INQUIRY TECHNIQUES FOR TEACHING SCIENCE

William D. Romey

Syracuse University

674141

PRENTICE-HALL, INC., Englewood Cliffs, New Jersey

PRENTICE-HALL INTERNATIONAL, INC., *London*
PRENTICE-HALL OF AUSTRALIA, PTY. LTD., *Sydney*
PRENTICE-HALL OF CANADA, LTD., *Toronto*
PRENTICE-HALL OF INDIA PRIVATE LTD., *New Delhi*
PRENTICE-HALL OF JAPAN, INC., *Tokyo*

Preface

Over the past few years, as I have evaluated books on methods of teaching science and the schedules of methods courses taught in various colleges, I have been impressed by the way so many authoritatively dictate to teachers how they should and should not teach. Others seem to describe all the methods their authors can think of but give no opinion about what methods to use under given circumstances. Few encourage teachers to experiment actively and constantly with teaching techniques and curriculum materials.

Inquiry Techniques for Teaching Science is an outgrowth of my own science methods course at Syracuse University. At first, my colleagues and I taught it as a lecture course. In a short while we were convinced that our goal of encouraging the use of discovery techniques of teaching and learning could hardly be reached by practicing the opposite of what we preached. Consequently, I have been trying to use a discovery approach in teaching the methods course itself. The object of the course is to force each student to develop his own curriculum materials and to work out his own style of teaching by making him "teach his way out" of various situations. Thus far we have used peer-group testing methods. Each student must teach certain kinds of lessons to a group of his peers, who at the end of the lesson become his critics. The instructor serves as a discussion leader or fellow critic and occasionally demonstrates special techniques. The instructor also helps lead summary sessions in which the class as a group decides which approaches have or have not been successful in achieving certain behavioral goals of the student teachers.

Part One of this book has served essentially as a laboratory manual in my own course, setting the stage for the various problems included herein as "Activities." Naturally it would be preferable if the students could teach actual elementary, secondary, and college students during their practice sessions. One of my colleagues, Professor Marvin Druger, has occasionally been able to enlist volunteer classes from local public schools to serve as subjects for the members of his classes. Probably at least some of the practicing should be done on peer groups rather than on actual school children so that the teacher-to-be will develop presence of mind, ease of manner, and an experimentive bent without having to cope with all the special psychological problems that must be dealt with in actual classrooms. There is time during the practice teaching experience for getting used to actual classes.

It should be obvious that my own approach to teaching is strongly discovery oriented. However, if users of this book who have tried the various activities in good faith are still clearly convinced that a discovery-oriented style does not suit them, they can use other styles without necessarily feeling that they are doing a bad job of teaching. The only essential requirement for all teachers is to continue throughout their careers to experiment with curricula and techniques and to strive to be creative. Creativeness implies a willingness to depart from textbooks, lesson plans, and old techniques that you consider good merely because they worked once upon a time.

This book is not intended to be a substitute for larger and more complete methods books. Many of them contain quite different kinds of information, suggestions, materials, and references. Instead, this book should supplement these larger works. In any course it will serve to supplement the part that deals specifically with discovery approaches to learning.

Many good, thoughtful articles on the history, philosophy, and methods of teaching science have appeared over the past few years. They have been published in numerous journals, and access to them is not usually easy without a great deal of bibliographic work in major libraries. Many methods books have paraphrased and adapted parts of these articles or referred to them in passing. I prefer that my own students have access to the original literature. Thus, Part Two of this book consists of a series of selected readings with some of my own commentary appended. Here again, from the selection it will be clear to the reader that my own bias is strongly in favor of learning by discovery. I wish to thank the various journals and authors who have graciously given me permission to reprint the articles included. Specific credits are included in the text.

Both parts of this book are aimed not only at undergraduate and graduate methods students but also at practicing teachers who desire to experiment with and improve their teaching. If they use this book as a guide in their search for a personal teaching style, their experimentation can take direction and perhaps be more organized and systematic. This book is also intended for any person interested in modern methods of science education. Parents who wish to encourage, to guide, and to reinforce the interest in science shown by their children may find useful some of the techniques discussed in these pages.

At what levels of science education can these techniques be used? Modifications of discovery approaches may be used successfully at all levels from nursery school through graduate school. The details of treatment may vary from one level to another, but the total view of science as a group of ways of looking at the world around us and gaining new knowledge should not change. At the higher levels more sophisticated procedures and more detailed coverage of subject matter will be desirable, but the need for treating learning as a process of inquiry remains paramount.

I wish to acknowledge the stimulation and ideas I have received from my colleagues at Syracuse University and from the large number of undergraduate and graduate methods students and practicing teachers I have had the privilege of working with at Syracuse University, during the course of numerous methods workshops, and in connection with the production and testing of materials for the Earth Science Curriculum Project. It is impossible to give adequate credit to all the people whose ideas have helped shape my own views, but I wish to thank especially John H. Merrill, Robert E. Kilburn, David L. Kendall and Harrie E. Caldwell.

William D. Romey

Contents

Part One

Searching for a Style of Teaching Science

Part Two

Readings on the Philosophy and Methods of Inquiry Teaching in Science

"If we indoctrinate the young person in an elaborate set of fixed beliefs, we are insuring his early obsolescence. The alternative is to develop skills, attitudes, habits of mind, and the kinds of knowledge and understanding that will be the instruments of continuous challenge and growth on the part of the young person. . . . All too often we are giving young people cut flowers when we should be teaching them to grow their own plants. We are stuffing their heads with the products of early innovation rather than teaching them how to innovate. We think of the mind as a storehouse to be filled rather than as an instrument to be used."

John W. Gardner
Saturday Review

Part One

SEARCHING

FOR A STYLE

OF TEACHING SCIENCE

What Is Science?

Books about methods of teaching science invariably begin with a section that defines "science." Perhaps this is the best place to begin.

If you should examine most college science courses, you might have to conclude that science is primarily a large body of knowledge. College teachers seem willing to accept without any objection the original meaning of the Latin word *scientia*; knowledge. Educators believe that beginning teachers generally imitate the person they consider to have been their own best teacher. This often leads to a series of lectures supported by a small amount of laboratory work and group discussion. In such a framework the teacher becomes a figure of authority, whose main function is to dispense knowledge. Teaching is then a matter of the teacher's demonstrating to his students how much he knows.

A number of years ago, after the author had handed in a mediocre report in field geology, the course instructor informed the author that geology was more an art than a science. However, as the author continued graduate study he found that the courses he took emphasized more and more the facts of geology and the conclusions of other geologists. As do most students in science courses, he had to memorize factual information and then reproduce it on examinations.

Then the author found he had to work on a thesis project for which there was no authority with a set of neatly prepared answers. Most of the knowledge he had gained in his courses was useful only as a tool to find answers to problems. He had to discover even the problems themselves. How much mental strife might have been avoided had his training in course work been aimed more at the recognition of problems, the formulation of hypotheses, the gathering and analysis of data, and the arrival at conclusions.

In a sense, the teaching of science can be compared to the teaching of art. Some art schools stress the history of art, whereas others are more

3

concerned with studio art; actual painting or sculpture. The difference between the two approaches is that one produces art historians whereas the other produces artists. The same is true of science. At present, many of our secondary schools and colleges are teaching the history of science rather than science itself. We burden students with factual knowledge, but few students get to *do* science until they reach the level where they must write a master's or doctor's thesis. Asking a high school or college undergraduate to learn science from a book or from a set of lectures is a little like asking a music student to learn the notes to a composition for the piano before he has been taught how to play the instrument.

Recent curriculum studies make it clear that young children, even at the elementary school level, are capable of doing simple scientific work. The word *scientific* comes from the two Latin words *scientia*, knowledge, and *facere*, to make. Thus "scientific" refers to the creating of knowledge. Students need not wait until graduate school to do scientific work in science classes. On the contrary, emphasis on the processes and methods of scientists should begin in the elementary school and continue throughout the student's academic career.

The main problem with which this book deals is how to make the teaching of science more scientific.

Defining Objectives*

Before beginning to teach a science course, as in any other course, you need a clearly stated set of instructional goals or objectives. The list you take to the store where you do your shopping is really a concise statement of your objectives. Strangely enough, many teachers forget that a classroom "shopping list" is badly needed for effective teaching.

Objectives can be phrased in various ways. One category of objectives might begin with the following prefatory phrase:

"My main objectives in teaching science are to . . ."

In order to complete the sentence, you might add such endings as:

1. "earn a living."
2. "keep children off the streets."
3. "stimulate young minds."
4. "cover the course of study contained in the textbook."
5. "cover the curriculum prescribed by the state."
6. "become qualified for promotion to a supervisory or administrative position."
7. "be able to keep dabbling in science myself."
8. "encourage and train young scientists."
9. "help all students become literate in science and competent to perform simple scientific tasks; help them to arrive at independent conclusions."

These are broad, general objectives and are not really useful in planning exactly how you are going to operate. On the other hand, we should

*I wish to acknowledge the contributions of David L. Kendall to this chapter. A number of stimulating conversations led to our sitting down together and preparing several parts of the chapter jointly.

pose the question, "what are my main objectives?" early in the course of a teacher preparation program. If you can honestly state objectives such as numbers 3, 8, and 9 above, the teaching profession needs you.

Another kind of objective described in many science education textbooks is what might be labeled a "teacher objective." As an introductory phrase the following can be used:

"During the course of this lesson (or unit or laboratory exercise or semester) I want to . . ."

Examples of terminations for this statement might include:

1. "show students the parts of a flower."
2. "teach students the principle of conservation of mass and energy."
3. "demonstrate what happens when chemicals A and B are mixed together."
4. "give a lecture on subject X."
5. "show a film on photosynthesis."

Perhaps statements of this type can be useful. However, they are simply statements of intention to perform some teaching function for or on the class. They tell nothing about what the student will take away from the lesson or how you will evaluate specifically what he has learned. As such, these are one-way objectives, which are perhaps better performed in an empty classroom than in front of live students.

Far more useful are what are termed "behavioral objectives." These are expressed in terms of the specific behavior a student is expected to exhibit after he has completed a unit of study. If you clearly specify the nature of the behavior expected, you also make obvious to both yourself and to your students the way in which you will be doing your testing and evaluating.

The following are examples of behaviorally stated objectives:

"After completing the work associated with this unit of study, the student should be able to . . ."

1. "make a leaf collection with all specimens properly labeled."
2. "interpret features on a topographic map he has never seen before."
3. "analyze the distribution of various kinds of energy in a model dynamic system."

Note that action verbs are used in expressing behavioral objectives. Some action verbs describe relatively simple, more or less mechanical kinds of behavior. Others require a complicated chain of mental operations that demonstrate a clear grasp of a major concept. The table below lists a few action verbs and separates them into rough categories showing the relative degrees of sophistication they require.

6

USEFUL WORDS FOR EXPRESSING OBJECTIVES IN BEHAVIORAL TERMS

The phrase preceding all these verbs is *"After completing all the work associated with this chapter, the student should be able to . . ."*

Level 1	Level 2	Level 3
(simple behavioral objectives)	(behavior requiring application of more complex mental operations)	(behavior showing that student has firm grasp of major concept or shows original thought)
find		
gather data	prove	
investigate	organize data	
describe	analyze	generalize from data
make	apply	synthesize
do	distinguish between	infer
compute	construct	discuss critically
measure	devise a method	predict
prepare	plot a graph	deduce
manipulate apparatus	state a problem	integrate
use	identify the variables	propose reasons and
recognize	contrast	defend them
examine	compare	formulate hypotheses
identify	specify limitations and	reorganize
recognize and cite	assumptions	discover
evidence for	suggest	manipulate ideas
classify	differentiate	
illustrate	relate	
	discriminate	
	reformulate	
	justify	
	estimate	
	interpret	

The table does not, of course, include all the words that validly describe kinds of behavior. You will notice that the table omits certain kinds of behavior that require mainly memorization of textbook material. This is not to suggest that memorization of certain key definitions and facts should be avoided entirely. If you wish to have students memorize certain things, use the following terms in stating behavioral objectives:

LEVEL "O" OBJECTIVES

"After reading chapter X, the student should be able to . . ."

recall	state	list reasons for
duplicate	define	explain
repeat	tell	imitate

One caution is necessary at this point. If you examine a list of behavioral objectives for a science course and find that a large percentage of them contain any of the nine verbs or phrases listed above, you should re-examine your intentions carefully. If you stress recall behavior rather than experimental, observational, interpretive, and synthetic behavior, you are not teaching science; you are teaching history of science.

Avoid one set of verbs altogether in stating objectives. These are verbs that, by their very nature, are so vague they give neither teacher nor pupil a clear idea of what is meant. Among these completely unacceptable words and phrases are the following:

LEVEL "NO" OBJECTIVES

"At the end of this lesson the student should . . ."

appreciate	develop an understanding, appreciation of
deal more effectively with	ciation of
understand	become aware of
know	become familiar with
have a feeling for	create an awareness of
comprehend	

There is no way to test for "appreciation," "understanding," "comprehension," and so forth. If you mean that you want the student to repeat what the book says about a subject, tell him so (and yourself) by using the verb "recall." The verbs listed above are not "honest" words because they do not clearly specify to the teacher or student what is expected.

In order to be completely honest with yourself and your students, include within your objectives a statement describing the conditions under which you will test for fulfillment of the objectives. For example, if you are doing a unit on mineral identification and wish to require a certain specified level of performance for a passing grade, you might state your objective as follows:

> At the end of this unit the student should be able to describe and identify correctly fifteen out of twenty unknown mineral specimens. During the examination the student will have access to a set of mineral identification tables and standard equipment for determining mineral properties.

With this kind of advance information, both student and teacher are at ease because requirements are clearly and specifically stated.

R. F. Mager has clearly analyzed the ways of stating objectives behaviorally in a book written in the format of a program. He emphasizes the following points:

1. An instructional objective is a group of words summarizing your intentions.
2. You will communicate your intentions to students only by describing accurately the kind of behavior you expect them to display at the end of the course.

3. In order to indicate accurately what you expect:
   a. Name the behavior required (e.g., identify minerals)
   b. List any conditions (given a set of mineral tables, etc.)
   c. State the criteria for a passing grade (make fifteen out of twenty correct determinations).
4. Write as many objectives as you need. The more clearly stated objectives you write, the more likely you are to achieve your instructional goals.
5. Give each student a copy of the objectives. If you do this you may not have much else to do.[1]

Specific behavioral objectives for *Inquiry Techniques for Teaching Science* and for a methods course in which the activities suggested in this book are completed will be found on pages 342–343.

[1]R. F. Mager, *Preparing Objectives for Programmed Instruction* (San Francisco: Fearon Publishers, Inc., 1962).

ACTIVITY 1

1. Write ten behavioral objectives for a unit or units in an eighth or ninth grade general science class. Be prepared to defend them orally.

2. Choose a chapter in any high school or college science text. Analyze the chapter to see if the author had clear behavioral objectives as he wrote the book. Write a set of behavioral objectives that fit the text. If necessary, suggest how the chapter might have been rewritten so that it could stress bringing about changes in student behavior.

3. Choose an activity or laboratory exercise in a high school or college laboratory manual. Analyze the exercise to see if the author had clear behavioral objectives. Write a set of behavioral objectives that fit the exercise. If necessary, suggest ways in which the exercise could be rewritten to stress student behavior.

4. Evaluate the levels of the objectives you have stated in 1, 2, and 3 above. (Assign levels 1, 2, 3, "O," "no" as described in this book.) Rewrite each objective that falls in levels "no" or "O" so that it belongs to level 1, 2, or 3.

Formulation and Teaching of Concepts

ACTIVITY 2

DO NOT TURN THE PAGE UNTIL YOU HAVE
COMPLETED THIS ACTIVITY!

Look through a high school or college textbook. Choose one "concept" from it. Make an outline showing how you would teach this concept.

There are various way of organizing scientific knowledge. One possible scheme is suggested below:

observations and facts   ⟶   concepts,   ⟶   conceptual schemes
(lowest level)   generalizations,   (highest level)
                       principles

Observations and facts are the basic data we have to work with in science. We gather data by looking at things, describing them, and measuring them. If the data are carefully gathered, essentially they remain forever as useful pieces of information. Qualitative information based on a quick look may later be improved by careful measurement and quantitative description. Improvements in analytical apparatus or in ways of looking at things may even show that data previously considered accurate are in error.

Scientists and science educators argue a good deal over the differences between "concept," "generalization," and "principle." In order to avoid a semantic discussion which would obscure rather than clarify the point, they have been included here in a single category and will be called *concepts*. A concept might be defined by any of the following phrases:

1. an abstraction that organizes a large number of ideas into a logical relationship
2. the resultant of a generalizing mental operation
3. a generalization relating the particular to the general
4. an idea comprehending the essential attributes of a class or logical species
5. an idea that includes all that is encompassed by a term
6. a network of inferences based on observation of a variety of objects and events in a variety of ways
7. a mental construct (a tight, logical assertion)
8. a theoretical construct (example: the concept of the atom)
9. the simplest patterns that help us order the world around us.

ACTIVITY 3

1. Now examine the concept you outlined at the beginning of this section. Does it fit any of the nine definitions given above? Does the way in which you proposed to teach it lead to student behavior that will appropriately demonstrate mastery of the concept? If not, rewrite the concept and outline so that they fulfill these requirements: A well-stated concept should indicate a generalizing mental operation and should suggest a network of ramifications and explanations. Statements that stand alone without further explanation generally turn out to be simple matters of fact or definitions. A concept should be stated in the simplest and briefest terms that will orient the student and the teacher.

2. Write one or more behavioral objectives that will help you lead students to master the concept you have chosen.

Why is it important to identify concepts in any course before you begin teaching? The concepts you choose to teach should provide basic threads running through your course. Stating them specifically gives direction to the course and ensures that none of the important threads will be omitted.

Reading Assignment: Read and be prepared to discuss the following:

1. Smith, H. A., "The Teaching of a Concept, an Elusive Objective," *The Science Teacher*, XXXIII, No. 3 (March, 1966), 103–12. (Also published as a pamphlet, Stock No. 471–14342, National Science Teachers Association, 1201 16th Street, N.W., Washington, D. C.)

2. *Theory into Action*, National Science Teachers Association pamphlet, Stock No. 471–14282 (Washington, D. C., 1964).

Conceptual Schemes

A conceptual scheme is defined in *Theory into Action* as a "big idea" or "a system of facts, principles, and concepts which . . . can be organized into a sound learning sequence from simple (capable of being taught to very young children) to complex (the level at which 'current problems' are being researched)." When several major concepts are gathered together, a conceptual scheme results. *Theory into Action* suggests seven major conceptual schemes into which the committee designated by the National Science Teachers Association feels that all scientific knowledge should fit. These conceptual schemes listed below are reprinted from *Theory into Action*, National Science Teachers Association pamphlet, Stock No. 471–14282 (Washington, D.C. 1964), by permission.

I. All matter is composed of units called fundamental particles; under certain conditions these particles can be transformed into energy and vice versa.

II. Matter exists in the form of units which can be classified into hierarchies of organizational levels.

III. The behavior of matter in the universe can be described on a statistical basis.

IV. Units of matter interact. The bases of all ordinary interactions are electromagnetic, gravitational, and nuclear forces.

V. All interacting units of matter tend toward equilibrium states in which the energy content (enthalpy) is a minimum and the energy distribution (entropy) is most random. In the process of attaining equilibrium, energy transformations or matter transformations or matter-energy transformations occur. Nevertheless, the sum of energy and matter in the universe remains constant.

VI. One of the forms of energy is the motion of units of matter. Such motion is responsible for heat and temperature and for the states of matter: solid, liquid, and gaseous.

VII. All matter exists in time and space and, since interactions occur among its units, matter is subject in some degree to changes with time. Such changes may occur at various rates and in various patterns.

The National Science Teachers Association also lists five "major items in the process of science."

I. Science proceeds on the assumption, based on centuries of experience, that the universe is not capricious.

II. Scientific knowledge is based on observations of samples of matter that are accessible to public investigation in contrast to purely private inspection.

III. Science proceeds in a piecemeal manner, even though it also aims at achieving a systematic and comprehensive understanding of various sectors or aspects of nature.

IV. Science is not, and will probably never be, a finished enterprise, and there remains very much more to be discovered about how things in the universe behave and how they are interrelated.

V. Measurement is an important feature of most branches of modern science because the formulation as well as the establishment of laws are facilitated through the development of quantitative distinctions.

Here then is a suggested set of conceptual schemes that might form the apex of a large triangle representing scientific knowledge. However, you will not go about "teaching" a conceptual scheme in a single class period, a week, a month, or even in a year. These are major ideas that should permeate the entire science experience of students throughout their school lives. Furthermore, although these particular schemes have been suggested by a group of eminent scientists and science educators, it would be a mistake to accept them blindly as the only worthwhile conceptual schemes. Professor Bentley Glass[1] in referring to these schemes, has stated "they may indeed supply an admirable basis for the organization of the study of physics, and possibly also of chemistry—although here I begin to have some doubt; but as a basis for organizing the study of the biological sciences they are not helpful—they are positively harmful."

In rebuttal, Morris Shamos, one of those who prepared *Theory into Action*, accuses Glass, a biologist, of "disciplinary bias."[2] It is unfortunate that some of the people involved in preparing *Theory into Action* apparently refuse to accept attempts to increase the number of valid conceptual schemes. As teachers you should be eager to search out other basic conceptual schemes and to make them the most important unifying threads of your courses.

[1]Bentley Glass, "Theory into Action—a Critique," *The Science Teacher*, XXXII (May, 1965), 29. (Reprinted on pp. 278–284 of this book.)

[2]M. H. Shamos, "The Role of Major Conceptual Schemes in Science Education, *The Science Teacher*, XXXIII (No. 1, 1966) 27–30.

The First Task:
Establishing a Need to Know

PARABLE

There once was a farmer from Missouri whose mule could not be persuaded to move. A neighbor, seeing the plight of the farmer, asked if he
might not help teach the animal some manners. When the farmer agreed,
his neighbor picked up a large stick and gave the mule a sharp crack on
the nose. When the farmer protested, the neighbor answered, "I always
figured that the first thing you have to do if you want to teach a mule
something is to get his attention."

The first task of the teacher is to attract the attention of the student.
This is true at all levels from first grade through graduate school. An
uninterested student is the despair of any teacher. In a sense, the whole
purpose of formal education is to attract the student's attention and
interest. Once interest is aroused, the student will learn far more through
his own efforts than you can ever teach him. Learning can occur only
when the mind of a student is prepared.

It is essential to establish a *need to know* before you begin any topics
in earnest. Any time spent on a science topic—or on any other topic for
that matter—is wasted until you have made the student want to know
what you have to say.

But how can you establish this need? How can you prepare the student so that he is ready to have you communicate with him? After
examining the behavior and success of many practicing teachers, we
might ask ourselves whether a need to know can be established by giving
an introductory lecture or demonstration to introduce a topic. Or can the
interest necessary to sustain a student through a unit of study that will
occupy several days of his time be established by assigning some advance
reading from a cleverly written textbook?

There is little doubt that a particularly clever lecture, demonstration,
or passage in a textbook is capable of arousing a certain amount of interest and need to know. But a more effective way of arousing student
interest is to conduct a laboratory experiment or discussion that *involves*

students more actively than does listening to a lecture or reading a book. We must begin by posing a question that leads the student to the brink of an intellectual dilemma, which can only be solved by his seeking for answers.

A lecture that pontifically tells the student a large number of answers is not likely to stimulate more than a passing interest. Similarly, a demonstration in which you "prove" something to the student will be unlikely to create sustained interest. When the author was a student in junior high school, he saw various science "magic" shows that featured elaborate demonstrations involving spark-making black boxes, oscilloscopes, and various elaborate electronic equipment. Looking back at these experiences, he realizes that, although mildly entertained by such spectacular displays of science in action, he learned little or no science and his curiosity was only mildly aroused. The demonstration that stimulates the greatest need to know is the one that asks a question and asks the student to find the answer.

One of the best ways to stimulate interest is to offend the student's intuition in some way or to confront him with a situation that is not readily acceptable. Then the student must be asked to find his way out of the intellectual maze that has been set up for him.

The following demonstration will offend the students' intuition. At the beginning of a lesson on density, they may be shown two beakers, both full of a clear liquid that looks like water. Ice cubes are dropped into the two beakers. In one liquid (water) the ice floats. In the second (alcohol) the cube sinks. Discussion centers around the reasons for this peculiar behavior of ice in "water."[1]

Another example of how to offend the student's intuition is a laboratory demonstration in which the teacher pours purple cabbage juice into several apparently empty test tubes. Suddenly in one tube the purple juice turns yellow, in another it turns green, and in yet another bright red! Discussion ultimately leads students to the conclusion that there must have been some colorless substance in the test tubes that caused the purple juice to change color. This can be the beginning of a profitable week-long study of chemistry with emphasis on pH, indicator solutions, and so forth.[2]

Virtually any unit in science can begin with some intuition-offending demonstration, statement, or exercise that will grasp the attention of your students. Also, either of the demonstrations used as examples could have

[1]An interesting discussion of two ways of presenting this kind of activity—one by an authoritarian approach and the other by an open-ended discussion and class activity is given in R. Samples, "The Death of an Investigation," reprinted on pp. 250–256 of this book.

[2]A number of similar demonstrations and suggestions can be found in W. Thurber and R. Kilburn, *Exploring Science*, Teachers' Editions of Books 7, 8, and 9 (Boston, Mass.: Allyn and Bacon).

been presented in a conventional, expository fashion. In the ice-cube demonstration or the cabbage-juice experiment the students could have been told in advance what to expect. That would have eliminated the need-to-know factor by telling the students what would happen rather than asking them to puzzle out the problem.

A discussion or short lecture without any accompanying demonstration can, however, be used to offend student intuition. John Merrill, a junior high school teacher with whom the author has worked, began a unit on astronomy by building up a scheme that made the sun, moon, planets, and stars all appear to revolve around the earth, as in Ptolemaic theory. Merrill's students listened to the presentation and then began to do laboratory work that somehow did not seem to agree with what they had heard. Gradually the students began to mutter about something being wrong. Finally the whole class became openly irate and challenged Merrill with a substantial number of considerations they felt indicated that he was in error. He had led them to the point he wished to make by advocating the Ptolemaic system and then helping them to disprove it through the laboratory activities that followed his introduction.

Films, filmstrips, and overhead transparencies are also good devices for establishing a need to know at the beginning of a unit of study. They cannot, however, be used in quite the conventional ways. Most films, to be used effectively in establishing a need to know, should be used with the sound track turned off. Or the teacher must switch the projector off at key points to bring in class discussion.

In summary, the need to know—which is essential at the beginning of any learning situation—can only be established by asking questions that your students must answer through discussion, experimentation, and reading.

ACTIVITY 4

1. Prepare a brief introduction that will offend the intuition of your listeners in such a way as to establish a need to know. Teach this introduction to the members of your class. You may use a discussion, laboratory exercise, a demonstration, or even (as a last resort) a lecture.

2. Write behavioral objectives showing what behavior you intend to elicit from the students.

The Role of Activities and Laboratory Exercises in Science Classes

Traditionally science classes at all levels have consisted of lecture and discussion groups as well as of a separate laboratory period once or perhaps twice each week. In some schools a double period is available for laboratory work.

Teachers normally use a textbook as the central point of focus for their courses. A supplementary manual or workbook used in conjunction with the laboratory may be more or less related to the textbook and lectures. The text and teacher assume the roles of authorities and dispensers of information. The laboratory commonly is a place where students prove the theories proposed by the teacher and the textbook. Workbook exercises are mainly concerned with vocabulary drill rather than with scientific processes.

This approach to science teaching is, in the author's opinion, the very antithesis of true science. Science is an experimental, observational, laboratory-oriented discipline. Effective courses in any subject should as faithfully as possible reflect the nature of the discipline. Thus effective science courses should be *laboratory centered* rather than text or lecture centered.

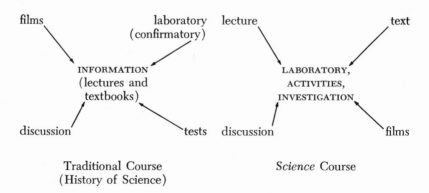

Traditional Course
(History of Science)

Science Course

Whenever possible, introduce topics in the laboratory. Effective laboratory activities may be set up in roughly the following manner:

1. Pose a problem.
2. Establish an experimental design aimed at solving the problem.
3. Have students gather data related to solution of the problem.
4. Have students graph, study, and interpret their data.
5. Have students generalize on the basis of their data.
6. Proceed to a group discussion of the meaning and limitations of the data, the relationship of the data to other problems, and so forth.
7. If enough interest has been generated and there is sufficient demand, a short lecture might even be in order at this point.
8. Related readings in a textbook take on genuine meaning now that they can reinforce and augment the results of the student's personal experience.

Above all else, the student's initial generalization should be the result of his own reasoning. He must have no preconceived ideas forced on him by textbooks or teacher. Some students may already have preconceived notions (some of them partially or wholly incorrect) from earlier courses. If this should happen, you as teacher must lead your students to trust what they do and see in the laboratory rather than what a textbook tells them they should believe.

Not all science topics, particularly in the natural sciences, lend themselves to *experimental* procedures. In biology and the earth sciences we arrive at many answers through careful observation of natural events. The principles of classification of animals, plants, rocks, and minerals become important. In order to teach students to observe, classify, interpret behavior, or reconstruct geologic circumstances, we must make it possible for students to step into the shoes of the biologist, geologist, meteorologist, or astronomer. Once again, we must pose problems—observational this time rather than experimental—and ask students to gather and interpret basic data. Rather than tell a student the function of a certain organ in an animal or plant, we must (whenever possible) allow him to discover it for himself.

You probably now are wondering how we can expect students to discover everything in science. Obviously it would be foolish to neglect all previous scientific work and require students to recreate man's scientific experiences of the past three-hundred years. As scientists make new discoveries, they give abundant credit to their predecessors and point out that recent conclusions would have been impossible without the foundation provided by earlier workers. Indeed, part of science teaching involves helping students learn how to use previous work—how to stand on the shoulders of scientific giants of the past in reaching for new knowledge. This subject will be further treated in the section entitled "The Role of Textbooks."

Structured Versus Unstructured Activities

In a structured activity the student is given instructions that lead him through a procedure designed to produce certain specific results. At their worst such exercises are so involved with instructions and procedural details that the student loses track of what he was trying to prove even if he comes out at the end with a perfect result.

Structured laboratory exercises can be written that still require the student to think about what he is doing. Procedures can be written out in complete detail but inserted among them must be questions requiring the student to analyze why he is performing a specified operation and why he is to do it in a certain way. In well-conceived structured activities the student is told how to gather the data and perhaps even how to graph the data. However, the student does not know in advance what his results will be. After he has gathered his data, certain leading questions may be asked to aim him in the direction of a reasonable analysis of the data and the desired generalization. Note, however, that if for some reason the student's data differ from those expected you must be prepared to analyze his results. The teacher in a well-taught laboratory section must never suggest that a student's *data* are wrong. For the particular procedure he has used, the student's data, as such, are valid. You must be prepared to suggest modifications of procedure if the student seems to have gone down a blind alley.

At the conclusion of an activity have several students show their data and summarize their conclusions for the rest of the class. For students whose data differ greatly from data gathered by other students, the class as a whole should analyze the reasons why: Did the student use a careless procedure? Did the student fail to control some important variable? Or is the student who appeared to be "wrong" perhaps the one who is actually right? Or are conflicting sets of data *both* reasonable, and conflicting generalizations both justified? Lead the students to suggest ways of resolving conflicting data.

22

A well-designed structured activity should do the following things:

1. Pose a problem.
2. Suggest a procedure for gathering data. (Procedure may be specified in great detail or only generally discussed.)
3. Allow the student time to gather the data in the way prescribed.
4. Require the student to organize his data in both tabular and graphical form whenever possible.
5. Require the student to answer a series of questions about his data.
6. Require the student to generalize on the basis of his data and to be prepared to defend his generalizations in front of the class.

On the other hand, let us examine the unstructured activity. A completely unstructured activity merely poses a problem and then allows the student complete liberty to devise his own procedure, organize his own data, and arrive at his own generalizations. The success of this approach depends on three things:

1. Properly stating the problem.
2. Having the class properly prepared to work in this manner.
3. Knowing how to lead the class by appropriately inserted suggestions and questions.

Proper use of unstructured activities can lead to the most exciting kinds of science experiences for both teacher and pupil. In such activities the student comes closest to following methods a scientist might use, and the possibilities for student discoveries are greatest.

Some topics lend themselves well to an unstructured approach. The teacher of a class investigating the effect of color on peripheral vision merely wrote the question on the blackboard, furnished protractors and paper of various colors, and let the students "structure" their own laboratory. The problem of procedure was simple enough, so that the class members had no difficulty making up their own experiments. When a single problem is approached by students using several different kinds of procedure, interesting conflicts of data may arise. Airing these conflicts can lead to excellent post-laboratory discussions and the proposal of new procedures to obtain definitive answers. Discussions may also lead to the posing of subsidiary problems that may excite and stimulate students to work on small research problems of their own.

Other problems may not lend themselves to an approach in which each student devises his own procedure. A way around this problem is to follow the plan suggested below:

1. Pose the problem the day before the experiment is to be conducted.
2. Tell the students specifically what equipment will be available to use in the experiment.

3. Ask the students to come to class the next day ready to suggest a tentative procedure.
4. At the beginning of the laboratory period ask the students to propose various procedures.
5. Through discussion, have the class decide on a procedure, or possibly two or three alternative procedures, which they might try for the experiment. You, as teacher, may want to throw in a comment from time to time, but be sure not to *impose* any procedure on the class.
6. Allow the students to proceed with the experimentation.
7. Hold a class discussion of results when experimentation is complete.

How do you go about preparing your class to do unstructured laboratories? It is unlikely that you will inherit a class already used to this kind of procedure. If you do, however, you can expect a pleasant and profitable year. (It pays to know just how students in earlier grades are taught in your school.) More likely you will have to train your own students. Many junior high school, high school, and even college students have never had the opportunity to handle laboratory apparatus. With such students or with students who are used to step-by-step directions you would be well advised to begin with labs that spell out procedures in moderate detail. Even the early labs should be *open-ended*, however. The student should not know in advance what his conclusions will be. Gradually, over the first few weeks of your course, reduce the structure of the laboratories as your students become progressively more self-sufficient and more willing and able to hypothesize, try modifications of specified procedures, and generalize on the basis of their own data. The next step in training a class to do unstructured labs is to let the group agree upon a procedure. Introduce a completely unstructured laboratory exercise from time to time to see how the group operates. You will probably want to use some structure in laboratory activities even after your class is well trained in working out their own procedures.

The particular schedule you wish to follow may dictate how often you can use purely unstructured laboratory exercises. In many situations it will take a class longer to do an unstructured activity than to do a structured one, although some activities may actually go faster if the students are not burdened with a large number of unnecessary instructions. Another risk of using unstructured activities is that the class may go in a direction different from the one you had intended. If they do, you should let them carry their investigation to its logical conclusion, but then later you will have to backtrack in order to lead the class to some generalization missed on the way. You will probably cover less ground if you use a large number of unstructured activities. On the other hand, though, the scientific skills developed by your students may be that much greater.

How Often
Should Activities Be Used?

In the author's personal opinion at least half of the class time should be spent on activities and laboratory exercises. While students are *doing* things, the likelihood of their learning something is greatest.

Some teachers protest that the physical layout of their classrooms does not permit them to run an extensive laboratory program. Generally this is an excuse rather than a valid reason. One very highly activity-oriented program known to the author is taught in a normal classroom equipped only with a few movable tables and very few of the "essential" furnishings most people think of as requirements for a "laboratory."

Other teachers protest that a forty- or forty-five-minute period is not long enough for laboratory exercises. Yet with proper planning, exciting activities can be planned for a normal classroom and for a class period of normal length. There is no need to complete an activity during a single period. Useful activities may stretch over several days. Professional scientists stretch experiments and investigations out over long periods of time and are often interrupted, but this does not prevent them from experimenting. The same is true for secondary school and college students.

Functions of the Teacher
During Laboratory Activities

Before a laboratory activity the way must be prepared by the statement of the problem. Pre-lab discussion must arouse student interest. Asking students to plan their own procedures is one way of doing this. Using a demonstration to confront the students with intuition-offending relationships is another.

In a good activity most of the teacher's work must be done before and after the actual class. Proper equipment must be made available. This requires a considerable amount of advance planning. It may be a matter of bringing in some cut flowers for a botany exercise, acquiring some sand for a geology lab, borrowing or ordering certain kinds of glassware for chemistry or physics, or making advance arrangements for a field trip. The wise teacher searches for ways to have his students find and bring necessary materials from home whenever possible. This procedure has a dual function:

1. It relieves the teacher of time-consuming outside work.
2. It further involves the student (and perhaps his parents as well).

During an activity you become a director of research rather than a teacher in the traditional sense. Your function is to discuss problems with individual students and groups as they request help, to recommend modifications of procedure, to encourage, to ask pointed questions, to challenge techniques, hypotheses, and generalizations, and to praise for work well done.

After the activity, in post-lab discussions, ask students to propose answers and to present results. Be prepared to direct the students to related literature and to appropriate textbook readings. You may want to show your own results from the same experiment and thus assume the role of fellow investigator. Or you may select results from technical papers to determine if results differ with more sophisticated equipment and procedures. If so, analyze the reasons for differences.

> Most important of all, as research director you must remain in the background during the lab work. Your students are the principal investigators; you are there only to help, to challenge, and to oversee.

ACTIVITY 5

1. a. Choose a laboratory exercise from a high school or college laboratory manual. Analyze the structure of the exercise. If it is "closed" (answers known in advance), rewrite it so that it is "open-ended" (answers to be learned through the activity).

    b. If the activity is structured but open-ended, rewrite it in unstructured form. Be prepared to defend your rewritten version.

    c. If the activity is unstructured, rewrite it in structured but open-ended form.

2. Write a structured laboratory exercise on a science topic. Include notes on planned pre-laboratory and post-laboratory discussion, necessary equipment, and so forth. Be prepared to teach the activity to a practice class.

3. Write an unstructured version of the exercise prepared for paragraph 2 (above). Include notes on pre-laboratory discussion, post-laboratory discussion, and equipment. Be prepared to teach your activity in this style also.

4. Write detailed behavioral objectives for the exercises you prepare.

(For numbers 2 and 3 above, make sure your pre-lab discussion notes include comments on how you will establish a need to know.)

Field Trips
in Natural Science

In general science, biology, and earth science courses, students should have the opportunity to make field observations. Field trips enable students to integrate into a total picture what they know about isolated parts of their environment.

Plan field trips that require a maximum amount of student involvement. Commonly, teachers use field trips to *show* students various natural features. The field trip under those circumstances simply becomes an outdoor lecture. Guided tours do not take full advantage of the potential inherent in field trips.

Any good field trip should be centered around a specific problem or problems. An effective trip should not involve many different problems at the same time. Otherwise the attention of the students is not sufficiently concentrated. Have students gather field data in the same way as does a professional field biologist or earth scientist. In biology, many ecology problems lend themselves well to *working* field trips. In earth science the following may be given as examples of useful problems for field studies: measuring stratigraphic sections, making simple geologic maps, and making quantitative studies of factors involving stream velocities.

If the field trip does not have as an important goal the gathering of basic data, it may as well be eliminated. Students should do the things that professional field investigators actually do.

ACTIVITY 6

Write a detailed proposal for a biology or earth science field trip. Pose a problem first, specify what kinds of data students will be expected to collect, and tell what you expect to have them do with the data. Be prepared to take a test class or some of your colleagues on the trip to evaluate its worth. Write behavioral objectives for the field trip. State the concepts you want the field trip to reinforce.

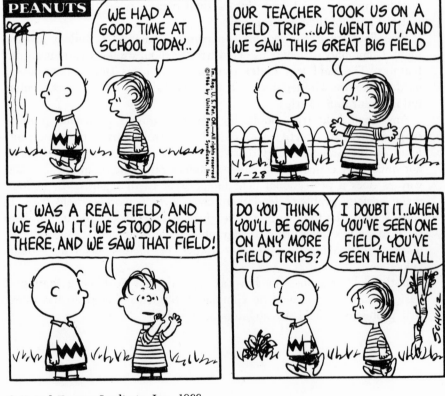

© United Feature Syndicate, Inc., 1966.

Invitations to Inquiry

Professor J. J. Schwab of the University of Chicago has proposed the use of a discussion device he calls an "invitation to inquiry." In a discussion of this type the teacher provides his students with a limited amount of basic data or evidence and then requires the students to interpret the data or to reason out a solution to the problem posed.

This is a particularly attractive instructional device because it gets right at the heart of the process of science. Experimenting and gathering data are essential to a science course and are usually interesting to students. However, they do require a lot of time. Furthermore, equipment problems for some experiments become virtually insurmountable. In an invitation to inquiry the student has a problem posed to him, but a set of data are furnished immediately. The essence of an invitation to inquiry consists of interpretation, generalization, and conclusion. The procedure is truly "scientific," and yet much time can be saved by eliminating the actual gathering of data.

Interpretation of the data is most satisfactorily done in a group discussion. First of all, set up the problem to be examined. Then provide a set of data relating to the problem. Next, encourage students to argue with you and with each other. The teacher, as discussion leader, should play the role of devil's advocate. It is important to keep the group discussion confined more or less to the topic. Let the class as a group develop its own chain of reasoning and interpretation as it seeks to generalize from the data provided. Students thus have the opportunity to discuss and argue over the meaning of data, just as practicing scientists do at their own professional meetings.

In order to set up the problem, tell a short anecdote or story to arouse the curiosity of your students. The data can be furnished in various ways:

1. Use an overhead projector to flash a data table, graph, or picture onto

the screen. Then ask a leading question or two to touch off the discussion.

2. Put the data on a blackboard.

3. Use Kodachrome slides to show a rock outcrop or some biological relationship. Instead of telling the students what the slide represents, ask them to interpret and explain what they see.

4. Use short clips from motion pictures to show some dynamic relationship. Film loops also serve this purpose admirably.

Be careful not to assume the role of the person with all the answers. Be continually alert for any alternate explanations of the data that do not coincide with your own explanation but may be partially or entirely valid nonetheless.

Where can you get data suitable for invitations to inquiry? If you teach biology, *The Biology Teacher's Handbook* is especially useful.[1] Professor Schwab and colleagues give detailed instructions about how to conduct a large number of invitations to inquiry. Several exercises in the course produced by the Earth Science Curriculum Project (ESCP) lend themselves to treatment as invitations to inquiry.[2]

You do not need any special source for information. Virtually any graph, data table, or diagram in almost any textbook, technical journal, or popular science magazine can furnish material for an invitation to inquiry. Draw the graph on a blackboard or prepare a transparency for an overhead projector. Make sure that any explanatory clues to interpretation found on the diagram are removed before you begin. Remember that your whole purpose is to get your students to do the explaining. Tell your class at the beginning what the problem was, how the data were gathered, what equipment was used, and so forth, and they will eagerly proceed to attack the problem of interpreting the data.

How often should a teacher use invitations to inquiry? This depends of course on many factors. Using such discussion techniques frequently —perhaps once a week—seems best. You may want to set up a regular day each week for an invitation to inquiry. The topics chosen for invitations should be carefully selected so that they will develop an important generalization related to your course objectives. Students should have had little or no advance reading on the topic selected. If they have too much prior exposure to the topic, they will parrot what a book says rather than abandon themselves to the joys of a heated discussion based on the data.

---

[1] J. J. Schwab, *The Biology Teacher's Handbook* (New York: John Wiley & Sons, Inc., 1963).

[2] *Investigating the Earth* (Boston: Houghton-Mifflin, 1967).

ACTIVITY 7

Prepare an invitation to inquiry on some topic in science and teach it to your class. Write a detailed outline showing how you plan to conduct the invitation. Specify your behavioral objectives for the invitation. State the concepts you are dealing with.

Simulation: The Use
of Games in the Classroom

Educators have recently shown much interest in the use of simulated situations to promote student interest and classroom participation. Carlson describes a number of games used in history, political science, business, mathematics, and other courses.[1] Some of these are not unlike a game of Monopoly. Others become as complicated as the elaborate war games used by the military. Games are being used more and more at all levels, from kindergarten to graduate school.

Is there anything useful in this idea that we in science might adopt for our own purposes? Can simulation problems provide an element of "need to know" that will be worthwhile?

The following will serve as examples of potentially useful games:

1. Trip to the moon (suggested by Mr. Roger Williams): In one version of this game students are told that at the beginning of the game they will be "landed" on the moon and that they will have a limited time to take whatever notes they wish and to collect a limited number of pounds of samples to take back to earth for analysis. Students are briefed about where they will be landed. Small teams of students are then sent behind screens where they find an array of rock and soil materials and perhaps some photographs or a plaster or cardboard model of the area where they are supposed to have landed. At the end of their "visit" to the moon the returning teams are then put into separate corners of the room where they are asked to determine exactly where they *actually* landed. They are also asked to study their materials, to produce as complete a description of the moon's surface as possible, and to formulate a set of hypotheses about the origin of the surface materials and of the landscape features. Each "landing site" should contain slightly different objects for study. The landscapes should differ, and each site should

[1]Elliot Carlson, "Games in the Classroom," *Saturday Review* (April 15, 1967), pp. 62–64, 82–83.

contain more rock samples than the students are allowed to "take back to earth" for study. Then each team is asked to report its findings to the entire class. The findings of the various teams will be different, and the questions should arise: Who is *right* or who is most accurate or are the areas really as different as the various teams have suggested they are? Later, a referee or referees can assign point values to determine which teams have performed best.

As an exercise for an earth science or general science class, such a game can integrate problems like rock sampling, description and identification of rocks, description and identification of landforms, description of climatic features, examination of materials for traces of microscopic life, solution of various problems in astronomy, and many others. Such a study can then be continued with examination of geologic maps of the moon. These are available from the U. S. Geological Survey.

2. A similar game used in a college geology laboratory and suggested by Mr. Richard Kroll involves dividing a class into oil prospecting teams provided with geologic maps, groups of rock samples, and a cardboard model from which to extract drill cores. Purchase of leases, choice of drilling sites, and other problems faced by petroleum geologists are part of the game. Winners are the team members who first bring in a major oil well. This game integrates many aspects of the study of rocks and maps and also introduces the nature of some practical problems faced in petroleum exploration.

3. Mr. William Garrabrant suggests a weather-plotting exercise in which students are assigned to a fictitious central weather bureau office and periodically receive reports of changing weather conditions from a number of outlying meteorological stations. Students are asked to plot incoming data and to make predictions about future weather conditions as more and more data become available. Points can be assigned to teams whose predictions are most nearly correct.

Many other such games could be proposed that would place students into situations involving applied physics, chemistry, or biology. The possibilities are limited only by your own imagination.

ACTIVITY 8

1. Prepare a classroom game involving the use of a situation leading students into practical problems that might be faced by a working scientist. The problem may involve either "pure" or "applied" science. Set up a point system for determining a winner.

2. Assign to a group of your students or peers the task of playing the game to test its workability.

3. Write behavioral objectives and concepts for the game that you design.

(If you are in an organized methods course, your instructor may choose to assign particular fields of science to various students in the class.)

Lectures in Science Courses

AVOID THEM!

It is unfortunate that lectures as a method of teaching are deeply ingrained in the fabric of our educational system. The most common justification for lecturing is that a lecture is the most economical way of getting a large amount of information across to a large group. Also, in lectures more ground can be covered.

The practical consequence of extensive lecturing is that virtually nothing you "get across" stays across for very long. Even the most dynamic lecturers often complain about the blank stares they observe on the faces of listeners. Various educational authorities have estimated that much less material can be covered in a pure laboratory and activity program than in a lecture program. This kind of statement is deceiving. If we examined regression (forgetting) curves for the two methods, we would probably find something like the curves shown below:

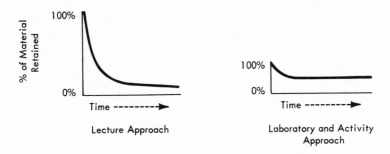

Lecture Approach

Laboratory and Activity Approach

(In the above diagrams, the length of the ordinate is proportional to the total amount of material covered in two courses of equal length.)

Thus, although much more material is covered in a lecture approach, a relatively small amount is retained. On the other hand, when the students are constantly involved in experimentation and have *derived*

37

many of the basic generalizations for themselves, the amount of regression (or forgetting) is significantly less. Although more may be covered by lectures, it is not only possible, but even likely, that at the end of a year or so more total information is retained from the laboratory approach than from a lecture approach.

Unfortunately, very little quantitative work has been done by science educators to show what actually happens. Many variables come into play, and subsequent detailed work may prove that those who believe in an activities approach are wrong. Experience with the new laboratory-oriented science curricula (Biological Sciences Curriculum Study, Physical Sciences Study Committee, Chemical Education Materials Study, Chemical Bond Approach, Earth Science Curriculum Project) however, seems to bear out the importance of laboratory work in science courses.

Concerning behavioral skills—manipulation, analysis, and synthesis—few science educators would deny that these are generally developed only through practice, and few educators would claim that listening to lectures promotes development of these skills, which many scientists and science educators consider among the most desirable in a scientifically literate student.

Must lectures be eliminated entirely? The author would not be so rash as to suggest this. When a working scientist hears a lecture on some aspect of science that especially interests him, he may profit greatly from the lecture because, although he is not physically duplicating the efforts of his colleagues, he is still intellectually involved in analysis of his colleagues' data and conclusions. He is carrying on a sort of mental "invitation to inquiry."

Members of a class may become so much interested in a particular topic that they will beg for additional information. The students' active desire to have lecture materials presented should be a clue that a short talk on the subject may be in order. If you do lecture, however, invite student interruptions and ideas. Avoid the dogmatism that many lecturers show, or you may undo some of the good work that your laboratory and activity program has accomplished. It is wise to keep lectures reasonably short. Hour-long lectures are likely to become taxing on high school students, college students, and even on professionals.

ACTIVITY 9

After what has been said above, you didn't really expect I would ask you to prepare a lecture, did you?

The Role of
Textbooks in Science Teaching

In science there is no *absolute truth*. The degree of truth of a proposition usually is proportional to the number of pieces of supporting data that serve as evidence in favor of the proposition. Even the great "laws" of physics are periodically doubted. Newtonian physics was considered adequate for many years to explain the behavior of important segments of our world. Then Einstein and others theorized about curved space. The old "truths," although they still can be used as models to help explain many physical phenomena, are not universal.

The average textbook is a compendium of scientific conclusions with few supporting data and few references to the original scientific work that led to the conclusions. Following such a textbook chapter by chapter, question by question commonly leads to authoritarianism on the part of the teacher and to blind acceptance and rote learning on the part of the student. Strict adherence to a textbook leads students to think that science comes from textbooks rather than from observation, experimentation, data analysis, and conclusion. The uncertainties built into scientific conclusions are generally only casually mentioned.

Textbooks, of course, have their uses, but they must be used intelligently. The teacher must analyze exactly what the role of the textbook will be in his course, and he must re-evaluate periodically just how well the textbook is serving him.

One way to diminish the problem of authoritarianism is to use several textbooks simultaneously. Instead of assigning the same pages in the same book to all students, assign parallel reading from four or five different textbooks. Have some students read one text, others a second, still others a third, and so forth. Set up class discussions in such a way that differences in viewpoint, approach, and even conclusions are brought out by the students rather than by you. Confront the students with conflicting views whenever possible so that they are forced to look for ways of resolving such conflicts.

Wherever possible it is important—even on the lower secondary level—to have copies of original scientific papers on various classroom topics available for the students. Unfortunately, the technical vocabulary of many such papers is beyond the comprehension of high school students (and commonly even beyond the comprehension of scientists in other specialties). Articles in such journals as *Science, American Scientist,* and *Scientific American* can be used to good advantage. Even when technical vocabulary is a problem, give your students the opportunity to see how working scientists interweave their own ideas with those of other scientists.

Proper use of text materials makes it possible to help students discover that important ideas are made up of many small discoveries. It is true enough that students cannot recreate all science in the laboratory. The most illustrious scientists are the first to acknowledge their debt to previous knowledge. Most scientists who make important discoveries recognize that in order to reach them they have stood "on the shoulders of giants."

Textbooks need not be authoritarian. Unfortunately, few existing textbooks have found the formula for nonauthoritarian approaches.[1] The most valuable kind of textbook is one that serves as a study guide, furnishing raw data wherever possible and inviting student interpretation rather than imposing author interpretation. References to original literature should be abundant.

Many textbook writers use other textbooks as the primary references for their own books. Few modern writers go back to original sources to see what new interpretations can be made. Erroneous ideas introduced in one textbook are often quoted in new texts and thus become perpetuated.

In this age of computers and elaborate, inexpensive copying machines the whole nature of the publishing industry may shortly be undergoing a drastic change. Most textbooks contain some good material and some that is of little value. Furthermore, what is useful text material for one teacher is less useful for another. Copyright laws have made it difficult to use parts of several different textbooks without making a large investment in a huge number of books. The new technology and copyright law revisions may soon make it possible for a teacher to select the best chapters or pages from several different textbooks and also original articles from the scientific literature and have all of these bound into textbooks that are custom-built for each teacher.

[1]For a notable exception among college texts see Eric Rodgers, *Physics for the Inquiring Mind* (Princeton, N. J.: Princeton University Press).

ACTIVITY 10

1. Choose any science topic of interest to you. Select at least five different beginning science textbooks. Compare and contrast the treatment of the topics you have chosen. How has each author dealt with the topic? What references to *original sources* have been made?

2. Seek out some original sources in scientific literature. How do they deal with this same topic? How much literature on the topic is available?

3. Outline a new text treatment on this same topic. Be prepared to explain and to defend your treatment of the topic as compared to the treatment used by the five authors whose texts you analyzed.

Quantitative Analysis of
Textbooks and Laboratory Manuals

Most teachers become involved at some time in the choice of textbooks and laboratory manuals or workbooks for their courses. The teacher of a discovery-oriented course must learn to recognize the textbooks or parts of textbooks that lend themselves well to this kind of use.

Simple reading of a textbook is not sufficient to bring out the good and bad points in any kind of quantitative way that will help the teacher make a clear choice of the book that best suits his purpose. One of the worst traps a teacher will face in choosing a suitable textbook is the physical layout and design of the book. Book publishers recognize the sales appeal of books that are physically attractive. Consequently, it is easy to be seduced by the external form of a book. Some of the worst textbooks have worn the prettiest coats.

Following is a sample sheet for quantitatively rating textbooks or single chapters of textbooks on the basis of their content. It shows how all the data for a given book can be combined so that a quantitative rating can be obtained for any book analyzed.

RATING THE TEXT

1. Randomly select and mark ten or more text pages from various parts of the book.

2. Read a block of twenty-five sentences on each of the marked pages and assign each sentence to one of the categories listed below. (If the page contains fewer than twenty-five sentences of normal text, continue on to the next page.) Do not include headings, figure captions, summary questions, or chapter introductions in your sample. Begin with the first new paragraph on the page. Your sample may thus span parts of more than one section.

a. Statements of fact. A statement of fact is defined for our purpose as a simple statement presenting a piece of data or an observation made by someone other than the student. *Examples:* (1) Red Lake is 200 feet deep; (2) The moon goes through all its phases in twenty eight days; (3) A cat eats mice; (4) When hydrochloric acid is placed on calcite, a reaction takes place in which carbon dioxide is formed; (5) Bees have stingers.
b. Stated conclusions or generalizations. A conclusion is defined for our purposes as the author's stated opinion about the meaning of or the relationships between items in a series of facts. *Examples:* (1) From their physical characteristics we conclude that whales are mammals; (2) Convection currents in the earth's mantle probably account for the subsidence and uplift of large parts of the earth's crust.
c. Definitions.
d. Questions asked but answered immediately by the text.
e. Questions requiring the student to analyze data.
f. Statements requiring the student to formulate his own conclusion.
g. Directions telling the student to perform and analyze some activity; statements posing problems to be solved by the student.
h. Questions that are asked to arouse student interest but are not answered immediately by the text.
i. Sentences directing the reader to look at a figure; procedural instructions in activities; sentences not fitting any of the above categories.
j. Rhetorical questions.

3. Calculate the index of student involvement for the text:

$$\frac{e + f + g + h}{a + b + c + d}$$

Items a, b, c, and d do not require student involvement or use of scientific skills. A large number of items included in these categories tends to make a book authoritarian and noninvestigative. On the other hand, a large number of items falling into categories e, f, g. and h is characteristic of a book suitable for use in a discovery-oriented course. If you have difficulty deciding whether to put an item in category a, b, c, or d, make a quick judgment. The important distinction to be made is to separate accurately sentences that would fall into categories a, b, c, and d from sentences that would fall into categories e, f, g, and h. Categories i and j have no real bearing on the usefulness of the book in a science course and can thus be eliminated from consideration.

RATING THE FIGURES AND DIAGRAMS IN THE TEXT

1. Randomly select ten figures or diagrams in the book.

2. Analyze each figure or diagram and assign it to one or more of the following categories:
   a. Used strictly for illustrative purposes.
   b. Requires students to perform some activity or to use data.
   c. Illustrates how to set up the apparatus for an activity.
   d. Fits none of the categories above.

3. Calculate the index of student involvement for the figures and diagrams:

$$\frac{b}{a}$$

RATING THE QUESTIONS AT THE ENDS OF TEXT SECTIONS AND CHAPTERS

1. Randomly select ten questions at the ends of ten different chapters.

2. Assign each question to one of the following categories:
   a. Answer can be obtained directly from the text.
   b. Definition.
   c. Question requires student to apply learnings from the chapter to new situations.
   d. Question requires student to solve a problem.

3. Calculate the index of student involvement for the questions:

$$\frac{c + d}{a + b}$$

RATING THE CHAPTER SUMMARIES

1. Select the chapter summaries from three different chapters.

2. Read two paragraphs of each of the three chapter summaries and assign each sentence to one of the following categories:
   a. Repeats the conclusions of the chapter.
   b. Raises new questions, the answers to which are not available in the text or are subjects of current research in science.

3. Calculate the index of involvement for the summaries:

$$\frac{b}{a}$$

Determining an Activities Index for the Book

Select at least ten pages at random and glance through each, assigning an index as follows: Count the number of proposed activities required of the students. To get an index number, divide the number of activities found by the number of pages examined.

Subjective Evaluation

At the bottom of the rating sheet, write your subjective opinion of how well the book seems to suit your own behavioral goals for a course. Include a comment on reading level, difficulty of mathematics in the text, and other factors with a bearing on the classroom situation.

Interpretation of the Data

Each index is calculated in a manner so that 0 represents virtually no student involvement; 1.0 represents material with an equal number of statements requiring no student participation and statements requiring some student thought. Progressively higher index numbers represent progressively higher ratios of investigative to noninvestigative material. Infinity would represent a book in which every statement and every figure would require analysis of some kind.

Every teacher must decide for himself just how much he wants his students to do. In general, chapters or books with indices much below about 0.4 will be primarily authoritarian and will contain few challenges to the student other than memorization of facts and definitions.

Conversely books with very high indices (much in excess of about 1.5) contain virtually nothing but questions. As such, they may not give the student enough data to work with effectively. Other reference sources or the opportunity to experiment extensively must be available to provide data upon which the student can base his generalizations and conclusions.

A very good teacher can use almost any textbook to good advantage. A highly discovery-oriented course can be run using the most traditional of textbooks if the teacher spends most of his class time on experiments and activities and uses the text as something to examine critically rather than as an authority upon which students base their conclusions.

Regardless of what approaches you elect to use, you should critically examine the textbook. Know how other parts of your course must be modified to take advantage of the useful features and to counteract the undesirable features of the textbook.

ACTIVITY 10 A

Make quantitative analyses of five science textbooks. For each book, complete a rating form such as the one on the next page.

NAME OF BOOK:

Text analysis

Number of page analyzed												Total
a. facts												
b. conclusions												
c. definitions												
I.												
d. questions asked but answered immediately												
e. questions requiring student to analyze data												
f. statement requiring student to formulate conclusion												
II.												
g. directions to student to perform and analyze activity												
h. question to arouse student interest: not answered immediately												
i. sentence directing student to figure; other types												
j. rhetorical questions												

Overall Involvement
Index for Text

$$\text{Total} \; \frac{\text{II}}{\text{I}} \; =$$

Figure and diagram analysis

Number of figure analyzed											
a. illustration only											
b. requires student to perform activity, use data											
c. illustrates way of setting up apparatus for activity											
d. fits none of above											

Overall Index for
Figures

$$\text{Total} \; \frac{\text{b}}{\text{a}} \; =$$

50

Activities index

Page number												
a. number of activities proposed per page												

Overall Index for Activities

$$\text{Total} \frac{a}{n} = \boxed{}$$

(where n = total number of pages examined)

Analysis of questions at chapter ends

Question number										Total
a. answer in text										
b. definition										
c. requires student to apply learning to new situation										
d. requires student to solve a problem										
e. fits none of the above										

Overall Index for Questions

$$\text{Total} \frac{c + d}{a + b} = \boxed{}$$

Analysis of chapter summaries

Chapter number												
a. repeats chapter conclusions												
b. raises new questions												

Overall Index for Summaries

$$\text{Total} \frac{b}{a} = \boxed{}$$

Subjective evaluation

1. Reading Level
2. Math Level
3. Other factors

Note: This form can also be used for rating single chapters of a textbook in which approaches vary greatly from chapter to chapter.

The Role of
Audiovisual Materials
in the Science Classroom

Teachers are often tempted to think of "film day" as a day off, when they can sit in the rear of the room and ignore everyday teaching duties. Many science films are made in a way that encourages this feeling. However, in order to use a film or other audiovisual aid properly, as much or more preparation time is involved as for a regular class session.

Before using any audiovisual aid (including motion picture films, film loops, filmstrips, overhead transparencies, and audio tapes) a teacher should have a clear behavioral objective in mind as a reason for using the aid. What will the student be able to do after he sees the audiovisual aid that he could not do before? What unique property of the audiovisual aid makes it the best way of reaching your behavioral objective? If you cannot state a valid behavioral objective, you will be wasting valuable class time even though the audiovisual aid might seem to make the class more "fun" for your students. (Once having fun becomes an objective of your course, whether explicitly or implicitly stated, you are probably in trouble. In a well-taught class the "fun" will come naturally as a consequence of student interest in the subject.)

In order to evaluate whether or not an audiovisual aid can be validly used, you will have to preview it. If this is impossible, it is better not to use the aid.

What properties of the various audiovisual media suit themselves specially to the attainment of particular behavioral goals and how, specifically, might you use these media to best advantage?

Motion Picture Films. Movies can bring dynamic events into the classroom: they show things in motion. Therefore, the first thing to look for in a film is the presence of scenes that live up to the capabilities of the medium. In a biology course for example, you might choose a film showing water birds landing on a lake. A valid behavioral goal to justify showing such a sequence might be stated as follows: After seeing this film the students should be able to write a detailed analysis of the way in which ducks land on water. Use of high-speed, slow motion photography to show landing of the birds would make the filmed sequence even more useful.

Many biological and physical events take place too slowly for a student to see dynamic details. Time-lapse photography being used in some of the better new films can provide a basis for developing scientific behavior in your students. Consider as an example the growth of a plant shown by a time-lapse camera. A behavioral goal that justifies the use of such a sequence might be phrased as follows: After seeing this sequence, the students should be able to describe and analyze the stages of growth of a given plant. A geological example is the movement of a glacier. The time-lapse method has been used to show the effects of glacier movement. Students may be asked to analyze the dynamics of this kind of situation also.

Another example of films that lend themselves to analysis by students is a well-known series on the behavior of bees.[1] The behavioral goal for such a series might involve asking your class to analyze how bees give instructions to each other about the locations of flowers and so forth.

These are only a few examples, but let us analyze what they and other suitable subjects have in common. First, they show dynamic relationships that cannot be observed in any way other than in nature or on a motion picture screen. In the case of time-lapse and slow motion photography, there is no other way than on film that the accelerated or slowed-down sequence can possibly be studied. (Note incidentally that much current original research on dynamic processes involves the use of these techniques.) Second, each of the examples cited above was presented to the students in the form of a sequence of events they were asked to observe, describe, and analyze. Third, films make it possible to isolate a subject and observe its action or behavior in a way that an untrained worker could not do without extensive specialized training (as in the case of the study of the bees). Fourth, films make it possible to bring large, expensive (and possibly dangerous) pieces of apparatus into the classroom so that students can become acquainted with the way in which they operate and the kinds of data they can furnish. Finally, films make it possible to bring into the classroom scenes and views of landscapes and objects the scope and size of which cannot be adequately demonstrated in still photographs or by verbal description. The motion picture projector has become a device for presenting raw data to the students rather than a device for presenting a summary of someone else's conclusions.

Unfortunately few films exist that fulfill these requirements. However,

[1] Studies by Karl von Frisch. Recent developments in the study of bees challenge some of von Frisch's conclusions. See *Science*, V. 158, 1967, pp. 1072–1077.

there are many films that contain excellent sequences surrounded by less suitable material. Here you have two alternatives. You can show the entire film and ask the students to concentrate their attention on certain parts of the film. However, a better technique is to show only the sequences that are going to be useful. This means extra work for you in that you will have to identify the good sequences and have the projector set just right before the class comes in.

One trouble with almost all existing motion picture films is that they have been made for the purpose of illustrating points rather than presenting data. As a result they usually have a detailed narration that tells the student exactly what he is looking at. Unless he finds this out for himself, he will probably not gain any new skills. The teacher can turn off the sound unit on the projector and use the film without narrative whenever the students are to do the analyzing themselves.

Another possible problem is the need to run sequences of film over again. If traditional films are to be used effectively, you will probably need a projector that can be reversed and run backward. For best possible results, use a projector equipped with a stop mechanism that enables you to hold any single frame on the screen and use the projector temporarily as a slide projector.

Many films show long sequences of details leading up to a final event or conclusion. In order to involve the students actively turn off the projector before the film gives its conclusion and ask members of the class to predict what they think is coming or what the conclusion will be. Then start the projector again so that the class can see what the film concludes. After this, if the class and the film do not agree, have the class analyze reasons for the disagreement.

Most motion picture films now available run from about ten to thirty minutes in length. When such long films are shown, the student is almost certain to become such a passive witness to the show that it is difficult to involve him. If you show a long film, prepare a script in advance that tells you where you should stop the film to interject class discussion, where you should turn off the sound to ask a question, where you should hold the film on a particular frame, where you should reverse the film or increase or decrease the speed. In order to use a long film in the most effective way you may have to spend up to two or three hours previewing and making notes.

Film Loops. A useful device that has recently become available is the film loop projector. A continuous loop of silent film up to four or five minutes in length can be shown over and over again with no rewinding. Work on these loops has been pioneered by the Biological Sciences Curriculum Study. Other organizations have also begun making similar loops. Commonly, film loops are accompanied by a teacher's guide or script that suggests how each loop can be used as a vehicle for discussion. If the guide does not state suitable behavioral goals for a given film loop, include some of your own. Sequences from longer films or from 8mm films that you have taken can be mounted in continuous loop cassettes if you wish to develop a school library of film loops.

Filmstrips and Color Slides. Filmstrips commonly come crowded with a number of title frames that give away most of the answers the students should determine for themselves. It is essential to preview all filmstrips carefully and to determine which frames provide the maximum opportunity for class discussion. Use only frames (or single slides) that raise problems worthy of discussion. A slide or filmstrip should nearly always be accompanied by a question from the teacher rather than by a statement of fact.

Overhead Projectuals. Many useful diagrams and charts can be effectively shown on overhead projectors. Most commercially produced projectuals (transparencies) concentrate on terminology and *showing* rather than on data and *asking*. Use the overhead projector as a supplement to blackboard space. Most overhead projectors come equipped with a roll of clear acetate, which can be used to prepare your own tracings of graphs and other materials before classes. Diagrams from books can be easily copied directly onto acetate overlays by various copying machines. The advantage of using overhead projectuals is that they can be reused and they leave the blackboard space free for other uses. The expense and time required to prepare your own set of projectuals are not great.

Several overhead projectuals giving additional data can also be overlaid on a basic transparency so that a set of data can be developed in the same sequence in which they would become available to an investigator. In the case of weather maps, for example, a sequence of overlays showing the development and movement of fronts can be used. As each overlay is added, students can be asked to predict what the situation will be three hours after the given set of data are received. Then the actual data for that period can be shown to check student predictions. The class can then analyze reasons for any substantial departure from the expected weather.

Overhead projectors may also be used in the same way that a bioscope or other relatively low-powered microprojector can be used. Growth of crystals in a solution, the geometry and details of larger structures on microscope slides, and the progress of certain chemical reactions are among the more or less "live" subjects suitable for projection onto a screen with the aid of an overhead projector. Using the overhead projector in this manner enables your whole class to observe the same thing at the same time. In this way you can be sure that all members of your class help each other learn how to observe systematically.

Audiotapes. Audiotapes can be used in biology courses where the sounds made by various animals might be analyzed in connection with the study of their behavior. In physics classes studies of frequency and pitch, Doppler effect, and so forth could be focused around audiotapes. Use such tapes for the purpose of analysis rather than for illustration.

ACTIVITY 11

1. Get a motion picture film on a science topic from a local film library (in your school or at a nearby university). Preview the film, analyze it, write behavioral objectives justifying its use in your classroom, and prepare a script showing where in the film you might make use of the following techniques:

    a. Stopping the projector to introduce questions.
    b. Turning off the sound.
    c. Reversing the film.
    d. Holding the film on a single frame while you bring up questions.

Try some of these techniques on a class and compare the response you get to the response you are used to getting in a traditional film showing that involves no attempt to use the films as a vehicle for discussion.

2. Acquire a film loop projector and film loops. Design a discussion activity around a film loop.

3. Select a series of color slides on a topic and prepare a short discussion activity using the slides as basic data requiring analysis by your students.

4. Find several diagrams suitable for reproduction as overhead projectuals and design a class discussion based upon them.

5. Acquire or make an audiotape presenting some scientific data and design a short activity around use of the tape.

Introduction of
Scientific Terminology

Science courses as taught by most teachers at all levels put special stress on science as a language. The presumption has been that, when a student is able to define correctly certain key terms, he "understands" the concept underlying the word. The concept of science as a language rather than science as a process is reflected in college board examinations, advanced placement examinations, and in state-wide examinations such as the New York State Regents examinations as well as in the average quiz or term examination in many classrooms.

Although scientists in each field have developed a special jargon all their own to facilitate communication on a professional level, the jargon should be regarded as the least important part of science. In courses concerned with the processes of science, technical vocabulary should be introduced only when it is clearly needed to facilitate communication.

However, science teachers should not avoid the introduction of technical vocabulary entirely. The following passage from Mark Twain's *A Tramp Abroad* makes it clear that complete avoidance of technical vocabulary does pose serious problems.

The man stands up the horse on each side of the thing that projects from the front end of the wagon, throws the gear on top of the horses, and passes the thing that goes forward through a ring and hauls it aft, and passes the other thing through the other ring and hauls it aft on the other side of the other horse, opposite to the first one, after crossing them and bringing the loose end back and then buckles the other ring underneath the horse and takes another thing and wraps it around the other thing I spoke of before and puts another thing over each horse's head, and puts the iron thing in his mouth and brings the ends of these things aft over his back, after buckling another one around under his neck, and hitching another thing on a thing that goes over his shoulders, and then takes the slack off the thing which I mentioned a while ago and fetches it aft and makes it fast to the thing that pulls the wagon, and hands the other thing up to the driver.

In Twain's description, more technical words are obviously needed to make communication easier.

How can a teacher decide what words are important and useful and what words are excess baggage? The author is against the introduction of conceptual notions through the use of words. Preceding pages have recommended extensive use of activities and open-ended discussions to introduce scientific processes, ideas, classifications, and facts. One good rule to adopt is never to give a technical word to a student until he *asks* for an easier way of expressing an idea. The following situations might serve as examples.

1. You are teaching a lesson on photosynthesis. Instead of introducing the word early in the lesson, conduct an activity in which students discover that plants produce sugars and starches from water and carbon dioxide by the action of sunlight on the green stuff in the plant. Throughout the discussion that follows the activity let the students continue to use long descriptive phrases to describe the process and to use "the green stuff" in referring to chlorophyll. As the discussion gets more involved, the need for a *handle* will usually become clear to the class. Finally a student will ask for some better words to refer to the process and to the green stuff. This is your clue to say, "Well, biologists call the process photosynthesis, and the green stuff is called chlorophyll." What do you do if the class never asks for the word? Then perhaps the word is not as essential as you thought and need not be presented to the class.

2. In a physics experiment, instead of giving students a large number of vocabulary words to refer to pieces of equipment they are using, let them find their own words. Ultimately they will end up in a situation similar to the one described by Mark Twain where they are putting this thing into that whatchamacallit and then that thing goes around and does such and so. At that point, your students may be shouting for *words* to simplify communication.

3. In a geology or earth science class you are working on a rock identification exercise. Let the students describe the particles of which the rock is made, but make no attempt to force mineral names into the discussion. Ultimately the students will tire of referring to "that clear stuff that breaks like a piece of glass" and will ask for a simpler name. At that point tell them that mineralogists call "that stuff" quartz. In any exercise on classification it is especially important to provide specific names only when a definite need for them arises.

Is this approach really useful? In his own teaching situations the author has recently tried to teach without stressing definitions. He has found that when he does not force rigid definitions on his own students they rapidly develop the ability to formulate their own definitions in a way that clearly indicates to him their familiarity with the ideas behind the word rather than a preoccupation with the word itself.

ACTIVITY 12

WHICH TECHNICAL WORDS ARE IMPORTANT?

1. Choose a long paragraph from each of five different textbooks.

2. Underline the technical words in each paragraph.

3. Rewrite each of the five paragraphs, replacing the technical words with ordinary language.

4. How many of the technical words were really essential to clear communication?

5. Take the lecture notes from a single lecture in one of your college science courses. Replace all technical words with ordinary language. How many useless words have you been asked to memorize in that lecture?

6. If you are a practicing teacher or student teacher, take the notes from one of your own lesson plans and underline all of the technical words you have introduced. Ask yourself how vital each of the underlined words really was.

The Art of Asking
Questions and of Leading Discussions

A teacher's task is to establish circumstances that favor the learning of certain specific concepts and the acquisition of specified skills and behavior. In the author's opinion lectures and highly structured activities and discussions rarely help you in any large measure to achieve this goal. Yet you cannot turn your students completely loose to do exactly as they choose.

In order to keep students more or less on the intended track the teacher must, of course, do some active leading. However, he must also develop the knack of guiding students without taking away from them the joys of discovery. When you ask a student to gather his own data and make his own generalizations, how can you help him without giving away the conclusions you hope he will formulate on his own? And if a student reaches a conclusion that is perhaps valid but not relevant to the concept you wish him to learn, how can you get him back on the right track? Effective leading involves learning how to ask useful leading questions and how to make helpful suggestions that still require the student to exert his own initiative in order to solve the problem at hand. You will have to be flexible and patient.

When a student asks a question, you have three main alternatives:

1. Give him a straight answer.
2. Answer his question with another question.
3. Make a specific suggestion about how he can find his own answer to the problem.

Which of these alternatives you elect in any given case will of course depend upon the circumstances. If you find yourself giving straight answers to too many questions, this is an indication that you may have adopted an authoritarian mode in your teaching. Teachers who "know" too many answers cannot expect their students to acquire much scientific behavior or to make very many discoveries.

The most effective teachers usually answer questions either with another question or with a suggestion. Yet even the best teachers sometimes give straight answers, so your technique should not degenerate to mere question asking. Developing the knack of asking useful and helpful questions requires practice and a great deal of attention on your part. When asked a question, many beginning teachers who want to get their students to do the thinking quickly throw back the question, "Well, what do *you* think?" The student's immediate reaction to this is usually, "If I knew what to think, I wouldn't have asked you in the first place!" Consider the following example:

Approach number 1

> Student: Mr. Jones, I've been looking at this mineral specimen for ten minutes and I'm still not sure. Is it quartz?
> Mr. Jones: Well, what do you think?
> (Student throws mineral at Mr. Jones, and stamps out of the room.)

Approach number 2

> Student: Mr. Jones, I've been looking at this mineral specimen for ten minutes and I'm still not sure. Is it quartz?
> Mr. Jones: Does it have a cleavage?
> Student: Not that I can see.
> Mr. Jones: How hard is it?
> Student: Harder than this piece of glass.
> Mr. Jones: According to your table, are those the properties you would expect to find in quartz?
> Student: Gee, yes!
> Mr. Jones: Do any other minerals on the chart seem to fit those properties?
> Student: No, I guess it must be quartz. (Big smile.)

In this example, by a series of questions and simple suggestions, Mr. Jones has helped his student through the process of observing and keying out a mineral. The next time, the student probably would not need to ask for help. If the specimen happened to have somewhat abnormal properties, Mr. Jones might have wanted to provide some extra information about how quartz occurs in many different forms, some of which might not quite fit the particular table the student happened to have available.

Suppose that during an activity or discussion a student makes a generalization or conclusion that either does not fit the data or is not relevant to the subject being studied. There is always the temptation to proclaim the student wrong and then to go hunting for a "right" answer. A more effective way of dealing with this situation is to ask a series of questions that lead the student to dissect and analyse his own conclusion. *He should be the one to say, "Why, I must be wrong then!"* Discovering through your own analysis that you are wrong can actually be an ego-building experience in itself. Usually the discovery that you were wrong also brings with it the discovery of an answer that is more acceptable and reasonable.

In leading class discussions you will commonly be in the position of having to ask appropriate questions to keep the discussion on the planned subject. A discussion that degenerates into a bull session is generally not productive. If the discussion involves analysis of data (as in the invitations to inquiry discussed earlier), questions that direct the attention of the students to certain aspects of the data may be necessary to get the discussion going. If you impose too much structure on a discussion or have goals that are too specific and inflexible, you may lose the very benefits you expected the discussion to produce.

ACTIVITY 13

Asking Questions

1. Make a tape recording of a session that you are teaching to either a peer group or a group of your students.

2. Play the tape over and write down each student question you were asked during the class period.

3. Write a short script showing:
   a. How you handled each question.
   b. What other ways you could have used to handle the same question.

Helping Students
Learn to Generalize

Early in a science course students should learn how to interpret data and make generalizations. Students, teachers, and scientists themselves often overgeneralize from their data. You should be cautious and try early in your course to develop good habits in your class. Some examples of valid and invalid generalizations are suggested below.

SAMPLE SITUATION

In a general science class a problem arises during a study of stream activity: What factors affect the velocity of stream water? You suggest that your students set up in the classroom a model stream and perform a series of experiments. The "model stream" consists of a length of eaves trough. You suggest (or let the class propose) the question, "Does the angle of slope of a stream bed have any relationship to the velocity of the stream?" Using a system of siphons, or a water tap opened a measured amount, your students hold constant the volume of water flowing down the trough. Then they time the rate at which a small cork floats down the trough while they vary the angle of inclination of the trough. From this information they calculate and graph the velocity of the model stream at various angles of slope.

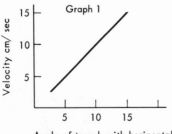

Other conditions specified
and held constant:
1. size of trough
2. 1 siphon ($\frac{1}{2}$" diameter)
3. height of head = 2'

Angle of trough with horizontal

The first generalization students will probably suggest may be approximately:

As the stream bed gets steeper, the velocity of the water increases at a constant rate.

This generalization would at first seem to fit the data. Nonetheless, this is an overgeneralization considering the available data. Let us examine what would happen at slightly higher angles of inclination:

Graph 2

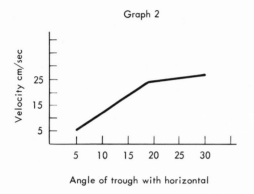

Other conditions specified and held constant:
1. size of trough
2. 1 siphon ($\frac{1}{2}$" diameter)
3. height of head = 2'

Angle of trough with horizontal

If the students had carried their measurements farther, they would have discovered that the slope of the curve became flatter at higher angles. The relationship changed and their first generalization turns out to be a serious oversimplification. How might the students have made a more cautious generalization on the basis of the more limited data in Graph 1? The statement below would have been a safer generalization to make:

As the angle of inclination of a model stream (consisting of an eaves trough x feet long and fed by a siphon with a half-inch diameter and a hydrostatic head two feet high) is increased from five to fifteen degrees with the horizontal, the velocity of the water increases at a constant rate.

This more cautious generalization is seen to specify the exact conditions for which the generalization holds true. Then if you wish to have students predict what they think will happen at higher angles, you may do so. But the more cautious generalization allows the student to modify his generalization without having to say, "My first generalization was wrong." Instead, he can say, "My first generalization was correct for the range of conditions I used in my first experiment, and now the additional data available allow me to amplify my generalization so that my ability to predict what will happen at higher angles will be improved."

A generalization should specify carefully the range of conditions for which it is applicable. When this rule is followed, students are not put in the position of having their generalizations turn out to be "wrong." It is easy to accept the idea that a prediction, which is clearly understood to be an extrapolation from the known to the unknown, can be erroneous because of changes that might occur over the unknown range.

Invitations to inquiry are especially appropriate for helping students learn to formulate careful generalizations from their data. In the above example you could have, for example, provided graphs for the students (without asking them to do the experimental work), asked them to make a generalization, and proceeded immediately to add to their information and caused them to question or modify their earlier generalization on the basis of Graph 2.

Evaluating Learning

Usually when we think of evaluating students and what they are learning, the words *test* and *grade* come to mind. In this section evaluation of learning will be considered in a broader sense than this. In the evaluation process, the main concern of a teacher should not be, "How smart is George, and what grade shall I give him?" but rather, "Has George gotten the idea, and, if he has not, how can I lead him to understand the relationship or learn the skill?"

In its broadest sense, evaluation can be thought of as the bridge between teacher and student. If evaluation in your classroom takes place only at the end of a lesson to determine what your students have and have not learned, you are playing a dangerous game. Essentially you are betting that most of your students will have learned what you intended them to learn. If they do not perform well on your quiz, the limitations of your teaching schedule may force you to leave an important concept, fact, or conclusion unlearned or incorrectly learned. True, most teachers at least review test answers with their classes, but does mere telling of what the "right" answer should have been necessarily guarantee that the class now knows what you wanted them to know? Evaluation in these circumstances becomes a drawbridge. You put down the bridge between yourself and your students only during quiz time, and you lose contact with what your students are learning between quizzes.

Think of every question you ask in class as part of a continuing process of evaluation. In evaluating every student response that you obtain—oral or written—you must decide whether or not the learning process is actively in progress. If your approach is not succeeding, you must be flexible enough to try new approaches to the subject.

Jerome Bruner suggests the interesting idea that:

. . . when children give a wrong answer it is not so often that they are wrong as that they are answering another question, and the job is to find out what question they are in fact answering.[1]

In a sense you must be like a boxer trying to get a punch in. You attempt several punches but they do not score. Finally you find an opening and are able to hit your target.

If you are not constantly evaluating whether or not you have succeeded in hitting your target—through the mechanism of constant evaluation of responses—you will lose contact with your students and thus fail in your teaching effort. The bridge between you and each student must be constantly open.

Many teachers develop the habit of listening to themselves and being mainly concerned with what they themselves are saying rather than in listening to and evaluating what the student is saying. As soon as you stop listening attentively to what each of your students is saying, you have lost contact. Evaluation cannot be truly effective on the level of a whole class. Instead, you must somehow find a way of constantly evaluating and keeping track of what each individual student in your class is learning.

In order to be effective with a large number of students, each of whom should ideally be treated as an individual, the teacher must train each student in such a way that he can correct his own errors. Otherwise, as Bruner suggests, you create a form of subject mastery that depends entirely on your perpetual presence.[2] One of your greatest goals very early in a course should be to evaluate carefully whether or not your students have learned *how to learn*. This can be done by correcting student errors in such a way that the learners learn how to correct their own errors. When this is achieved, the student becomes his own teacher and your direct contacts with him can become less frequent. A teacher's most important function is to make himself unnecessary!

In the preceding paragraphs we have been considering evaluation from a philosophical point of view. Now let us consider some practical ways of conducting a day-to-day program of evaluation in which each student's individual progress can be watched carefully.

1. Oral exchange of questions and answers. Whether you are conducting a laboratory activity, class discussion, or small group discussion, ask questions designed to focus the attention of your students on important relationships between various pieces of data they are obtaining or interpreting. If your class is accustomed to an activities approach, you will be able to deal with questions and problems of individual

[1]Jerome S. Bruner, *Toward a Theory of Instruction* (Cambridge, Mass.: Harvard University Press, 1966), p. 4.
[2]*Ibid.*, p. 53.

students or of small groups of students while they proceed more or less independently with their laboratory work.

2. *Written assignments.* Require your students to turn in brief laboratory reports and problem sheets often so that you can keep a record of individual progress and spot places where perhaps several students are being bothered by a similar problem. Then this smaller group can be given collective rather than individual help. If your class is well organized, you can require students to do again work that has not been satisfactory. Do not be satisfied with low grades. Insist instead that a certain minimum level be attained by each student on each major activity before allowing a student to go on to the next assignment.

3. *Anecdotal records.* Some teachers keep card files in which they make brief records of behavioral trends for each student. Such cards might be set up as shown:

```
┌─────────────────────────────────────────────────┐        Code letter
│                                                   │        suggestions:
│  Name ................     Date ........          │   wc — worked carefully
│  Code letters          Capsule description of     │   oh — offered hypothesis
│  to designate          what the student did       │   th — tested hypothesis
│  behavior              in lab: difficulties,      │   co — changed opinion
│                        successes                  │   sr — saw relationship
│                                                   │          etc.*
│                                                   │
│                                                   │
│                                                   │
└─────────────────────────────────────────────────┘
```

*Design and categories for card modified from Arthur Carin and Robert B. Sund, *Teaching Science Through Discovery* (Columbus, Ohio: Charles E. Merrill Books, Inc., 1964), p. 146.

Notations about progress in written work can also be added to show how each student is improving in his approach to problems. If you are able to maintain a file of anecdotal records of this sort, you will be able to keep close track of individual student improvement.

4. *Check Lists.* A check list including headings categorizing various kinds of student behavior and attitudes is perhaps easier to handle than the anecdotal record system and provides almost as close a check on how well the students are progressing. Such lists must be used regularly, however, if you are going to benefit from them. See the list on page 70 for an example of a form that might be used. For each student the teacher makes a check or minus under the various columns depending on whether the student is or is not doing what the chart lists. Alternatively, "A" for always, "S" for sometimes, and "N" for never might be used.

Student's names	Able	Baker	Craft	Dodd	Jones	Smith	Zilch
comes prepared							
follows directions							
plans ahead							
modifies procedures and equipment appropriately							
cooperates with group							
handles equipment properly							
dexterous with equipment							
observes carefully							
works effectively, neatly							
records data systematically in notebook							
makes independent decisions							
assesses the meaning of data frequently							
relates to specific problems							
aware of assumptions and limitations							
makes use of references							
overall performance							
used "I think" or "I'm not sure"							
offered hypothesis							
changed opinion							
tested hypothesis							
saw relationship between facts							
admitted mistake and tried to correct it							
admitted he didn't know							
criticized and evaluated own work							
gave credit to others when deserved							
repeated work to validate results							
used more than one resource							
applied science learning to new situation							
determined difference between truth and fiction							
asked good science questions							
avoided jumping to conclusions							

Modified from A. Carin and R. B. Sund, *Teaching Science Through Discovery* (Columbus, Ohio: Charles E. Merrill Books, Inc. (1964), p. 147.

5. *Quizzes.* Give frequent short quizzes. Make most or at least some of these quizzes noncredit or "diagnostic" quizzes. Allow the students to grade one another's papers. Return the papers immediately to their owners and conduct a short discussion on points with which students had difficulties. Then collect the papers so that you will personally have a chance to spot where specific students are having special difficulties. Announce to your students that failure to solve a problem in a satisfactory manner will not count against them but will give both you and them a chance to find out just how much has been learned. Quizzes of this type might on some days be substituted for laboratory reports. Whenever possible, quizzes should involve a problem to be solved or a situation to be analyzed rather than a conclusion or definition that the students might have memorized.

One way in which to emphasize the teaching and learning value of quizzes is to have them graded strictly on a "pass or fail" basis. If a student turns in a paper with a failing grade, require him to continue working on the subject and give him retests (using either the same quiz or different but similar quizzes) until he does achieve a passing grade. Let him know that only the "pass" gets recorded in your book and that he can try as many times (within reason) as necessary in order to succeed. Instead of forcing students to compete against one another, get each student to compete against his own past performance.

It may take some students longer than others to achieve the level of learning you desire, but your ultimate goal must be for every student to achieve a certain level. You should always feel some disappointment about your own abilities as a teacher when you have to leave a topic that you feel is still not understood by some of your students. At the same time, you have to face the fact that it will be rare for all of your students to be achieving at the level you hope for. You will have to learn to live with a certain degree of disappointment in your ability to reach all of your students. This is good, however, because it will force you to be constantly searching out new and better ways of reaching your students. When a teacher begins to think that all his students always achieve everything he wishes, he had better re-examine his whole program.

6. *Major Examinations.* It is traditional in most courses to give major, period-long examinations. These tests can be made an enjoyable experience for both teacher and students if the class is well prepared. Questions on longer examinations should be similar in style to the questions used regularly in oral exchanges, to questions given on quizzes, and to questions that accompany student laboratory work.

7. *Testing for Your Objectives.* If you have developed a good set of behavioral objectives for your course, the writing of good test questions should be a simple task. Since good behavioral objectives specify *in detail* the behavior you expect your students to exhibit at the

end of a unit of study, all you will need to do is go directly to your objectives and write questions based on the objectives. The more detailed and carefully written your objectives are, the easier is your task of preparing meaningful examinations that test directly for what you have been trying to teach. Objective writing gives both direction to your classroom activities and serves as a basis for evaluation.

Psychologists have written a great deal about the *transfer* of learning. Transfer can be thought of as the ability of a student to use behavior learned in one kind of situation and to adapt and apply it successfully to different kinds of situations. It involves the ability to take entirely new situations, approach them in a systematic way based on past experience, and to come up with reasonable solutions. Helping develop in students the ability to transfer their learning is obviously a highly desirable goal. Carefully written behavioral objectives, well-designed examinations and quizzes, carefully phrased questions at the teacher—pupil level, and well-organized laboratory and discussion activities can lead to this kind of result.

One way of forcing yourself to write examinations that do not stress simple memorization is to give open-book tests. When you allow students to use their books and notes, you are forced to ask questions that require transfer behavior. You obviously cannot merely ask them to copy definitions out of the book or repeat facts that can be looked up and copied quickly. You are forced to present problem situations, which the students must analyze using their books and notes as sources of data to help them formulate their own conclusions and generalizations.

8. *Types of Questions for Tests and Quizzes.* The large majority of questions on modern examinations seems to be either of the types called multiple-choice or true-false. In the author's opinion, it is difficult to measure learning or behavior through these kinds of questions. Questions that require students to outline their chain of reasoning are much more useful, because they make it possible to determine just why the student may need help and where he goes astray in his analysis. If an analysis is rated only "right" or "wrong" as in a multiple-choice or true-false test, all you can do is give the student being tested a grade. You are not helped in finding out how to lead the student to a better analysis. Objective examinations often turn out to be subjective by demanding that the student show the same bias the teacher has in order to get a high grade. In this sense, the author does not believe objective tests serve a very useful teaching function. Their main value is in getting a quick, cheap grade for the student.

Essay questions and problems must be graded very carefully, which takes time, but they do provide a unique contact with the level of student learning and behavior.

There are many interesting kinds of problems and questions that teachers do not commonly use. Many of us tend to think of an examination as a sheet of paper containing a number of questions with appropriate blank spaces left for "blackening in between the lines," marking "T" or "F," writing a fill-in word, or writing a short sentence or essay. Students get bored by always having the same kind of test. When possible you should attempt to find ways to make exams more interesting and challenging.

Laboratory courses lend themselves well to *practical examinations.* When your students come into the room, have a different lab set-up at each place with a question or two written on a card at each station. Give each student a set period of time, perhaps two or three minutes, at each station to answer the questions on the card. Set-ups might include: microscope slides; partially dissected animals; things to classify; physical relationships to observe and interpret; a simple chemical change to describe, interpret, and write an equation for; a rock or mineral to describe; and so on depending on the subject being studied.

Some teachers have taken their students on field-trip examinations. At each station the students are given certain definite questions to answer. Student performance on this kind of activity can be made an important factor in determining the course grade. Students can also be taken on vicarious field trips by means of slides or films. On a recent geology examination the author showed two slides of rock outcrops. The students were asked to: (1) Describe what they saw. (2) State how they might interpret the relationships they saw. Students were given a five-minute "visit" to each outcrop. One of the main objectives of this exercise was to evaluate whether or not the students could distinguish between an observation and an inference, a fact, and a conclusion. This kind of question provided specific information about how certain students could be helped to improve their abilities to distinguish between these two fundamental scientific activities: observation and interpretation. Short clips of motion pictures or of film loops might be used in similar fashion if you were concerned with the dynamics of a process rather than with the essentially static configuration of a rock outcrop.

Using a hypothetical situation is especially useful in evaluation of transfer. In an astronomy unit, for example, if a student has been studying the solar system, set up a hypothetical grouping of planets and stars that differs in certain ways from the solar system but to which students can nonetheless apply some of the principles used in interpreting relationships in the solar system. Ask the class to analyze and interpret statements about observations pertaining to the hypothetical configuration.

9. Outside-Observer Techniques of Evaluation. In order to get outside opinions on how successful you are in getting students involved, band together with some of your colleagues and sit in on one anothers' classes occasionally during a free period. Learn to furnish one another with objective opinions about possible improvements. Several objective techniques for having your classroom activities evaluated might be proposed.

In one such technique the observer sits in the back of the room with a seating chart. Each time a student responds, the observer classifies the response and marks a code on the seating chart so that a running record of the kinds of responses made by each responding student is obtained. The following code was suggested to me by John H. Merrill:[3]

I. Motivation for response by student
>v—*voluntary* response to a question or unsolicited statement from the student
>t—the student answers a question directed to him by the *teacher*
>s—*student* answers a question initiated by another student

II. Nature of response by student
>f—statement of *fact*
>r—*reasoned* statement which demonstrates that the student must be doing some thinking or analyzing
>q—*question* asked by the student
>o—no response (as in case where student is asked a question by the teacher and answers, "I don't know," or doesn't answer at all)

III. Quality of response by student
>r—right
>w—wrong
>a—appropriate
>i—illogical
>t—trivial
>p—poorly expressed
>*—extremely so

Sample of a portion of a seating chart and interpretations

seat 1	seat 2	seat 3
v-r-a		t-f-w
vt-f-rp		t-o
v-q-ap		vt-f-r

According to this scheme you would obtain the following information:

Student Number 1 responded three times:

[3]Technique suggested to me by John H. Merrill, formerly a teacher at Fox Lane School, Bedford, New York and in the public schools of West Hartford, Connecticut, and now with Educational Services, Incorporated.

74

a) He volunteered a reasoned statement appropriate to the discussion.

b) He volunteered a response to a teacher-initiated question. His response was a fact that was correct but poorly expressed.

c) He volunteered a question that was appropriate but poorly expressed.

Student Number 2 did not respond at all during this period.

Student Number 3 responded three times:

a) The teacher asked the student a question, which he answered with a statement of fact that was wrong.

b) The teacher asked him a question that he could not answer at all.

c) He volunteered an answer to a teacher question. The answer was a statement of fact judged by the teacher to be right.

Put your colleagues to work on this kind of mutual teacher-evaluation program and you may be able to learn who are the students who need to be called on more; who are the ones who consistently give incorrect or inappropriate answers and thus need extra help; and who are the alert ones, who might be moved ahead more rapidly or given extra project work to keep their interest high.

Another technique of evaluating teacher-pupil interaction has been described by Flanders and others.[4] In this technique an observer sits at the back of the room and every few seconds records an index number from a list of categories designed to include all possible forms of teacher and student interaction. The categories are mutually exclusive, and well-defined ground rules tell the observer what to do in ambiguous cases. Use of such sophisticated evaluation techniques requires a certain amount of practice, but well-trained observers achieve fairly reproducible results. This technique gives the teacher an overall view of the general kind of verbal behavior that he and his students are displaying. However, evaluation schemes of the Flanders type do not identify the strong and weak points shown by individual students. Furthermore, they also do not indicate the percentage of students who are responding. A teacher can obtain a very high rating on a Flanders-type scale by interacting only with two or three bright students and allowing the others to flounder.

---

[4]Ned Flanders, *Interaction Analysis in the Classroom*, School of Education, University of Michigan, 1966.

ACTIVITY 14

1. For Activities 1, 4, 5, 6, 7, 8, and 10 you have been asked to state behavioral objectives in conjunction with activities you have been asked to prepare or analyze. Go back over these activities and prepare the following:

a. Three objective-type (multiple choice, true-false, or single word fill-in answers) questions that would help you evaluate whether or not your objectives had been achieved.

b. Three short essay or problem-solving questions to test for your objectives.

2. Prepare three quiz questions that involve the use of special techniques (slides, films, practical exercises, and so forth).

3. Prepare three questions you would use on an open-book test. Make sure that the questions are not such that mere copying from the book will provide a correct answer.

4. Design a short section of a practical laboratory examination. Describe in detail the objects that are to be located at each of five different stations, how long each pupil would be allowed at the station, and exactly what you would expect him to be able to do at the station.

5. Visit a classroom and conduct an "outside observer" analysis of the type proposed by Merrill and described in the preceding pages. Alternatively, prepare and use an evaluation sheet of your own, which you think would be useful to you in evaluating how successful you are in getting your students involved.

6. Use a tape recorder to record a class you teach. After the period, replay the tape several times and analyze your own performance, using one of the "outside observer" techniques of objective analysis.

Teaching by Contract
and Independent Study Methods:
Programming Your Course

Learning behavioral skills lends itself well to various forms of programmed instruction, although many existing programmed textbooks involve a highly structured group of questions stressing learning of vocabulary and factual information. These will not be treated here, for they are mainly an aid to memorization. Memorization of factual information should be a minor goal of any science course.

Well-planned programs with proper behavioral objectives enable a teacher to ascertain that no student leaves a particular unit of study until he has demonstrated a minimum level of competence. Teaching by program or contract can be done in many ways, ranging from an approximation of traditional group teaching to a completely independent study program. For variety, a course may be divided into modules, some of which involve programmed, independent study and others of which involve more conventional group teaching. As you begin to experiment with programmed study, choose small units of study and gradually work toward more complete programming.

One convenient way of programming a unit of study is to have your students sign learning *contracts*. In one kind of contract, students are given a list of tasks and informed that their grades for the particular unit of study depend directly on the number of tasks that they perform satisfactorily. The tasks may include laboratory exercises, problems, reading assignments, written papers, and quizzes. Rate each task on a pass-or-fail basis. If the students do not perform the task satisfactorily, they must do it over or revise their materials in some way before resubmitting them if they wish to get credit for that particular section of the unit. Certain essential parts of the unit should be required in order for the students to pass. Other activities are made optional, and the number of these activities satisfactorily completed determines the level of the passing grade: A, B, C, or D. The students are not allowed to submit optional tasks until they have satisfactorily completed the required work.

77

Why is the word "contract" applied to these programs? At the beginning of the unit each student is given a complete list of the requirements, both required and optional, and is asked to sign a statement such as the following:

I understand that in order to receive a minimum passing grade (D) for this unit of study, I must complete all of the tasks marked "required" on the above list. In order to receive a grade of C, B, or A, I must in addition complete the optional tasks specified above as required for those grades.

Signed _____

Some teachers carry the contract a step further and require each student to contract for a specific grade by completing a sentence such as:

The grade I wish to contract for is _____

Signed _____

This statement can be used in one of two ways:

1. As a nonbinding contract. Here the contract merely informs you generally about the level of effort various students intend to put forth, and it helps you to know something about how each student rates himself.

2. As a binding contract in which the student receives an extra grade penalty if he fails to meet the grade requirements he signed for and in which he must do special extra work if he decides to try for a higher grade than the one for which he initially contracted.

Making your students contract for a specific grade has the advantage of forcing them to evaluate their own abilities and to learn how to estimate their capabilities in realistic terms, but if penalties are established for not meeting the terms of the contract, tension in the classroom is raised. If a student has underestimated his ability and has no way of renegotiating for a higher grade, he may lose interest in the subject and create problems. Therefore, it might be profitable for the student to allow him to renegotiate his contract halfway through the period of time allowed for completion of the unit. Once he has signed this final contract, he must either meet its terms or be penalized. This enables the student who thought he could do B work but has realized that he cannot reach this goal to complete the rest of the unit at the C level. It also permits a student who suddenly discovers that he loves the subject and is able to do well in it to receive without penalty of extra work the higher grade his performance merits.

An example of a binding contract used by Kilburn is on pp. 80–81.

Using a contract unit of the type reproduced in this example makes it possible to be sure that every passing student in the class has attained a certain minimum level of achievement in a given time period. It is also possible to keep the members of the class working on approximately the same topic for the same period of time. Thus, although different students may be working on different activities during laboratory periods and reading different materials in class and at home, it is still possible to schedule regular group discussions and arrange for students doing special projects to report their results to the rest of the class.

One important pitfall to avoid if possible is to put your students so much on a plane of independent study that they do not have a chance to interact with each other in group activities. Science is not a one-man affair, and students must learn to cooperate and exchange information as well as to work independently.

Another approach to programmed teaching is a system used by L. H. Parsons of Central Technical High School, Syracuse, New York. No actual contract is signed in this approach. Each student is provided at the beginning of each unit of study with a sheet of specific directions, and problems relating to the unit of study. Each student must complete all of the specified activities and problems and submit an appropriate written report on the unit. Upon satisfactory completion of the program and completion of a unit test taken by each student individually when he is ready for it, the student proceeds to the next study unit. No attempt is made to keep the whole class working together. The better students can proceed to the end of the course at a rapid pace and have time for certain optional work at the end of the school year. The slower students may lag behind a specified number of chapters. Grade in the course is based on the total amount of work completed satisfactorily.

A CONTRACT UNIT ON ROCKS AND MINERALS*

NAME _____

The grade you will receive depends on the work you do!! Contract to work for a letter grade as listed below.

F—Required work incomplete
D—Complete only required work
C—Required work + 2 from I.
              2 from II.
              2 from III.

B—Required work + 4 from I.
              4 from II.
              6 from III.
A—Required work + 6 from I.
              6 from II
             10 from III.

Place a check mark opposite the work you select. Keep an account on one copy of the contract and return the other with your work plan and contracted grade.

Contract terms:

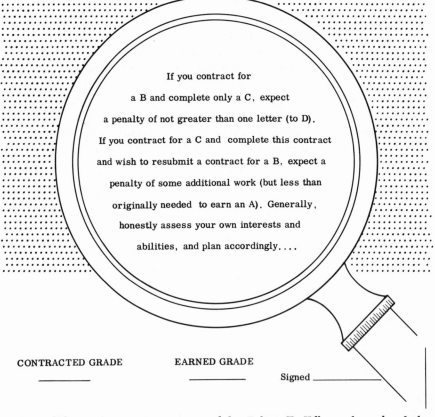

If you contract for

a B and complete only a C, expect

a penalty of not greater than one letter (to D).

If you contract for a C and complete this contract

and wish to resubmit a contract for a B, expect a

penalty of some additional work (but less than

originally needed to earn an A). Generally,

honestly assess your own interests and

abilities, and plan accordingly....

CONTRACTED GRADE   EARNED GRADE

_____   _____   Signed _____

*This contract unit was prepared by Robert E. Kilburn, formerly of the Fayetteville-Manlius New York School district and presently a supervisor of science education in the Newton, Mass. school system. I wish to thank Mr. Kilburn for permission to reproduce this material.

SELECTIONS	CONTRACTED	COMPLETED	SELECTIONS	CON'TED	COMP.	SELECTIONS	CON'TED	COMP.
I Reading and Writing			II Rock and Mineral Identification Skills			III Activities		
Required			Required			Required		
A			A			A		
B			B			B		
C			C			C		
D			D			D		
E						E		
F						F		
						G		
						H		
						I	Any 12	
						J		
						K		
						L		
						M		
						N		
						O		
						P		
						Q		
Optional			Optional			Optional		
A			A			A		
B			B			B		
C			C			C		
D			D			D		
E			E			E		
F			F			F		
G			G			G		
H			H			H		
I			I			I		
J			J			J		
K			K			K		
L			L			L		
M			M			M		
N			N			N		
			O			O		
			P			P		
			Q			Q		
						R		
						S		
						T		
						U		
						V		
						W		

CONTRACT UNIT ROCKS AND MINERALS

The following lists contain the course content for the next few weeks. The grade for this time will be determined by the amount of this work you successfully complete in the next four weeks.

I. Reading and writing

Required

A. Read N&S, 8–18; submit list briefly defining each italicized word: Due ————————

B. Read T&K, 209–234, submit answers to review questions. Due ————————

C. Read N&S, 20–40 major ideas, not ital. words, examed orally, due before D.

D. Read T&K, 242–268; submit answers to review questions. Due ————————

E. Read N&S, p. 43–55; submit key-styled outline of all rocks mentioned in text. Due ——

F. Read one of the selections from the optional list. Due at end of the unit.

KEY

N&S: Namowitz and Stone, *Earth Science Text*

T&K: Thurber and Kilburn, *Exploring Earth Science*, Allyn and Bacon Inc., 1965

R&R: Read and report orally

OE: Oral Exam

Optional

A. "Interaction Between Light and Minerals," Nat. Hist., 53–57, Oct. '65, R&R.

B. "Sediment. Origins of Rock Layering," Nat. Hist., 50–55, Dec. '65, R&R.

C. "Time's Traces in Sediments," Nat. Hist., 53–61, Feb. '63, R&R.

D. "Diamonds in Meteorites," *Sci. Am.*, p. 26, Oct. '65, R&R.

E. "Rocks and Minerals," in *The Crust of The Earth*, pp. 128–146, R&R.

F. "The Formation of Mineral Deposits," same as E, 146–154, R&R.

G. "Rockhounds Uncover Earth's Natural Beauty," *Nat. Geog.*, p. 631, Nov. '51, R&R.

H. Read one issue of "Rocks and Minerals" for one hour-report on its worth.

I. "Notes on the Clintonville Dikes, Onondaga County, NY," NYS Museum Pub. #286, p. 119. OE including locating local deposits on top sheet.

J. Skim "Gypsum Resources and Gypsum Industries of New York," reading all local references. OE including locating local deposits on top sheet.

K. Skim either NYS Museum Pub. #434, 343, or 14 or ————. Brief written summary.

Reading and writing (cont'd.)

Optional

L. Read and understand organization of U.S. Geol. Survey Bulletin 1072 F. Written summary.

M. "Minerals and Mineral Ores" in *The Earth* (Fenton). Written summary.

N. "The Great Treasure Hunt" in *The Earth* (Life). Written summary.

II. Rock and mineral identification skills

Required

A. Learn names of minerals in collection. Tested by identifying same mineral types. Passing score—90%

B. Learn names of Hardness Scale of Mohs and devise a method to remember it.

C. Learn names of rocks in collection. Test as in above.

D. Pass test in identifying microchips of minerals.

Optional

A. Prepare a display of unweathered surfaces of fifteen local rocks. Identify all you've studied.

B. Same as in A (above), with minerals.

C. Learn six additional important minerals. OE.

D. Learn five important additional ores. OE.

E. Learn five different varieties of quartz. OE.

F. Collect minerals from two sites listed in "Field Trip Guide to Onondaga County" (or other sites you know).

G. Make a display of cardboard models of different crystal shapes.

H. Perform chemical tests to identify several minerals (tests such as bead tests, charcoal block tests, flame tests).

I. T&K p. 235 #3

J. 236, #4

K. 237, #12

L. 238, #7

M. 269, #3

N. 271, #5

O. 271, #6

P. 271, #9

III. Activities (T and K)

Required (A + 12 others)	*Optional*
A. 211, include color, luster, hardness, streak, cleavage-fracture, and specific gravity of galena, hematite, gypsum.	A. Compare the specific gravity of two rocks by three different methods.
B. 218–219[1]	B. Attend Syracuse Gem and Mineral Soc. meeting. Write report.
C. 221	C. Attend Syracuse University Dept. of Geology outside lecture.
D. 222	D. Determine weight and volume of eight different pieces of a mineral. Graph and explain.
E. 223	E. Calculate % of weight lost when gypsum is heated. Calculate % of water in $CaSO_4 \cdot 2H_2O$. Propose and defend possible explanations for the difference in these two values.
F. 225 (2 analyses)	F. Analyze six or more different rock samples from a cliff for % calcite.
G. 227[1], 227[2] (any one chemical)	G. 217[23]
H. 235, #2 (do heating at home)	H. 220[3]
I. 236, #5 (at home or school)	I. 235, #3
J. 243[1]	J. 236, #4 prepare a collection
K. 244[2]	K. 237, #9
L. 246	L. 237, #13 or 14
M. 255	M. 238, #6
N. 258[2]	N. 239, #13
O. 270, #1	O. 247
P. 271, #3 (locally important) or NY state important)	P. 249 sketch observations
Q. 237, #11	Q. 250
	R. 266–7 (counts as two)
	S. 269, #1
	T. 269, #3
	U. 269, #6 (5 different igneous or metamorphic rocks)
	V. 270, #10
	W. 271, #6

In an elementary college geology course that the author teaches at Syracuse University, he is presently experimenting with a contract of the nonbinding type. This contract is a full-semester contract involving about thirty required tasks, each graded on a pass-or-fail basis. Required tasks include regular weekly laboratory reports. regular outside problem sets, field trip reports, short essays, and short, single-skill quizzes (mineral identification, rock identification, map study, and so forth). Each of these tasks must be satisfactorily completed in order for a student to receive a minimum passing grade. When quizzes are retaken, the second quiz is not a repeat of the first quiz, but a new one. This discourages rote learning of answers to the first quiz and puts emphasis on the ability to apply skills to new situations.

In addition to the required tasks, an additional thirty optional tasks are designated, including optional readings, film viewings, attendance at approved lectures, participation in independent or extra field trips, and approved independent research projects (either original or library research). Satisfactory performance of optional tasks is evaluated in short oral interviews between individual students and course instructors. Students may propose their own optional readings and other tasks in keeping with their own interests. Some students try to spread their optional work over several topics. Others select one or two main areas of interest and do studies in depth. In order to qualify for a course grade of C students must in addition to completing all of the required tasks submit five optional tasks. A grade of B requires fifteen optional tasks, and an A requires twenty optional tasks. Further check on quality of performance is maintained by a mid-term and a final examination. No credit is attached to the mid-term examination, but in addition to completing the appropriate number of required and optional tasks a student must obtain an A or B on the final examination in order to receive an A or B in the course.

Advantages to this type of contract are:

1. The class as a whole can be kept working on the same general required topics, although the slower students may also be finishing work formerly judged unsatisfactory.

2. The better students are able to get appropriate credit for doing outside work in areas of special interest to them.

3. No student passes the course without achieving a certain minimum competence in certain critical skills.

4. Passing the course becomes a matter of hard work and application rather than of skill in taking examinations. Examination pressure is lower (except, of course, for the A and B students).

Elaborate independent study systems involving study in carrels equipped with audiovisual materials, laboratory equipment, programmed study material, and tape-recorded instructions are being introduced in some schools. Other institutions have begun experimenting with computer-monitored analysis and response techniques. Such systems will allow teachers to handle heterogeneously grouped classes in optimum fashion. But even when elaborate machinery and facilities are available, teachers must still provide opportunities for student—group interaction and student—teacher interaction. Good independent study programs also can be designed and put into operation without elaborate equipment. Contract systems provide a means of being sure that behavioral goals set up for your classes are achieved, even in heterogeneously grouped classes. Note, however, that you will usually have to set up the details of your own programs. You must be certain that you have developed adequate behavioral goals before you begin setting up a contract.

ACTIVITY 15

1. Select a unit of study suitable for teaching in a period of two to four weeks and write a detailed contract indicating what tasks your students must be able to perform in order to pass the course. Specify in detail what the basis for assigning grades will be and how you will evaluate whether or not a student has reached the minimum level of achievement. List in detail all required and optional laboratory activities, specify reading assignments, and other work.

2. State your behavioral goals.

3. State the specific concepts with which your contract unit deals.

4. Try your unit out on a class, and, afterwards, solicit their opinion on the approach.

Problems of Discipline
in an Activity-oriented Classroom

The word discipline has several meanings. Most commonly, teachers think of discipline as having students submit to authority and control. If we go back to the Latin roots of the word *disciplina*: *dis*, apart, and *cipere*, to hold or to take, we discover that the authoritarian view of discipline is not what the word should really convey to the teacher. We have discipline in a classroom when students are disciples who follow but nonetheless who are taking ideas apart—pupils who are *learning*. A better definition for the teacher to adopt is that discipline is "training that develops self-control, character, or orderliness and efficiency."[1] A classroom in which students sit with hands folded is no more a disciplined classroom than is a classroom characterized by general rowdiness.

You will have to expect a fairly high noise level in any classroom where activities are in progress. In order to decide whether or not learning is in progress, you will have to listen to the conversations. If students are talking mainly about the activity and arguing over techniques, data, and conclusions, then you have good discipline in your classroom.

The main problem in establishing good discipline is to get off on the right foot at the beginning of the year. With an untrained class, start the year with somewhat structured activities and discussions. Train your class to come in and start working immediately. Convey the idea that your classroom is to be a place where serious study is in progress. One device to help establish this kind of relationship early in the term is to have a snap quiz, activity, or discussion prepared to begin as soon as the class arrives. When your students realize that the moment they step into the room their study of science begins, you have won the major part of the battle. You must, of course, find your own special tricks for

[1]*Webster's New World Dictionary of the American Language*, College Edition (Cleveland: World Publishing Company, 1960), p. 416.

establishing an aura of "science in progress" for your classroom. Once the tone of your relationship with the class is properly set you may proceed to more open-ended exercises in which you give the students progressively more liberty to approach problems in their own ways.

Developing a
Personal Style of Teaching

The author has not intended in the preceding pages to try to impose any particular style of teaching. Necessarily, there must be as many different styles as there are teachers. What works for one teacher will not necessarily work for another. Furthermore, in order to be effective, a teacher should be the master of several different styles or approaches, because not all students will respond to the same style.

First try to discover the *style of learning* of each of your students. In the early stages of evaluating your class, attempt to categorize your students according to the techniques to which they as individuals respond best. (Note the importance here of keeping careful records evaluating each student. Anecdotal records will probably be most helpful in categorizing your students.) Once you have recognized differences in learning styles you can gradually help students with poor learning techniques improve their study habits. Point out to the class as a whole interesting differences in learning behavior and style of individual students. Members of a class should be able to see and evaluate the relative effectiveness and speed of methods used by their peers to work out problems in different ways. Exploit differences within the peer group to fullest advantage rather than attempting to shape a class in your own image. The ability to perceive differences in learning behavior of various students and to adjust teaching style accordingly is one of the most important attributes of an effective teacher.

Even with individual students you must vary the style of your teaching. A classroom without variety and surprises quickly becomes dull. All of the methods with which you have experimented during the preceding pages and also other techniques you will find described in other methods books should be used from time to time.

Basically, ways of teaching and learning in the classroom can be divided into three main categories:

1. Activities. This category includes laboratory experiments, workbook exercises, problem solving, student demonstrations, preparation of reports and projects, and any other student research activity in which the students are physically involved in independent or group work and the teacher merely supervises in a general way and from a distance.

2. Discussions. Any discussion involving both teacher and students would fit into this category. Discussion involving only students (student—student arguments and conversations) might more appropriately be considered under the activities category.

3. Presentations of information. Lectures or straight talk by the teacher, presentation of oral reports by students, use of many kinds of audiovisual materials, teacher demonstrations, and any other presentations in which the class as a whole passively listens or simply reads would be included in this category.

Naturally, what goes on during any one class period will rarely fit exclusively into one or another of these categories. More likely at least two and perhaps all three of these categories might be in use in some kind of blend. For example, lectures are often interrupted by short discussions of unclear points. Laboratory investigations may be introduced by teacher talk and interrupted at appropriate times by teacher talk or by class discussion of problems in technique or presentation and examination of results. However, at any one moment what is going on in the classroom may be assigned exclusively to one or another of these categories.

A useful way of representing the kinds of blends of categories that might be used is a triangular diagram such as the one below. In the diagram, each corner represents 100% of the teaching method named in the corner. For example, point a in the diagram represents a class period devoted entirely to activities. Point b represents a period in which

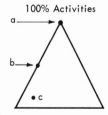

100% Activities

100% Discussion   100% Presentation of Information

50% of the time was spent in discussion and 50% in performing activities. Point *c* represents a class period during which most of the time (about 80%) was spent in class discussion, but during which the teacher spent a small percentage of the time (about 10%) presenting information and in which the students spent about 10% of the time working on an activity. Any point on one of the sides of the triangle represents a blend of the two behavioral types described by the words at the ends of the line, the percentage of each being proportional to the distance away from the opposite end of the line. Any point within the triangle represents a blend of the three categories.

Not only can single class periods be rated on such a triangle, but a whole unit of work or a whole course can be plotted so that we can see graphically just what teaching method predominates in any classroom. This can be done qualitatively, by making a rough guess as to what particular blend was involved in each day's class and then plotting a point on the diagram to characterize the class period. Or it can be done quantitatively by developing a rating scale such as the Flanders scale described in the chapter on evaluation so that an objective measure of the amount of time spent on each of the categories may be obtained. The figure below is an example of a diagram representing about five weeks of classroom time (twenty-five class periods). From the distribution of points, each of which represents the blend of activities in a single class period, it can be seen that the teacher represented spends most of his class time on combinations of activities and discussions with an occasional lecture, report, demonstration, or reading period.

100% Activities

100% Discussion   100% Presentation of Information

The diagram below summarizes a unit of twenty-five class periods, which would be characteristic for a teacher with quite a different emphasis:

100% Activities

100% Discussion   100% Presentation of Information

In this example the teacher is primarily engaged in the presentation of information and the students are apparently given little opportunity to perform activities of any kind. Some class discussions do take place, but there is always a strong element of "presentation of information" in the lessons.

Thus, triangular diagrams such as the examples shown above representing a continuum of variation among the three categories of teaching (and learning) behavior can be divided up roughly into fields that give broad information about the kinds of things going on in the classroom. The diagram below is divided to show what the average positions might mean.

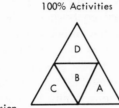

100% Activities

100% Discussion   100% Presentation of Information

Field A represents basically a lecture–textbook approach, which is probably a course mainly in history of science rather than in science. Field B represents a classroom in which there are few purely investigative things going on but in which there is great variety of teaching behavior. Field C includes classes where discussion is the primary activity. Field D is a classroom in which student activities predominate.

Which field of the triangle should you aim for in planning your own course? This must be determined by your own specific classroom goals. In general, however, if you wish to teach *science*, avoid an average level of performance that would fit into Field A. The triangle below shows where the author feels that teachers should operate:

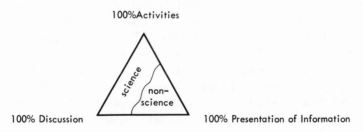

100% Activities

100% Discussion   100% Presentation of Information

If, in the course of evaluating your own teaching behavior, you find that your classes on the average fall into the zone marked "non-science," perhaps you should re-evaluate your teaching methods.

Developing an effective personal style of teaching science involves more than simply looking at your teaching from the viewpoint of activities, discussions, and lectures. One man's lectures may be more potent than another man's discussions or activities. In addition to evaluating whether an activity, discussion, or presentation is going on in the class-room you must also examine, evaluate, and develop another dimension: the *mode* of your approach. Let us consider two main *modes of teaching*:

1. The authoritarian mode.
2. The investigative mode.

The *authoritarian mode* appears in lectures when the instructor presents conclusions as more or less absolute and when he stresses rightness or wrongness—with his own answers and ideas representing the absolute "right" in the class. Note an apparent contradiction however: many so-called activities can also be taught in the authoritarian mode. This would apply strictly to books with fill-in answers that are "right" or "wrong" and in which the student *must* prove some predetermined result in order to get credit for having done the exercise. Many workbooks impose an authoritarian mode on activity situations. Many textbooks are inherently authoritarian in nature. They present science in terms of absolutes. Discussions may be taught entirely in the authoritarian mode. For example, the teacher may ask questions that the students must answer in certain words. Or the "discussion" may be entirely a matter of having students define words assigned as homework or of having students parrot conclusions from previous lessons or from the book.

The *investigative mode*, on the other hand, appears when you require your students to formulate their own classifications, definitions, and conclusions, when you require them to analyze data and accept, discuss, and analyze their results whether or not these results coincide with what you as teacher had expected. It is entirely possible to lecture in the investigative mode. In order to do this you would carefully outline all data leading up to a generalization and then proceed to analyze the generalization in terms of its limitations and general applicability. Textbooks written in the investigative mode ask frequent questions, which force the student to analyze situations and make his own conclusions. Discussions conducted in the investigative mode involve acceptance, recognition, and analysis of student answers and ideas rather than a striving to get at some predetermined answer. Activities in the investigative mode may be either structured or open-ended, but they must never spell out procedures too carefully, and they must not lead inexorably to some single conclusion or answer.

Obviously there is a continuum of variation between the two modes. This continuum can be represented as the line segment shown below.

Investigative _____ Authoritarian mode
mode 100%   100%

On this line, a point near the "investigative" end would mean that the

94

teacher generally uses the investigative mode of teaching and only occasionally brings in an authoritarian note. The author doubts seriously if it is possible to teach entirely in the investigative mode. On the other hand, it is clear that far too many science teachers limit themselves almost entirely to the authoritarian mode.

As you develop, analyze, evaluate, and modify your own teaching style, it is more important to be concerned with the mode of your teaching rather than with whether or not you have a high "activities rating." It is probably safe to make a few tentative generalizations about the relationship of the triangular diagrams representing the classroom blend of activities, discussions, and presentations to the linear diagram representing variation in mode of teaching.

1. In general, teachers who stress presentation of information in the long run teach mainly in the authoritarian mode.

2. Teachers who stress activities and discussions may or may not teach in the investigative mode. This depends entirely on how they conduct their classes.

In short, do not feel confident that just because you are doing a lot of activities and conducting a lot of discussions, you are necessarily doing a good job of teaching science. In any science course the mode of teaching you choose to adopt and the relative proportions of activities, discussions, and presentations must be consistent with your goals. If you wish for your students to use scientific approaches to problems, the teaching style you develop must help you attain this goal rather than hinder you. As you write and analyze the detailed behavioral objectives for your course, make sure they are expressed in the nonauthoritarian (investigative) mode. Consider the following examples:

a. At the end of this unit of study the student should be able to show that the angle of reflection of a ray of light is equal to the angle of incidence.

b. At the end of this lesson the student should be able to define density as the amount of mass in a given volume.

Both of these objectives, although properly stated in behavioral terms, are stated in the authoritarian mode. They specify exactly how the student must phrase his conclusions and define his terms. The obvious way to test for these objectives is to ask simple recall questions requiring only rote memorization—a very low level of behavior. The two examples given can be restated in the investigative mode so that they require more sophisticated (and scientific) behavior:

a. *(Revised)* At the end of this lesson the student should be able to formulate conclusions about the relationship between incident and reflected rays of light, and he should be able to apply his conclusions to the solving of new problems.

b. *(Revised)* At the end of this lesson the student should be able on the basis of his experimental work to formulate a definition of density and to differentiate among density, weight, volume, and mass.

Using the revised set of objectives written in the investigative mode will force you to use a more open-ended approach in both teaching and evaluating your students.

One of the biggest problems teachers face is to keep out of the way of the students. You cannot learn for them. All you can do is point out directions and help facilitate their learning. Remember that, on the part of the teacher, talking is not necessarily teaching, and, on the part of the student, listening is not necessarily learning. The primary goal of all teaching is to make students self-educating people. They must learn not only what happened last year or the year before, but how to deal with new information and how to analyze, evaluate, and integrate new knowledge into their overall system of concepts. Furthermore, where the old framework of knowledge seems faulty, we want our students to have the courage and skills to challenge old ideas and to replace them with new, more soundly based conclusions and generalizations.

A final word of advice with regard to developing the teaching style that will take advantage of the particular gifts you have to bring into science teaching:

$$\boxed{\text{E X P E R I M E N T}}$$

ACTIVITY 16

EVALUATING YOUR TEACHING STYLE

1. Keep a log book to evaluate your teaching methods:
   A. Each day mark a point on a triangular diagram to deter-mine over a period of several weeks where your teaching falls with respect to activities, discussions, and presenta-tation of information.
   B. Each day mark a point on a line representing the con-tinuum of mode of teaching between authoritarian mode and investigative mode.

---

* * * CERTIFICATE * * *

I _____ HEREBY CERTIFY THAT I WILL CONDUCT
SYSTEMATIC EXPERIMENTS WITH MY STYLE OF TEACHING. I CERTIFY THAT I
WILL AT LEAST GIVE A FAIR TRIAL TO EACH OF THE TEACHING METHODS
PROPOSED IN THE PRECEDING PAGES.

I ALSO CERTIFY THAT I AGREE NEVER TO BECOME SATISFIED WITH MY TEACHING.
I WILL CONTINUE TO EXPERIMENT AND TRY TO EVALUATE NEW APPROACHES AS
LONG AS I REMAIN A TEACHER.

Signed:

_____

Part Two

READINGS ON THE

PHILOSOPHY AND METHODS

OF INQUIRY TEACHING

IN SCIENCE

Concept Formation and the
Nature of the Learning Experience

You were asked several times during Part One of this book to consider the nature of concept learning and to experiment with the recognition, formulation, and teaching of concepts. The articles included in this section on concept formation further explore the reasons for being concerned with concept learning. Professor Bruner, for example, makes the observation that the so-called information explosion that bothers many scientists, teachers, and students may well be an information implosion, if we observe that the more and more powerful generalizations and conceptual frameworks being developed are actually reducing and clarifying the most important scientific understandings and making them ultimately easier for man to grasp. The basic problem becomes one of recognizing what is significant in science and what is clutter. A great deal has recently been written and said on how learning experiences should be best organized so that teachers can most effectively lead their students to an understanding of science. The following five articles consider what is to be taught, how curriculum materials may be structured, and how the formation of concepts in students may be evaluated.

Liberal Education for All Youth*

Jerome S. Bruner

I propose to explore four or five questions that are at once philosophical, partly answerable, and profoundly practical in their implications. They are practical in the sense that they may guide the manner in which we deploy our educational resources, prepare our teachers, construct our materials to be taught, and view our pupils. They are questions that should be reopened often enough to assure that our educational enterprise is remaining receptive to new knowledge, yet not so endlessly debated that we grow weary of them. For they deal with matters of wearying difficulty.

I

Has anything been discovered about the nature of human intelligence that suggests we can better assist its growth than we are now doing?

The evidence is overwhelming now that the evolution of intelligence came as a result of bipedalism and tool-using. The large human brain gradually evolved as a sequel to the first use of pebble tools by early near-man. Natural selection favored the primitive tool-user. As human groups stabilized, tools became more complex and "shaped to pattern," so that it was no longer a matter of reinventing tools in order to survive, but rather of mastering the skills necessary for using them. In short, after a certain point in human evolution, the only means whereby man could fill his evolutionary niche was through the acquisition of the skills necessary for him to use the implements, devices, and techniques that were available to him.

*Reprinted from *The Science Teacher*, V. 32, No. 8., Nov., 1965, pp. 19–21. ©, by permission.

Two parallel evolutionary developments might also be noted. First, man's prolonged and impressionable childhood made possible the acquisition of skills for manning the evolved system of tools. Second was, of course, the emergence of human language, a system for communicating unlike anything seen before in the animal kingdom. Whatever else its uses to man as a species, one of the supreme benefits of language was to increase man's power to instruct the young.

In general, the tools or implement systems that have served to amplify man's powers are three—amplifiers of the muscles, amplifiers of the senses, and amplifiers of thought processes.

The acquisition of skills is the proper occupation of the prolonged childhood that is characteristic of man—of skills and the attitudes of mind and heart that make possible their wise use later. The skills must be such as to make it possible for the person to utilize the powerful technologies of the culture as multipliers of mind: the technologies of the hand and arm, of the senses, not only for seeing and hearing, but for looking and for listening, and for reflection and analysis.

Man's mind, because of its capacity to be increased in power from the outside in, has a potentiality that can never be estimated without considering the tools he has available for using his mind. His powers, then, are not simply his own but are communal in the sense that their unlocking depends upon the success of the culture in developing means for the individual's use. The proper aim of education, the proper design of a curriculum, the very shape of a school must, then, take into account the task of empowering the hands, eyes, and minds of men with the wherewithal to use what the culture can offer. At the same time, the culture must maintain itself in order to fulfill this function.

II

What characteristics of intellectual growth in children need especially to be taken into account better to assist the individual to the achievement of his full powers? The activities that foster intellectual growth are, in the main, self-rewarding. That is to say, given an opportunity, infants will exercise curiosity to drink in their environments, the more so as they are given intervening opportunities to do so. No outside reward seems necessary. They will manipulate and perambulate and construct and take apart—provided there is an opportunity for them to carry out these activities without resultant injury or harm or frustration that may inhibit such activity. Such competence-building activities are very early supplemented by another self-rewarding human tendency to pattern oneself and one's activities on some "identification figure," some emotionally significant adult human being. Taken together, these two self-sustaining forms of activity can provide a highly durable program for keeping intellectual growth going. But while they are durable, they are not indestructible, for they are dependent on freedom from injury and upon maintaining a tolerable level of frustration. The exploring and learning with a tutor present should be less punishing than exploring and learning without one.

The course of cognitive growth can also be thought of as the mastery of a set of prerequisites, with the mastery of one skill making it possible to go on to the mastery of ever more powerful and complex ones. Whether the prerequisite is of the kind that constitutes the mastery of components for a higher skill, or the mastery of a skill to reach a higher skill, or is of the kind that involves suppression, it is quite plain that we need a relatively clear sense of what has to be attained at the later stages to plan the order of learning at the earlier levels.

Intellectual growth appears to go through what may roughly be called phases or emphases. It may well be that these phases reflect the three major amplifier systems that man uses for achieving his full potential. At the outset, most of what the child is learning is motoric in nature: to do things and to get to know things in terms of what one can do to or with them. In time there is added a rich array of techniques for imaging things, and the perceptual world gradually becomes autonomous of action: A thing can be considered without references to what one is doing with it. In time we learn to conceive of the world not only in terms of acts and images, but also in the symbolic coin of words and sentences. Act, image, and symbol, then, all become the means whereby the adult knows his world.

To put it in an instructional context, one can know the classical mechanics in physics first in the playground sense of understanding how to get a seesaw to work, a lever which provides further means of knowing it. With language, one can strip the image down to a schematic diagram, and eventually be able to state its properties not only pictorially, but also in the more compact language of mathematics as Law of Moments, or more simply as the fact that a weight of 50 pounds placed 3 feet from the middle of the seesaw can balance a weight of 150 pounds one foot from the center. And what then of 3 pounds at 50 feet or a half-pound at 300 feet? To introduce the beautiful symmetries of the seesaw to the young child, one does far better to begin with the physical exploration of balancing, then to go on to diagrams, and finally to the ideas of fulcrum, force, distance, and the like. As long as one has some sense of where one expects the child to go, it is challenging and delightful to organize or invent materials to help him find his way there by using such modes of knowing as he already has established.

In short, if I may repeat a phrase that deserves to be repeated end-lessly, *it is possible to teach any subject to any child at any age in some form that is honest—and interesting.* The challenge is to find how to represent the idea in a mode that is within the child's reach and then to proceed from there to a more precise and deeper representation. It is this that I once called a spiral curriculum.

This much having been said, it is no surprise that the evidence of a quarter century of research underlines the importance of early childhood for intellectual development—the years before ever the child arrives in school. School itself is a relatively new invention in the world. It should not be astonishing that we have not yet discovered a proper means of preparing the child for school. There exists neither a decent theory of toys *per se*, and hardly an inkling of the educational use of toys. Nor do we know what role early dialogue between parent and child has, beyond language learning, where it is crucial enough. It may also be critical in helping the child organize his thoughts. One of the best ways of predicting how well a child will do in school is to base the estimate on how often he is involved in conversation with parents—at the breakfast table, for example, where he learns to fit his thoughts to the measure of language.

Perhaps the most important thing that we can do for a growing child from the intellectual point of view, is to design curricula for him that permit him to achieve skill in at least one area of knowledge, to experience the self-rewarding and confidence-giving pleasure of going deeply into something. . . . What I am proposing suggests that we should cut down drastically on the coverage in what we teach to any one child and concentrate instead upon a multiple approach to a few basic ideas, attitudes, and skills in order that we keep alive a sustained satisfaction in mastery.

III

Have we learned anything about the nature of knowledge and knowing that alters our conceptions of how best to organize it for learning, retention, and use? The past half-century has surely been one of the richest in the history of our effort to understand the nature of knowledge. Advances in the foundations of mathematics and logic, in the "theory of theory" in science, in the general theory of information, in linguistics and psychology—all of these have led to a deeper knowledge of knowledge.

The first thing that has changed—and perhaps it comes principally from the revolution in physics in the last half-century—is the conception of what a theory is. A theory is far more and far less than an unproved statement of the facts. It is something more than a generalization about what happens—or more than a statistical statement about what is more and what is less likely to happen. It is, rather, a formal model, a set of propositions about things and ways of reordering those propositions that generate, from time to time, predictions about the world to which the theory hopefully relates. Armed with a theory, one is guided to things to look for and, if the theory is any good at all, it should provide one with a terse account of what is known without the burden of details. A theory is not only the fruit of experience with what is known, but a product of imagination and careful fantasy in ways of expressing it so that one can go beyond the known. It is a canny way of keeping in mind a vast amount while thinking about a very little.

What is perhaps most important about this way of viewing theory is the attitude it creates toward the use of mind. Theory is a construction of the scientist, a result of using the disciplined imagination. It is a way of humanizing knowledge, of recognizing that to know is to have done far more imaginative things than simply to search successfully.

The second thing about knowledge is that it can be expressed in many forms. No matter how abstract the theory may be and no matter how compact its expression, it can still be rendered in ordinary English or in diagrams, provided one has enough time to say it. There are idioms into which knowledge can be translated that are of the form or in the mode that are within the grasp of children.

The third thing that can be said about knowing is that there are a relatively small number of general operations used and ways of stating what one has come to know, no matter what the subject. The small set of knowing skills and of ways of stating what one knows has many variations. There are many fewer forms of matter than were thought to be the case before Mendeleev, many fewer ways to convert external nutriment into a cellular substance than there are kinds of nutriments and cells, many more kinships beneath the surface of things than meet the untutored or innocent eye. One can, in short, become alert and deft about using the mind, the eye, and the hand for a variety of purposes.

Knowledge has a structure, a hierarchy, in which some of what is known is more significant than the rest of what is known about some aspect of life or nature. The task of the curriculum maker and of the teachers is to give to the student a grasp of this underlying structure so that he may be saved from that most common blight on human thinking: clutter. Do not take a charitable view toward irrelevant detail. It is not harmless. It is lethal.

The fourth thing that can be said about our knowledge of knowledge is that very little of it can be dealt with by the human mind at one time. A concept, or the connected body of concepts that is a theory, is man's only means of getting a lot into the narrow compass of his attention at one time. Without some such aid, there is clutter.

The fifth and final thing to be said about the nature of knowledge is that it is exploding. The knowledge explosion, to be sure, is something of a hoax. From outside it looks like an explosion. From inside it seems more like an implosion. For not only is there ever more of it around, but it turns out on closer inspection that it is all more interconnected than ever before suspected. Though there are many more facts, there are far more powerful theories with which to reduce or implode them to an order than can be understood. The working solution to the knowledge explosion is to cultivate the arts of connecting things that are akin, connecting them into the structures that give them significance. If one needed a single argument for reemphasizing concepts and structure in the design of a curriculum, this one would, I think, suffice.

IV

How shall our image of ourselves as men be kept intact and instructive while that image is also kept responsive to the new forms of knowledge and sensibility that come into our possession? Let me propose a view. Our population is becoming increasingly urban, and it is characteristic of urban life that it is marked by a certain protective anonymity. Our great metropolitan areas have not only a problem of urban rot and urban renewal at their centers, but a problem of increasing blandness and remoteness from life at their bedroom-suburban peripheries. We may be suffering a loss of moral richness at the periphery of our cities. At the center, in our slums, the problem is quite different and in the short run far more serious: it is a problem of loss of hope.

Yet, for all our deep worry over hopelessness in the city and suburban provincialism outside, neither seems to blunt one particular human capacity that overrides both: the sense of drama, the mysterious device by which we represent most vividly the range of the human condition. I would urge that in fashioning the instruction designed to give children a view of the different faces of man, you consider more seriously the use of this most powerful impulse to recognize the human condition in drama, and, thereby, the drama of the human condition.

V

Let me now bring together our various threads with a view of reexamining our conduct and philosophy of education.

It would seem to me, first, that at the very least, elementary education might well receive a fresh and very complete overhaul—including an overhaul in our approach to the training of teachers. We should, I believe, give a much higher priority to the early years—the elementary school and the pre-school years, for it is likely the case that well begun is better than half done. Our emphasis should be upon the cultivation of the skills of mind, the skills of inference and reasoning needed for grasping the connectedness of knowledge and its patterning that gives significance to particulars. The road to skill and to delight in the acquisition of it is probably in shape like a spiral. One begins at some lower level, exercising one's understanding of a great idea in some intuitive way, usually in some way that has to do with action, with what and how one does something, returning to it again and again with more and more powerful ways of picturing it, of symbolizing it, of acting in its behalf. Let the ideas we teach be great enough to warrant the revisits and to absorb the increase in skill that a learner brings to them. The ideas that are worth considering at the frontiers of knowledge are worth considering in the elementary school in their appropriate form.

We have, I believe, already achieved a revolution in American education in the last decade. It has again become a preoccupation of the community at large, but more interesting still, a passion in the intellectual community as a whole.

Does Experience Equal Understanding?*

David P. Butts

Once we recognize that one of our primary tasks is to help the student develop conceptual understandings, the first question is: How can this be done? What causes a concept to be developed? What can a teacher do to insure that each student will, in fact, develop conceptual understandings? Certainly we all agree that the student must have such understandings as the foundation for further study or interpretation of his environment.

First, we must understand what a concept is and how it develops. Suppose we assume that *a concept represents an interpretation of an event by an individual.* Then, let us see whether we can begin with the event and work forward to the concept. Obviously, the experience of the event must precede interpretation. It may also be that the more the student is permitted self-direction within his experiencing of an event, the greater the meaning this experience will have for him. Firsthand experience and independence in handling the experience seem to be necessary conditions for meaningful interpretation of an event—or for conceptual understanding.

We reason that independence is important because complete freedom within the experience permits the student to select those parts of the experience for interpretation that are meaningful to him. This should enable him to develop a greater conceptual understanding of that event.

If we set up an equation for the development of conceptual understanding we have:

Experience + Independence in manipulation of the experience = Conceptual understanding

*Reprinted from *The Science Teacher*, V. 30, No. 8, Dec., 1963, pp. 81–82. ©, by permission.

The logical arrangement of experience and independent manipulation as a prerequisite for concept development sounds good. Is it practical? Does it work? Is the equation complete? Do we have any evidence that students learn in this way?

Unfortunately, there is little conclusive evidence that the equation is complete or even accurate. For example, Watson and Cooley suggest that

> We have little clear evidence as to how and when the developing child, provided with selective experiences, can form dynamic classifications. Our intentions must be consistent with what the child can do; and we do not know much about the child.[1]

To test the accuracy of our equation, as well as to learn something more about the child if possible, we conducted a small study with children at the University of Illinois.[2] Within the experimental design, the student was confronted with the phenomena of a science experience and little else. He was given the freedom to do with the experience what he wished. The phenomena of these experiences were centered around four concepts—displacement, inertia, action-reaction, and depth-pressure relationship. For each concept, four experiences were provided in which problems were not identical but attention was focused on events related to a single concept. The researchers thought that by using four experiences it might be possible to determine whether any growth in understanding occurred *between* these experiences. The structure of each experience included three phases: experience, question, and manipulation.

Experience Phase

During the experience phase, the students observed an illustration of a science principle. They were seated around a demonstration table set up with equipment necessary for the experience. Each student was asked to predict what would happen when certain things were done and to write a rule explaining why this would happen. The students observed the demonstration but remained silent. The experiences were designed to afford each student the opportunity to formulate rules for

[1]Fletcher G. Watson and William W. Cooley. "Needed Research in Education." In *Rethinking Science Education*. Fifty-Ninth Yearbook of the National Society for the Study of Education. Chapter 16, Part 1, p. 302.

[2]This article discusses some of the implications which seem apparent from a study "The Degree to Which Children Conceptualize from Science Experiences." The investigation was conducted at the University of Illinois during 1961–62. The author was the principal investigator. For a description of the methodology and analysis of the data from the study, see David P. Butts, "The Degree to Which Children Conceptualize from Science Experience." *Journal of Research in Science Teaching*, 1:135–143. June 1963.

what he thought he would see. As an illustration for the concept of displacement (*two things cannot occupy the same place at the same time*), these experiences were used:

I. The children saw a bell jar partially filled with water. A drinking glass was held above the jar, inverted, and pushed down into the water. As they observed, the water did not go into the glass. The students were asked to explain in writing why the water did not rise in the glass.

II. A thistle tube was inserted into a one-hole stopper. A gallon jug about two-thirds full of water was placed on the table, and the stopper placed in the top. The students predicted what would happen if water were placed in the thistle tube. They then wrote the explanation of their prediction.

III. One thickness of cheesecloth was fixed tightly over the opening of a flask. This was placed near a stream of water which was about one-fourth inch in diameter. The students predicted what would happen if the flask were placed under the water and explained the reason for their prediction.

IV. A glass filled with water was held in an inverted position under the water's surface. A second glass was inverted and held slightly below the first glass and to its left. The students predicted what would happen if the second glass were tilted and explained the reason for their prediction.

QUESTION PHASE

The question phase followed the completion of written responses. The procedure was specifically designed to try to keep each student independent in his search for understanding. The student was forced to rely upon his own cognitive capacities in order to see the relationship between the phenomena of this experience and his past experiences. He could ask any questions he desired. It was explained, however, that the teacher would only answer those questions which could be answered by a "yes" or "no." In the event that there were questions which asked for explanations (directed learning), the investigator responded with "How would you find out?" This was an effort to return the student to independent learning. Thus the students were forced to depend on their individual understanding without the direction of the teacher giving information and explanations.

MANIPULATION PHASE

When the group's inquiries were satisfied, the students were permitted to manipulate the apparatus of the demonstration in any way they desired. Since this class was involved in other activities, the apparatus was placed on a separate table and was not the main focus of attention. Usually, however, for the remaining portion of the class meeting time, the apparatus was in constant use. It was not unusual for the students to come to the next sessions with more ideas about the experience and more questions or suggestions about the verifications of their ideas.

RESULTS

By careful analysis of the students' written responses on each of the four experiences, it was possible to evaluate their understanding at the beginning and their understanding at the completion of each group of experiences which dealt with the same concept. Their conceptual understanding was inferred to be the result of experience plus independence as per our equation.

What evidence does this study have to offer concerning the adequacy of the equation on conceptual understanding? Although this group of fourth-, fifth-, and sixth-grade children were bright (median IQ 124), there was no significant progress in understanding. Some made progress, others did not. Does this mean that the equation is completely wrong or in need of a revision?

WHAT IS NEEDED?

At this point, we can only hypothesize. From what is known about children and how they think, some useful clues are suggested. A child perceives a new situation from the vantage point of his past experience. That is, concepts represent the dynamic interaction of the student with the phenomena of experience. Within this experience, specific data have been organized and the organization perceived. From a pattern or configuration of these perceptions comes the concept. This interaction is twofold. In addition to developing from perceptions, concepts also help focus the attention of the student within the new situation. The data of that new situation do not change. Which of them are perceived by the student is determined by that student's conceptual background. The greater the fund of knowledge, the more direction the student has within his experience. Lacking an adequate fund of knowledge, can the student find science meaningful? Isn't the teacher's direction of the student's observation of the concrete experience important at this point? This help is related to the student's need to see those aspects of the situation which will help him form more accurate, complete, and functional conceptual understandings. Thus, could it be that the younger the child, the less helpful is his past experience and the more necessary the direction of the teacher? Does he need not only firsthand experience and opportunity to manipulate, but also the intellectual guidance of a teacher in order that this new experience will be a set of puzzle pieces that fit together in an understandable manner? This suggests that the equation should be modified to

Experience + Independence in manipulation + Direction depending upon cognitive maturity = Conceptual understanding

What does this new term in the equation mean for the teacher? When and how much direction should the teacher give to the student? Atkin and Karplus suggest that:

During [the introduction of a new concept], the teacher must make clear which previous observations of the children can be interpreted (or perhaps reinterpreted) by using a concept. Further, he must follow the introduction with opportunities for the children to discover that new observations can also be interpreted by using a concept. This type of discovery is made possible by the availability of a concept to the children, because their perception is oriented by the teacher's formulation of the new idea.[3]

It is important to emphasize that the teacher is not "telling the students" or playing the role of "information giver." The teacher is clarifying the relationships within the student's experience in such a way that he is motivated to *continue* to search for understanding. The attitude of the teacher in this intellectual guidance may well be the most important determining factor of future cognitive growth of the student. The degree to which the teacher's attitude controls the student's desire to continue to search for understanding represents another area of needed research.

At present, there is no empirical evidence to support the accuracy of the equation's modification. As an intuitive beginning, this modification appears to be helpful. We need to know more about the student in our classrooms and how he develops conceptual understandings. This knowledge will enable us to be more intelligent directors of his search for meaning in science.

[3]J. Myron Atkin and Robert Karplus. "Discovery or Invention." *The Science Teacher*, 29:47. September 1962.

Concept Learning in Science*

Milton O. Pella

Concepts have been cited as the products of scientific processes, as the basis for further scientific studies, and at times as the knowledge that is applied by the technologist. Concepts in and of science, according to some educators, are to be the desired outcomes of science instruction.

Concepts are important not only because they are the warp and woof of science, but also because they provide the possessor with a means of coping with the development of knowledge in the future. It seems that one way known to provide for maximum coverage of old and new knowledge is through the development of a classification system. The formation of concepts or conceptual schemes is one method of classification which results in such economical use of human intelligence. As stated by Philip Phenix:

> The only satisfactory answer to the crisis in learning lies in the formulation and persistent use of key concepts. . . .
>
> Key concepts probably should not be taught explicity and directly, at least to beginners. It does mean that particular items of knowledge should be selected and used with an eye to their exemplification of the basic concepts of the field.
>
> Ineffective teaching and learning, according to this thesis, are due in no small degree either to the failure to understand the need for comprehensive organizing concepts and their function in the economy of learning or to using the wrong key concepts (e.g., mistaken idea of what science really is).
>
> It is claimed that some concepts of high generality can be found which will provide truer insight into a field than could be gained by mere heaping up of isolated scraps of information. As knowledge develops the organizing principles change—old disciplines decline and new fields open up. Discovery of powerful key concepts applicable to a given group of ideas is the best way of defining a field of knowledge. [9]

*Reprinted from *The Science Teacher*, V. 33, No. 9, Dec., 1966, pp. 31–34. ©, by permission.

Concept formation results in a simplification of past, present, and future experiences, because individual facts become parts of the ideas. *A concept may be viewed initially as a summary of the essential characteristics of a group of ideas and/or facts that epitomize important common features or factors from a larger number of ideas.* Because of their comprehensive nature, concepts are useful to the individual in gaining some grasp of a much larger field of knowledge than he has personally experienced. He is able to interpret and assimilate new information into the old schemes through the modification of existing concepts.

WHAT IS A CONCEPT?

Reflection upon the nature of a concept given here "initially" reveals that such a definition is not fruitful in answering teaching-learning questions. There is need for a more specific definition or description before the many questions essential to teaching and learning concepts may be studied; there is need for an epistemology of concepts so that intelligent communication is possible. A first attempt to develop a definition or description leads to the question "Are concepts in all disciplinary areas the same?" Is the concept "mother" in a social sense the same as "mother" in a biological sense? Are these two parts of the same concept "mother"? Does the social concept "mother" depend upon higher level emotional factors than does the biological concept "mother"? Are the concepts of citizen, revolution, Uncle Sam, love, hate, etc., structurally similar, not in elements, but in design, to the concepts of force, mass, time, electron, atom, cell, living things, etc.? These questions lead no-where—their answers are included in the basic question.

Such questions, however, do have value in that they suggest that some concepts have been identified. A fruitful procedure may be to examine certain science concepts for the purpose of determining their individual characteristics. A list may be made of their individual origins, nature, etc., and then the items may be compared.

A concept of "insect" is used as example A:

An insect is an animal with six legs and three main body divisions. This statement

1. is a symbolic representation.
2. is a decision made by man.
3. is a decision based upon human experience with natural phenomena.
4. is an abstraction from a field of experience.
5. is a generalization that includes more than a field of personal experience.
6. involves the conscious or rational relating of facts. (The facts that are alike are placed together; the facts are classified.)

115

7. describes a man-made idea.
8. describes an idea that may exist at various levels of complexity (incomplete and complete metamorphosis).
9. is useful in making predictions and unifying information.

Example B:

A force is a push or pull which tends to change the motion of a body. This statement

1. is a symbolic representation.
2. is a decision made by man.
3. is a decision based upon human experience with natural phenomena.
4. is an abstraction from a field of experience.
5. is a generalization that includes more than the field of personal experience.
6. involves the conscious or rational relating of facts. (The push or pull is correlated with a change in motion.)
7. describes a man-made idea.
8. describes an idea that may exist at various levels of complexity (contact and noncontact forces).
9. is useful in making predictions and interpretations.

Example C:

An atom is the smallest particle of an element possible and is composed of electrons, protons, neutrons, and other particles. This statement

1. is a symbolic representation.
2. is a decision made by man.
3. is a decision that is not based upon direct human experience with natural phenomena.
4. is an abstraction of a created idea. (It is a verbal symbol representing a mechanical model.)
5. is a generalization that includes more than the field of human experience.
6. involves the conscious or rational relating of facts. (The intent is to explain rather than describe human experience.)
7. describes a man-made idea.
8. describes an idea that may exist at various levels of complexity (atom as a unit or atom as an aggregate of units).
9. is useful in making predictions and interpretations.

A comparison of these three concepts reveals many similarities and a few differences. There is one difference between concepts A and B; concept A is concerned with the classification of facts, and concept B is concerned with the correlation of facts: if *a* then *b*. Concept C is different from A and B in two ways:

Concepts A and B are

1. Abstractions from a field of direct experience
2. Descriptions of human experience

Concept C is

1. Abstraction of a created idea
2. Explanation of human experiences

This type of analysis may be repeated with other concepts, such as:

1. Matter occupies space and has mass.
2. A vertebrate is an animal with a backbone and an internal skeleton.
3. The digestive system is a group of organs with the common functions of preparing food for assimilation.
4. Spermatophyte plants form seeds.
5. Matter may be changed by adding or subtracting energy.
6. The structure of the digestive system of animals varies.
7. Digestion is the process of changing food from an insoluble to a soluble form.
8. The electrical current in a circuit varies with the resistance if the voltage is constant.
9. Matter is made up of particles called atoms.
10. The structure and habits of animals are adaptations that are the result of evolutionary development.
11. In the process of digestion, the molecular structure of the elements contained in the food is changed.
12. Light is an electromagnetic wave.

Note that 1 to 4 are similar to concept *A*, 5 to 8 are similar to concept *B*, and 9 to 12 are similar to concept *C*. Concepts of type *A* could be labeled as *classificational*, concepts of type *B* could be labeled as *correlational*, and concepts of type *C* could be labeled as *theoretical*. Concepts of type *C* go beyond sensory experience or facts, yet fit the human reasoning that has been tempered or indoctrinated by facts. One outstanding similarity is that all are "created by man" from direct real experience or from other created "ideas" that may be the result of real experience.

Before elaborating on the similarities, another source of information may be examined: definitions or descriptions given by other individuals concerned with the problem. Here is a selection of such definitions:

A concept is an idea, a mental image of an action or thing, a generalization about related data. It is an understanding of the immediate based upon the impact of present impressions on past experience, usually labeled with a verbal symbol or symbols. [7]

Every concept is an apperceptive system: a mass of experience functioning in a condensed form. [1]

When an element common to many experiences is not merely recognized when it appears, but (1) is thought of without being perceived, and (2) is capable of being combined in thought with other elements, it becomes a concept of general meaning and application. To be a general concept the element must be something for consciousness apart from its perceptual setting and it must be applicable to a different setting. [6]

A concept is a network of significant inferences by which one goes beyond the set of observed critical properties exhibited by an object or event to the class identity of the object or event in question, and thence to additional references about other unobserved properties of the object or event. The working definition of a concept is the network of inferences that are or may be set into play by an act of categorization. [2]

Physical concepts are free creations of the human mind, and are not, however it may seem, uniquely determined by the external world. [5]

A concept is a psychological phenomenon, complete description of which will be contained someday in a theory of explaining the numerous empirical laws involving the concept. [8]

We have a concept when we recognize a group of situations which have a resemblance or common element. We usually give a name or label to the group. [4]

A concept deals with the meaning an individual attaches to a word or symbol rather than the mere fact that any given symbol is associated with any given object. [10]

Conceptual schemes are more or less general systems of abstract propositions of empirical references which shape the determinate conditions under which empirical phenomena are related among themselves. [3]

The variability with some similarity is noted in these definitions and in many others which can be found in the literature. The next step in the attempt to describe or define a concept is a second examination of the place of concepts in science.

The ambition and hope held in the last century that science could offer a photographic replica or true image of reality have been abandoned. Science as understood today has two major assignments: (1) the description of certain phenomena in the world of experience and (2) the establishment of general principles for their prediction and for provision of a system of concepts that assist in their explanation. The system of concepts that facilitates description of phenomena is largely *classificational* in nature, the system of concepts that facilitates prediction is largely *correlational* in character, and the system of concepts that facilitates the explanation of phenomena is made up of *theories* of verbal, mechanical, or mathematical varieties.

The selection or development of concepts from the chaotic diversity of sense experience is determined by many factors other than the facts themselves. One factor may be the sequence of receipt of the sensory experiences that were the result of uncontrolled observations of natural phenomena or the result of experiments. A second factor may be the cultural pattern of the time and its effect on subconscious patterns of thought.

These two notions result in the demand for consideration of the belief held by some that the meaning of a concept is identical with the procedure that led to its formulation. Is it possible that the redefinition of concepts or the meaning attributed to a given concept has some part of its origin in the changing sense of values accepted by the scientific community? The historical record of such concepts as "force" and "electron" give some credence to a positive answer.

Characterizing a Concept

A list of the characteristics of concepts in science based on the preceding statements may now be risked.

1. Concepts are ideas possessed by individuals or groups. They are a type of symbolism.
2. Concepts of any particular object, phenomena, or process exist in a continuum from simple to complex.
3. Concepts emerge as a result of experience with more than one object, phenomenon, or fact. They are generalizations.
4. Concepts are the result of abstract thinking that embraces the many experiences.
5. Concepts involve the relating of facts or supposed facts to each other by the individual.
6. Concepts are not always based upon a physical encounter.
7. Concepts are not inherent in nature or reality.
8. Concepts are not photographic images of reality.
9. Concepts are neither true nor false; they are, rather, adequate or inadequate.
10. Concepts have five primary relationships: relations to people, relations to things, relations to other concepts, relations within conceptual systems, and relations to processes.
11. Concepts are useful in making predictions and interpretations.
12. The individual concepts formed in any area may be determined by the sequence of the sensory experiences received or available.
13. The individual concepts formed in any area may be determined by the cultural pattern at the time of formulation. As the culture changes, the meaning and value of a given concept may change.
14. The nature of a concept may be determined by the procedure that led to its formulation.
15. Concepts and conceptual schemes are rendered inadequate as a result of new knowledge and must undergo constant revision.

Concepts and Teaching

It is reasonable that these 15 recognizable characteristics of concepts should be carefully considered in the processes of teaching and learning where the concern is not essentially the development of personal concepts of the creative variety but rather the development of concepts of product and process acceptable to the discipline of which they are a part. The continuation of science in any culture must depend upon transmission of the accumulated knowledge and strategies of science from one generation to another. The emphasis on concept development in science has been important and is becoming increasingly important with the rapid growth of knowledge. It is the one way known to provide the maximum coverage of knowledge because it is a kind of classification or summarizing system which results in the conservation of human intelligence. To go further, it may be said that a conceptual scheme is a summary of the essential characteristics of a group of concepts that epitomize important common features or factors from the larger group of concepts. Because of their comprehensive nature, concepts enable the possessor to have some grasp of a much larger field of knowledge than he has personally experienced. He is able to interpret the new and to assimilate it into the old through the modification of existing concepts. The current product and process concepts of science are the heritage of each generation.

Concepts may be taught or formulated by indoctrination, induction, deduction, extrapolation, interpolation, analysis, synthesis, and probably other means.

With reference to the development of science concepts with children, the following questions are asked:

1. How important is the level of mental development of the child to learning *classificational, correlational,* and *theoretical* concepts?
2. How important is the intensity of the physical encounter which the learner has with the facts from which a concept is formulated?
3. How important to the learner is extensive physical encounter with the facts from which a concept is formulated?
4. How important to the learner is the sequence of the stimuli offered?
5. How representative of the total class covered by the concept must the stimuli offered be?
6. How remote from reality may the stimuli be for individuals of different experiential maturity?
7. When in their lives can learners utilize facts or ideas not based on physical reality?
8. To what extent is the cultural background of the learner a factor in concept learning?
9. How important are the procedures involving telling, demonstrating, or laboratory experience in concept learning?
10. Is it reasonable to expect learners of all school ages to develop concepts of the classificational, correlational, and theoretical varieties at some level during each year of their educational preparation?
11. Is it reasonable to expect the learner to discover a concept as a result of free inquiry?
12. How important is the vocabulary and language development of the learner in concept development?
13. Should we be satisfied with allowing pupils to formulate their own concepts whether or not they conform to those accepted by the discipline?

14. How deeply imbedded is the problem of transfer in concept learning?

These questions have been probed slightly by Piaget, Inhelder, Gagné, Loveall, and others; however, they are far from answered. The answers are fundamental to effective teaching, curriculum design, and teacher training. Surely it may be speculated that concept learning depends upon the characteristics of the learner and the circumstances under which he is guided.

What evidence is sought out to indicate that a specific concept has been developed or accepted by the learner? To date all that seems to be known is included in the words "transfer" and "verbalization." Are these valid?

Research is the avenue to determining whether the basic thoughts are credible. Much of this should and can be performed in the classrooms of the schools of this nation. This will lead to the answer to a more important question, "How do children of different ages, cultural backgrounds, and abilities learn concepts in science?" This is far more fundamental than "How do we teach concepts in science?"

REFERENCES

1. Bagley, William Chandler. *The Educative Process.* Macmillan, New York. 1905. p. 144.
2. Bruner, Jerome S.; Goodnow, Jacqueline J.; and Austin, George A. *A Study of Thinking.* Science Editions, Inc., New York. 1956. p. 244.
3. Conant, J. B. *Science and Common Sense.* Yale University Press, Oxford. 1951. p. 25.
4. Cronbach, Lee J. *Educational Psychology.* Harcourt, Brace & Co., New York. 1954. p. 281.
5. Einstein, Albert, and Infeld, Leopold. *The Evolution of Physics.* Simon and Schuster, New York. 1938. p. 33.
6. Hobhouse, Leonard Trelawney. *Mind in Evolution.* Macmillan, London. 1901. p. 329.
7. Kranzer, Herman C. "Children and Their Science Teachers." *Journal of Research in Science Teaching* 1:181; 1963.
8. Melton, A. W., Editor. *Categories of Human Learning.* Academic Press, New York. 1964. p. 226.
9. Phenix, Philip H. "Key Concepts and the Crisis in Learning." *Teachers College Record* 58:137–43; December 1956.
10. Woodruff, Asahel Davis. *The Psychology of Teaching.* Longmans, Green & Co., New York. 1951. p. 285.

A Model for the
Interpretation and Analysis
of Concept Formation*

J. D. Novak

Introduction

At the Woods Hole Conference sponsored by the National Academy of Sciences, an important concern of the participants was with the importance of *structure* in the process of learning. [5] What the participants meant by the term structure cannot be defined in a brief phrase; they resorted to examples from various subject areas. Central to their concern was the way in which knowledge and problem solving (with associated skills and attitudes) combined together in the understanding of major ideas in science or other fields. This paper will focus on the process of concept formation in science, though there is no basic reason why the illustrations could not be extended to include other areas of human endeavor. Major concepts in a discipline can be interpreted as providing the principal structure for the discipline. To be sure, understanding a given discipline requires more than memorization of statements summarizing concepts in the area; a student must discover how the concepts are derived and elaborated in order to *understand* the concepts and to grasp the structure of the discipline.

The *structure* of a science may be viewed as the system of major generalization or concepts together with the *process* by which these concepts are obtained and enlarged. For this paper we will use the following definition:

Concepts in science are broad generalizations regarding some aspect of the physical or biological world; they are a composite of individual facts and emotional experiences.

*Reprinted from *Journal of Research in Science Teaching*, V. 3, pp. 72–83 (1965). ©, by permission.

The term *concept* is used in many ways; it has been used to refer to apprehension of a letter, *e.g.*, the letter A, to indicate understanding a word, *e.g.*, the concept of the word fast, to represent a group of related facts, *e.g.*, the concept osmosis, to represent an image of some kind, *e.g.*, a concept of a building, or to represent some composite of knowledge, *e.g.*, the concept of evolution. Though these meanings differ in the extent to which they encompass experiences, they are all similar in that each describes some aggregate of sense impressions recorded and manipulated by an individual. For the purpose of this paper, with concern focused on concepts that can be major components in the structure of a discipline, the more restricted meanings of "concept" are of limited value. Hence, the definition above is one of convenience; the term *conceptual scheme* may have been more appropriate, at least in reference to science, but this would be more awkward to use.

The development of concepts begins at birth; with the first booming, buzzing confusion, as William James termed it, the infant begins to form sense impressions of the world around him. These sense impressions are soon combined with "problem solving" experiences (primarily by trial and error) such as how to get mother's attention, food, a dry diaper, etc. As experience (cognitive and emotional) accumulates, the "confused" mass of sense impressions "organize" or "are assembled" into collections or groups to form a "general" sense impression with generalized response patterns. These cumulative, general impressions could be called rudimentary *concepts*.

An individual's acquisition of concepts follows a unique course; the specific experiences he has result in apprehension of a concept that may have essentially the same meaning to the individual as that held by other individuals, but the experience pathway used in arriving at this concept can vary appreciably. Studies by Piaget, [38] Ausubel, [3] Atkin, [2] Butts, [7] and Ervin [14] well illustrate this point. A model for concept formation must accommodate varying patterns of concept attainment and yet provide for a conceptual product that is similar in different individuals.

Some of the most significant advances in the behavioral sciences and biology have resulted in part from the application of information theory. The early work of Shannon [42] and Wiener [49, 50] has been followed by applications to learning by Miller [25, 26] and others. [15, 18, 30–32] The beauty of utilizing information theory in learning models is that it provides a close link with important concepts in other areas of science; certainly the future of learning theory will depend largely on new applications of fundamental principles in other sciences just as recent advances in biology derive largely from such applications. To be sure, the complexity of learning will require new insights before elucidation is approached, but it would be naive to assume that fundamental differences in mechanisms exist between learning phenomena and other basic organismal characteristics. Therefore, the theory described in this paper is based on the assumption that learning of concepts has an underlying biochemical basis that may eventually explain information acquisition, storage, and utilization. The theory as developed in this paper has common elements with suggestions in other work on concept formation. [6, 16, 18, 22, 48]

A final word regarding the *structure* of science. Recently, a conference was held to attempt a description of the major concepts of science that might serve as a basis for kindergarten through grade 12 science programs. [29] This conference grew out of a recognized need for a conceptual framework that might guide science teaching and lead to successively better development of children's understanding of science as they progress through the grades. The conference was attended by fourteen distinguished scientists from various fields and a few science educators. Based on the conference and work of a summary conference held later, seven basic "conceptual schemes" were described which summarize the major achievements of science (or the *products* of science) and five statements were developed summarizing the methodology or *process* of science. The hypothesis developed was that curriculum materials could be designed which would provide a sequence of experiences for students leading them to an understanding of the basic conceptual schemes and the process by which these were obtained. An example of the conceptual schemes described is the following: [29]

> Matter exists in the form of units which can be classified into hierarchies of organizational levels.

DESCRIPTION OF THE MODEL

Beginning with a simple cybernetic model suggested by Wiener [49, 50] the important role of information input, processing, storage, output, and feedback were indicated. Partly because of the derivation of emotive or *affective* information from internal signals, and partly because the use of this internally derived information may be different in concept formation from that derived by external senses, the model differentiates between *affective information* and *cognitive* information. There is some organic basis for this distinction also. [36] Schematically, the overall model would be as shown in Figure 1.

As the child acquires experience, information is stored. We do not know the neurological basis for this storage though important advances are likely in this area within the near future. The storage mechanism could be molecular engrams, [9, 11, 41] but changes in membrane per-

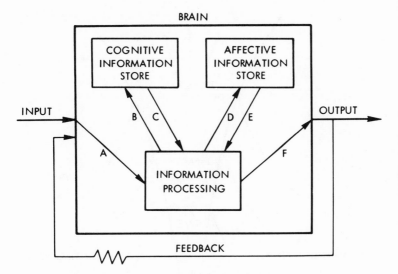

Figure 1. Schematic representation of the relationship between component parts and pathways involved in concept formation.

meability and other mechanisms are also possible. There is evidence that information acquired is not stationary, for experiments with split-brain animals [44] show that information acquired in one hemisphere can be replicated into the other hemisphere. Some of our data suggest that information "bits" (in our study these were individual botanical facts) are stored independently [27] even though the individual bits appear to relate to a single concept. Therefore, the location of individual information bits relative to a given concept might assume some complex distribution in the brain, and yet these bits can be utilized in concert when behavior requires that many bits of information be utilized, such as in the solution of problems. Whatever the localization of individual information bits may be, the observed behavior of students is that they can draw on this information to see new relationships and to solve problems. This behavior indicates that the individual has some organized pattern of eliciting information and we may refer to this pattern as a *concept*. For illustrative purposes only, the growth of a concept could be diagramed two-dimensionally as in Figure 2. It is important to note that a concept would develop in *n* dimensions where *n* is some index of interaction between concepts. Also, the rate of development of various concepts would differ. Figure 3 suggests some developmental patterns.

One of the principal sources of information utilized in concept formation is postulated to derive from problem solving experience. Furthermore, it is postulated that the "breadth" of a concept can be indicated by the relative complexity of relevant problems an individual can solve. For example, students given an examination with problems dealing with

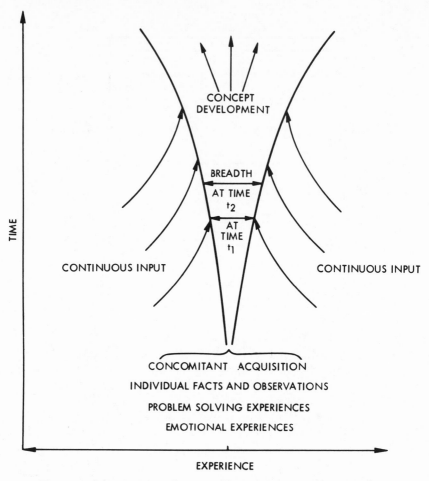

Figure 2. Schematic, two-dimensional representation of concept formation.

atomic structure will show variance in scores with some of the most difficult problems solved only by a few students. These students can be said to have the broadest concept of atomic structure and the whole group can be arrayed from broadest to most limited concept attainment on the basis of their problem solving scores. Thus, problem solving-ability, if it were possible to devise an adequate examination, could be taken as an index of concept attainment. Students who could solve problems for which there were no prior solutions, *i.e.*, could perform original research, would advance the concept as it exists in the discipline and would also demonstrate unusual concept attainment.

An important area of concern in science and school instruction is the nature and role of creativity. Descriptions of creative students have been provided by Torrence, [46] Getzels and Jackson, [17] Taylor, [45] and others. In the model presented here, we would interpret creativity as

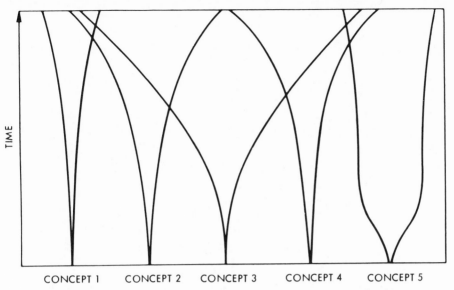

CONCEPT 1   CONCEPT 2   CONCEPT 3   CONCEPT 4   CONCEPT 5

Figure 3. Schematic, two-dimensional representation of concept development and association.

the act of moving from one conceptual level (see Fig. 2), say at time t_1, to a higher level at time t_2, without direct instruction as to how to solve more complex problems. Obviously, at the "frontier of knowledge" in a given area, direct instruction is not possible and creativity is most often recognized here. The student who moves from any one level to a higher level independently is demonstrating *creativity*. The difficulty in making an assessment lies in the fact that we cannot always decide when a student makes a conceptual leap independently.

The central role assigned to problem solving in the model for concept formation requires that this process be described further. Returning to the initial premise that a cybernetic model could apply to concept formation, as has been suggested by others, [18, 24] problem solving can be fitted into the scheme as shown in Figure 4.

In computers or in man, problem solving involves the processing of stored information (cf. Newell [31] and selection of "behaviors" or response patterns (output). Successive attempts at the solution of a complex problem adds new information (via feedback) and new emotional experience. The procedure may be diagramed as shown in Figure 4. Attitude or emotional predisposition can play an important role in the selection of behavior (in man, but not in present computer programs), and in psychotic individuals, we can postulate that "irrational behavior" is a result of the "masking" of cognitive information by affective information in behavior selection. [43] Various physical handicaps can alter the feedback or introduce "noise." Where dexterity or skill is important, *e.g.*, preparation of specimens for microscopic analysis, even without physical

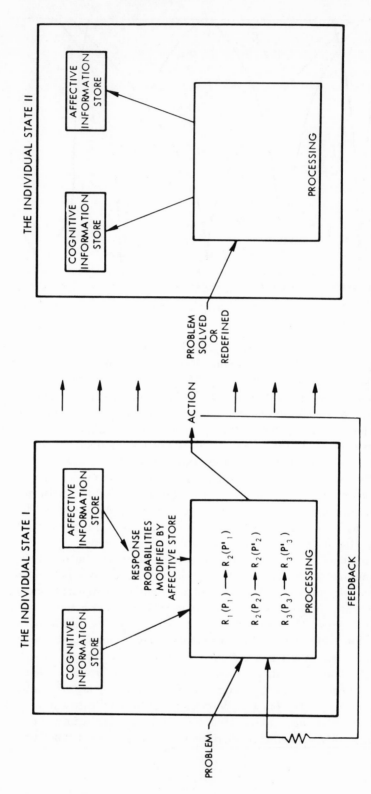

Figure 4. Schematic view of the problem solving process. (R) Possible responses, R_1, R_2, R_3, . . . R_n. (P) Probability responses will occur. (P') Probability response will occur after "emotional" input. Broken line indicates "noise" or perception distortion.

defects, an individual will receive varying information from a behavior depending upon his skill. The major activity in the scientific enterprise *is* the successive solution of problems (cf. Conant [8] and Nagel [28]; an analysis of the process of problem solving is also an analysis of science as a process.

MEASUREMENT OF CONCEPTS

With the model presented above, we have three categories of variables which require measurement, *i.e.*, cognitive information, affective information, and problem solving or information processing efficiency. Though all of these variables may change simultaneously, we can consider simple systems where the focus is on changes in only one of the three categories.

1. Measurement of Cognitive Information. If we restrict our definition of information to dates, names, measurements, and similar relatively discrete "bits" of information, somewhat analogous to the "bits" which are programed into a computer, it is possible to devise reliable, valid tests with relative ease. These are, in fact, essentially the types of tests most teachers prepare: *e.g.*, in history, who shot who, when, where; in biology, give the function of the ovule, lenticel, etc. This is the type of evaluation described under the category of 1.10 in Bloom's Taxonomy. [4] We can measure with relatively good precision, comparable to that in the natural sciences, the extent to which the "information" parameters change as a result of instruction. This measurement is important, *but* is only one of the three categories which we need to define to measure level of concept development. It can be seen from the scheme illustrated in Figure 4 that cognitive information is critical for development of alternative behaviors in problem solving. If an individual's ability to select alternative behaviors, that is, his ability to process stored information, is constant, it could be postulated that success in solving problems (for any one individual) is principally a function of the amount of relevant information he has, assuming no major aberrations result from his emotional set. We have some evidence that this is true, [20, 27, 35] but the question needs further study. One of the difficulties in analyzing the extent to which new relevant information affects concept development lies in the fact that we cannot easily determine what information is relevant to a given concept for a given student. Also, our index of concept attainment, a score on a problem solving test for the concept, is itself a rather unreliable estimate.

2. Measurement of Affective Information or Attitude. By contrast with the measurement of cognitive information, measurement of emotional predisposition or attitude is exceedingly difficult. It is possible to

129

determine changes in certain emotional predispositions or attitudes and an outline for the measurement of scientific attitudes has been developed. [34] The results we have obtained on attitude inventories requiring that students indicate their emotional predisposition or *feeling* toward ideas, activities, or objects show no correlation with information acquisition or problem solving ability (which would include information processing). The reliability of these inventories has been high. Our results from attitude appraisal suggest that this component in the model is real and measurable and that normal students are relatively stable in this dimension. We must acknowledge that assessment of changes in this component of concept growth will remain crude for some years to come. Moreover, the role of attitude is confounded with perception of events and problem solving *per se*. Nevertheless, we might ignore measurement of this parameter for the time being with the hope that with normal students under normal classroom procedures, no markedly aberrant effect will occur.

3. *Measurement of Problem Solving Ability.* Problem solving in science is a complex process. An outline of an attempt to interpret the nature of problem solving and measurement of problem solving ability is available elsewhere. [33]

One of the tests we have used to measure problem solving ability requires the student to select from a pair of alternatives, proceed to a second pair of alternatives according to his first choice, and select from a third pair of alternatives. This successive selection of appropriate responses was built into the test to correspond with the model shown in Figure 4. Each problem in the test could be diagramed as shown in Figure 5. The selection at each part would require a new evaluation of information, since some new information is available once a specific alternative is selected. Originally it was thought that "good" problem solvers, *i.e.*, those who score high on the test, would make almost all of their errors on Parts II or III, since they could make one or two correct appraisals but might fail on the third. Poor problem solvers, *i.e.*, those who score low on the test, were expected to make most of their errors at Part I. The results from 302 botany students did not support this

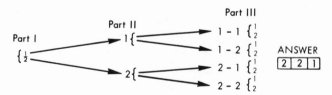

Figure 5. Diagram representing choice alternatives in the three-part problem solving test item.

hypothesis. [33] Figure 6 shows that students getting five out of six problems correct made approximately the same number of errors at

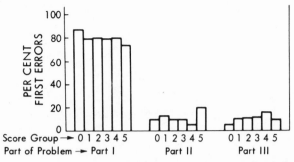

Figure 6. Per cent of "first" errors made on each of the three parts of a problem for each of the score groups.

Part I as students missing all six problems; approximately 80 per cent of the students who missed a problem made an incorrect selection at Part I. Similar results have been obtained subsequently. [35] Though these results were unexpected at first, we now interpret this to mean that the total information required to solve a given problem is largely present within the individual, and the contribution of feedback information is relatively slight. Examination of the problems used [33] would suggest that this is true. Continued study of the relation between information stored and problem solving success suggests that the principal determinant in problem solving success is the amount of relevant information an individual has. [27]

Further study is needed on the relation between information processing ability (which we have measured largely as ability to interpret data, solve problems, etc.) and total quantity of stored information. Some of our results [27] suggest that information processing is less a determinant in utilization of stored information than a determinant of the quantity of relevant information that might be stored. Figure 7 shows that students with high analytic ability (high information processing efficiency) acquire more botanical information in less time.

These data could be interpreted to mean that information processing operates most critically on the *input* side for our model, not on the output side. If this is true, important educational implications can be derived; sequences of experiences should be planned to facilitate information acquisition, perhaps with different regimes for high analytic ability and low analytic ability students. The emphasis of this study would be on how to maximize information gains, not on measurement of information utilization, an objective we have been working toward for many years (cf. Johnson [21] and Tyler [47]). Getzels and Jackson's finding [17] that highly creative students do as well in school achievement as their high IQ counterparts in spite of their non-conforming school habits suggests that creative students seek out effective, but atypical, schemes for information acquisition.

131

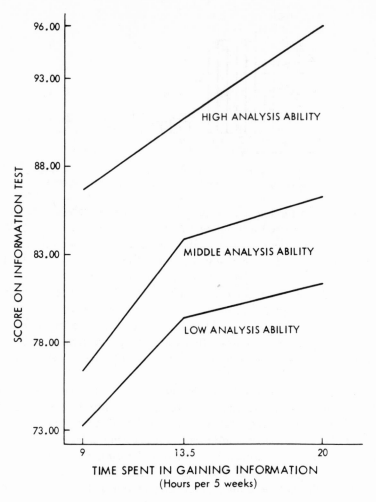

Figure 7. The effect of analytic ability and time spent in gaining information on information store.

4. Appraisal of Concept Growth. As indicated above, problem solving and information acquisition are considered to be closely tied to concept development *per se.* In the model presented here, problem solving success is taken as an indicator of concept attainment; in turn, acquired information is important in problem solving and some evidence suggests that the rate of acquisition of information is a function of an individual's information processing efficiency or analytic ability.

Referring back to Figure 1, two sources of information input are indicated, though these can be considered as a single input. Perceptual distortion, *e.g.,* poor eyesight or hearing, can alter the input. Moreover, emotionally derived information might affect the processing of cognitive input to the point that considerable alteration may occur; experiments and studies showing the effect of high emotion in perceptual distortion are common. [43] Ismail [19] has found that certain motor tasks, *i.e.*, those involving balance, are highly correlated with academic success. The role of motor-linked information input may be important to isolate in future studies, but at this time it is simply included with over-all input.

Summarizing some of our studies and work of others, the following description of concept growth is suggested (cf. Fig. 1):

(*1*) Information obtained through the senses is carried to the brain for processing (some processing and selection occurs at the receptors also). We will assume that transport from receptor to the processing unit (whatever this might be in the brain) is efficient and little information is lost, though experiments with drugs suggest that transmission of information may be blocked or distorted at any juncture. In other words, the pathway (*A*) is relatively noise free. The same assumption will be made for pathways (*B*) through (*F*). If these pathways are real, the course of psychopharmacological research may show specific inhibitory chemicals for each pathway. [23, 40]

(*2*) Information processing includes the biological mechanism of molecular engram formation or other mechanisms, one for short-term memory and the other for long-term memory. Information stored may affect the information processing activity with the result that varying amounts of information could be stored for a given input. The relationship between information passed in pathway (*A*) and pathway (*B*) may not be linear and may vary considerably between individuals. However, our data suggest that information once stored can probably be utilized, and hence the flow of information in pathways (*C*) and (*F*) may be more closely correlated with less variability in ratios between different normal individuals. The information processing efficiency, *i.e.*, the ratio of information transmitted in pathways (*A*) and (*B*) or pathways (*D*) and (*F*), though primarily the former, may vary considerably between individuals. It is this difference in processing efficiency that would determine the sum of information stored and thus the potential level of concept formation.

(*3*) Emotional experience can result in information storage that can play a role in affecting information processing. [10] The effect of emotionally derived information on processing of incoming and outgoing information remains an area of speculation. Polyani [39] has suggested that emotion plays an important role in selecting behaviors, but he has no data to support this position. The psychological concept of motivation is undoubtedly closely linked or identical to the action of affective information on information processing. The student who will not look through his microscope cannot perceive the structure of a tissue and if he is inclined to view the specimen only casually, the flow of information in pathways (*A*) and (*B*) is likely to be limited.

(*4*) The components identified above must be considered to operate in rapid sequential fashion. In even a simple behavior such as deciding which of two stones is heavier, many cycles of input, → processing → storage → processing → output →, feedback may occur. Even very small genetically determined differences in information processing efficiency [13] can be amplified to conspicuous differences between an individual's behavior after several years of such cycling. It is almost frightening to think of the enormous differences that might appear between individuals if and when appropriate drugs are applied differentially.

Summary and Implications

The educational Policies Commission of the National Education Association published a statement entitled *The Central Purpose of American Education* [12] in which the Commission identified, "The purpose which runs through and strengthens all other educational purposes—the common thread of education—is the development of the ability to think." In science education this would require that students understand how data are obtained and problems in science are solved. Successful observation and interpretation in science derives from orienting conceptual schemes or as referred to in this paper, from the concepts of science. The purpose of this paper is to outline a model for interpreting the mental process of concept formation that may be useful for classroom research; the parameters suggested can be measured using available testing procedures and the interpretations of the results can be applied directly to science classroom instruction.

Figure 1 shows a schematic representation of the component parts and pathways involved in concept formation. Though much of the biochemistry underlying the function of these components is not understood, there is evidence that functions of the type ascribed to the components exist in the brain. The two principal factors to be observed are information storage and information processing, the latter identified through tests requiring data interpretation and/or analysis. Storage of cognitive information may be partly dependent on the manner in which information is processed; some of the data presented indicates that differences in total information stored may result from differences in the manner in which students approach learning tasks and their manifest analytic ability or information processing ability. Further study of these relationships is needed.

Research in science teaching has often involved questions that can be related to a learning model only with difficulty or not at all. Such research, *e.g.*, lecture only versus lecture—laboratory teaching of a subject, is not likely to contribute to our understanding of the learning process and in general "methods comparison studies" probably will not advance our knowledge of how pupils learn or consequently, how to improve instruction. It is hoped that the model for concept formation presented here may provide some guidance to research in science education which will be more fruitful than much of the research in the past.

The writer acknowledges with appreciation the critical reading of this manuscript by D. M. Murray and H. H. Hagerman.

REFERENCES

1. Ashby, W. R., *Design for a Brain*, 2nd ed., New York, Wiley, 1960.
2. Atkin, J. Myron, "Teaching Concepts of Modern Astronomy to Elementary School Children," *Sci. Educ.*, **45**, 54–58 (1961).
3. Ausubel, David Paul, *The Psychology of Meaningful Verbal Learning; An Introduction to School Learning*, Grune and Stratton, New York, 1963.
4. Bloom, Benjamin S., Ed., *Taxonomy of Educational Objectives I: Cognitive Domain*, Longmans, Green, and Company, New York, 1956.
5. Bruner, Jerome S., *The Process of Education*, Harvard University Press, Cambridge, Massachusetts, 1960.
6. Bruner, Jerome S., Jacqueline Goodnow, and George A. Austin, *A Study of Thinking*, Wiley, New York, 1956.
7. Butts, David P., "The Degree to which Children Conceptualize from Science Experience," *J. Res. Sci. Teaching*, **1**, 135–143 (1963).
8. Conant, James B., *On Understanding Science*, Yale University Press, New Haven, Connecticut, 1947.
9. Cook, L., "Ribonucleic Acid: Effect of Conditioned Behavior in Rats," *Science*, **141**, 268 (1963).
10. Denenberg, V. H., "Experience and Emotional Development," *Sci. Amer.*, **208**, 138 (1963).
11. Dingman, W., and M. B. Sporn, "Molecular Theories of Memory," *Science*, **144**, 26 (1964).
12. Educational Policies Commission, *The Central Purpose of American Education*, National Education Association, Washington, D. C., 1961.
13. Erlenmeyer-Kimling, L., and L. F. Jarvik, "Genetics and Intelligence: A Review," *Science*, **149**, 1477–1479 (1963).
14. Ervin, Susan M., "Training and a Logical Operation by Children," *Child Development*, **31**, 555 (1960).
15. Estes, W. K., "Toward a Statistical Theory of Learning," *Psychol. Rev.*, **57**, 94–107 (1950).
16. George, F. H., "Machines and the Brain," *Science*, **127**, 1269–1274 (1958).
17. Getzels, Jacob W., and Philip W. Jackson, *Creativity and Intelligence*, Wiley, New York, 1962.
18. Hunt, Earl B., *Concept Learning*, Wiley, New York, 1962.
19. Ismail, A. H., N. Kephart, and C. C. Cowell, "Utilization of Motor Aptitude Tests in Predicting Academic Achievement," unpublished study, Purdue University, Lafayette, Indiana, 1963.

135

20. Jerkins, Kenneth F., "An Exploratory Study of Learning and Retention in General Science Classes Utilizing the MPATI Telecast Course 'Investigating the World of Science.'" unpublished Ph.D. dissertation, Purdue University, Lafayette, Indiana, 1964.

21. Johnson, Palmer O., "The Measurement of Outcomes Other Than Information," *School Sci. Math.*, **34**, 26–33 (1934).

22. Kendler, Tracy S., "Concept Formation," *Annual Rev. of Psychol.*, **13**, 447–472 (1961).

23. McGeer, P. L., "Mind, Drugs and Behavior," *Amer. Scientist*, **50**, 322 (1962).

24. Mark, H. J., "Elementary Thinking and the Classification of Behavior," *Science*, **135**, 75–87 (1962).

25. Miller, G. A., E. Galanter, and K. H. Pribram, *Plans and the Structure of Behavior*, Henry Holt and Co., New York, 1960.

26. Miller, G. A., and F. C. Frick, "Statistical Behavior and Sequence of Responses," *Psychol. Review*, **56**, 311–324 (1949).

27. Murray, Darrel L., "The Testing of a Model for the Interpretation of Concept Formation Using College Biology Students," unpublished Ph.D. dissertation, Purdue University, Lafayette, Indiana, 1963.

28. Nagel, Ernest, *The Structure of Science*, Harcourt, Brace and World, New York, 1961.

29. National Science Teachers Association, *The Science Teacher*, **31**, 10–13 (1964).

30. Neisser, Ulric, "The Imitation of Man by Machine," *Science*, **139**, 193–197 (1963).

31. Newell, Allen, and Herbert A. Simon, "Computer Simulation of Human Thinking," *Science*, **134**, 2011–2017 (1961).

32. Novak, Joseph D., "A Comparison of Two Methods of Teaching a College Botany Course," unpublished Ph.D. dissertation, University of Minnesota, Minneapolis, Minnesota, 1958.

33. Novak, Joseph D., "An Approach to the Interpretation and Measurement of Problem Solving Ability," *Science Educ.*, **45**, 122–131 (1961).

34. Novak, Joseph D., "The Interpretation and Measurement of Scientific Attitude," Mimeograph, Purdue University, Lafayette, Indiana, 1961.

35. Novak, Joseph D., "Further Study of Problem Solving Ability," Mimeograph, Purdue University, Lafayette, Indiana, 1963.

36. Olds, James, "Pleasure Centers in the Brain," *Sci. Amer.*, **195**, 105 (1956).

37. Penfield, W., "The Interpretive Cortex," *Science*, **129**, 1719–1725 (1959).

38. Piaget, Jean, *Logic and Psychology*, Basic Books, New York, 1957.

39. Polyani, Michael, "Passion and Controversy in Science," *Bulletin of the Atomic Scientists*, **13**, 114 (1957).

40. Roth, L. J., and C. F. Barlow, "Drugs in the Brain," *Science*, **134**, 22 (1961).

41. Schmitt, Francis O., *Macromolecular Specificity and Biological Memory*, M.I.T. Press, Cambridge, Massachusetts, 1962.

42. Shannon, C. E., "A Mathematical Theory of Communication," *Bell System Tech. J.*, **27**, 379–423, 623–656 (1948).

43. Sidman, Murray, "Normal Sources of Pathological Behavior," *Science*, **132**, 61–68 (1960).

44. Sperry, R. W., "Cerebral Organization and Behavior," *Science,* **133**, 1749 (1961).

45. Taylor, Calvin W., *Scientific Creativity: Its Recognition and Development,* Wiley, New York, 1963.

46. Torrence, E. Paul, *Guiding Creative Talent,* Prentice-Hall, Englewood Cliffs, New Jersey, 1962.

47. Tyler, Ralph W., "Needed Research in the Field of Tests and Examinations," *Educ. Res. Bull.,* **15**, 151–158 (1936).

48. Vinacke, W. E., "The Investigation of Concept formation," *Psychol. Bull.,* **48**, 1–13 (1951).

49. Wiener, Norbert, *Cybernetics,* Wiley, New York, 1948.

50. Wiener, Norbert, *The Human Use of Human Beings,* Doubleday, New York, 1954.

Science Teaching and the Nature of Science*‡

James T. Robinson

Today's teachers of science are confronted with an almost over-whelming volume of materials—texts, programs, pamphlets, etc.—pur-porting to provide information which will enable the student "to understand science." Science kits with packaged laboratory exercises in many forms are available. It is suggested that by using these materials the student will learn how to "inquire," will learn the "processes" of science. The possibilities of keeping students actively engaged in labora-tory activities and well-supplied with reading material in most of the fields of science is no longer a problem. Rather, the problems reside in much more profound questions: Have the students, as a result of doing the activities, reading, and discussing what they have read, indeed increased their "understanding of science?" What is the nature of science which they are to understand? Can aspects of the nature of science be identified and so specified as to provide for guidance in the selection and organization of elements which are to be included in science curricula?

Many articles in the professional literature suggest that it is the "processes" of science which are most important in teaching science rather than the "products" of science. Other articles suggest that the "structure of science" as a discipline and the "processes of inquiry" are of the greatest importance. Many science guides developed within school districts emphasize the teaching of "science concepts" as well as "science processes."

These many suggestions, and others could be cited, raised numerous questions for the writer. Not all of these questions have been fully explored, and for many it has been possible only to refine them for

*Reprinted from *Journal of Research in Science Teaching*, V. 3, pp. 37–50 (1965). ©, by permission.

‡Based on an unpublished Ed.D. dissertation, Stanford University, 1964: "An Investigation of Selected Frameworks of Science."

further investigation. Implicit in the suggestions for science teaching cited above was the separability, identifiability, and teachability of the processes and products of science. But can process be separated from product in science? How do product and process relate to the structure of science, and what is meant by the structure of science? Does this structure become most significantly stated as an array of products, concepts, facts, theories, and laws of nature? The list of questions may be expanded almost indefinitely; the study reported on here makes its central contribution in relation to the nature of what may be termed in current parlance "the structure of science."

In order to make some entry into this field of interrelated problems, and with the purpose of searching for eventual clarification of the nature or structure of scientific knowledge which might become a framework to provide guidance in curriculum development in the secondary schools, an investigation into the nature of scientific knowledge seemed in order. With such a framework one might be able to develop answers to such questions as the following: Is the language used in instructional materials consistent with the structure of science? Are the scientific relationships developed in materials consistent with relationships which characterize the structure of science? While these questions were initial goals of the inquiry, more specific questions were to be found that could be formulated and more fruitful answers were to be proposed as a consequence of the study.

The dissertation was based upon an analysis of six writings concerned with the nature and organization of scientific knowledge: three written by physical scientists [1–3] and three written by biological scientists. [4–6] These writings were selected from a working bibliography of more than one hundred works. A preliminary list of writings was selected from this bibliography on the basis of publication date, authorship by men who had taken a Ph.D. or received recognition in biology, chemistry, or physics, and who had a special interest in the nature and organization of scientific knowledge. The list of writings of physical scientists was sent to a selected group of physical scientists and the list by biologists was sent to a selected group of biological scientists. The final selection of the six works used in the investigation was made on the basis of the responses of the scientists, the recency of publication, a balance of works by biologists and physical scientists, and the writer's judgment.

The framework or structure of science which will be presented below must be considered as preliminary, since it has been based on a limited number of writings and represents the writer's selection of those aspects of the writings which he evaluated as central to the formulation of a structure of science which would be relevant to education in the sciences.

The reporting of the findings from this dissertation will be carried forward in two phases. First, four aspects of the structure of science will be discussed. At the present time, it is these four aspects which the writer feels have particular significance for curriculum implementation: (1) the distinctions as between the correlational and the exact sciences, (2) the constructional nature of scientific reality (including the circuit of verification and the inextricable interrelationships of the processes of induction and deduction), (3) the processes of observation and the emergence of rules of correspondence, and (4) the considerations which lead to the verification and acceptance of scientific theories. Second, the writer will present a statement of selected understandings which characterize an individual who is growing in scientific literacy. While only four aspects of these understandings will be discussed in phase one in any detail, the reader is referred to the dissertation and the six original works upon which it was based for substantiation of the additional emphases in these understandings.

CORRELATION AND EXACT SCIENCES

Although the sciences may be seen to consist of observations, experiments, theories, and hypotheses, the findings of this investigation support a necessity to go beyond this simple formulation in developing an understanding of the structure of science. First, a distinction must be made between correlational and exact procedures in the sciences; for the discussion in this article will be concerned primarily with the methodologies of the exact sciences. The history of science provides evidence that the various sciences began with observation and speculation, moved to the correlational level, and are developing, albeit at varying rates of speed, toward a theoretical or exact level.

Correlational procedures are characterized by data collection and by comparisons. Such comparisons may result in groupings or classifications, for example, the groupings of organisms into the categories plants, animals, or protists. Correlations of quantitative data may result in a mathematical relation, the correlation coefficient, developed by agreed upon rules of procedure. The biological sciences are characterized by correlational procedures. The inductive generalizations resulting from these procedures may summarize or describe, but they do not predict, and thus do not seem to satisfy investigators as they search for basic explanations. As Margenau indicates, ". . . they feel the urge to probe more deeply, to *derive* . . . (these uniformities) of experience from principles not immediately given." [7] In support of this observation Margenau gives the example of the use of the three-four-five rule by Egyptians as a correlational procedure but states that we honor Pythagoras for his mathematical demonstration for ". . . through his act a *theory* was born; the surface of mere correlation was broken, subsurface explanation had begun. To put it another way; the contingency of correlation had given way to logical necessity."[7]

This search for subsurface explanation was evinced by Paul Weiss in the transcript of the Lee Conference at which "Concepts of Biology" were discussed. Weiss asked if there might be relationships in the morphology of a flock of starlings and a slime mold colony. He explains these phenomena by stating:

> The outline of the starling cloud is very sharp, nearly spherical. Now, when this is broken in two, each half almost simultaneously rounds up into a separate unit. It isn't exact; it has almost an ameboid motion, with distortions and elongations. The remarkable thing is that despite these deformations, they cohere and retain a very sharp outline. We don't know what the communication system could be that would tell a bird the differential equation of a smooth, spherical surface. This is the analogy I wanted to investigate because that is what really happens. [8]

Frank Brink, Jr. continued the discussion and extended the analysis by stating:

> . . . the similarity here is a little bit like certain mathematical formulations; you have an operator, differential equations with the function in which it is going to operate not specified physically. . . . [9]

Paul Weiss related this comment to concerns in biological studies:

> . . . isn't a lot of our present biological work impoverished by the fact that people don't look for these operators? Take endocrinology—how much we know about the agents, which we can purify and extract and even synthesize, and how comparatively few people worry about their mode of action. Not until we know both do we have a complete and consistent understanding. [9]

This illustration points up the qualities of thought which characterize the movement from correlational to exact or theoretical procedures. The biological sciences have been predominantly correlational, but the thrust of these sciences, as with the physical sciences, has been toward exact or theoretical procedures. A discussion of a limited number of these procedures is the central purpose of this paper; for such procedures serve to form the paradigm of science and this may be considered of greatest importance in the search for the nature or structure of science.

The distinctions between inductive generalizations and the generalizations of the exact sciences are more clearly delineated by Frank Brink, Jr. when he commented regarding the framework of biological principles developed at the Lee Conference:

> I am trying to get my own ideas straight as to what kind of generalizations these are. With other generalizations that occur in science, and

141

perhaps a subsidiary set of rules of procedure, one can go back to the instances that suggested the generalization. . . . It's not clear that I can do this and, therefore, I am not sure that this is a basic set of generalizations. But if it is a basic set of generalizations, what must be added to it in the way of rules of procedure? Without these formal symbolisms, and rules for manipulating the symbols, it doesn't seem to me that you can work backwards to the instances that suggested the general principles. [10]

In this statement several of the essential characteristics of the exact sciences are presented: a basic set of generalizations is presented with formal symbolisms and rules of procedure by which one may go back to the specific instances that are suggested by the general principles.

The findings reported in the dissertation were formulated into statements of understandings which would characterize those individuals who are increasing their understanding of the structure of science as developed from this study. Each major aspect of the nature or structure of science was followed by a summary in the form of understandings. Understandings which relate to the distinctions as between the exact and correlational sciences are as follows:

Accordingly, an individual who is developing scientific literacy will increasingly

understand that the thrust in all sciences is for them to become increasingly theoretical and exact, the biological sciences being currently more correlational and the physical sciences more exact,

understand the current theoretical framework of the exact sciences, and where such frameworks are developed in predominantly correlational sciences, and

understand the limitations of current patterns of explanation in the biological sciences and understand the attempts to devise explanatory systems in the biological sciences which will be predictive.[1]

The writings of Morton Beckner reflected a point of view which was more expressive of the correlational than the exact thrust in science. He was concerned with documenting and clarifying the processes for rationalizing data now current in the field of organismic biology. In the transcript of the Lee Conference [11] some of the same strands of thought were in evidence. The general statements of the biological sciences are most characteristically inductive generalizations rather than theoretical systems of explanation, and thus the biological sciences are

[1]The "understands" presented in this paper represent a selection from, and in some instances a revision and reordering of, a longer and more comprehensive development in the dissertation.

142

more generally correlative or descriptive rather than exact sciences. But the thrust of the biological sciences is clearly toward the methodologies of the exact sciences.

In attempting to understand the nature of organisms, the biological sciences began with description and classification. This taxonomic stage of investigation was supplemented by morphological investigations and then progressed into investigations of the dynamics of living systems. The complexities of living systems has led some biologists to investigate organisms through levels of organization: molecular, organelle, cell, organ, individual organism, small group, population, and community. The investigations at the molecular level have utilized the methodologies of the exact sciences more fully than those investigations at the "higher" levels of organization. Investigations at each of these levels has produced large bodies of discrete facts and concepts, but the ordering of these facts and concepts into theoretical frameworks has lagged. The thrust of biological investigation toward the logico-mathematical systems characterizing the physical sciences is coupled with a belief by some biologists in the uniqueness of life and the questioning of the usability of such methodologies, especially at the higher levels of organization.

Some biologists evince concern with the fragmentation of their discipline into many non-communicating sub-disciplines with special concepts and special language. The breakdown of existing disciplinary boundaries with a reorganization into a "levels" organization has been given impetus by advances in information theory, systems analysis, symbolic logic, and the application of the methodologies of the exact sciences to living things. Such a movement to a more unified discipline with greater attention to deductive systems of explanation was commented upon by Margenau who, in discussing "causation in biology," stated:

> In biology, multiplicity of causal schemes is probably important enough to be studied in its own right. It may give rise to levels of explanation, perhaps to an entire hierarchy of explanations, each a causal one, and each at a different stage of organizational integration. Thus there may be encountered a theory framable in terms of molecules and molecular forces, another one in terms of thermodynamic systems, another in which cells and cytological interaction are basic concepts, and perhaps one that speaks of stimuli and responses. If a prognosis can be based on physics, one may judge it to be a very long time before the vertical connections between these schemes are completely understood. [12]

Thus, an understanding of science in this period of history must include understanding the divergent ways of thought which characterize contemporary biology.

Accordingly, an individual who is developing scientific literacy will increasingly understand the development of inquiry in biology with movement from simple observation to taxonomy, to descriptive morphology, to comparative morphology, and to the addition of analysis to description,

understand the diversity of methodological approaches by which practicing biologists are attempting to explain living systems,

understand that some biologists accept inductive generalizations as being currently satisfactory for living systems, and

understand that inductive generalizations formed into law-like statements preclude prediction in the sense usually required by the exact sciences;

understand the logical, mathematical, and syntactical structure of the physical sciences since the physical sciences are being used as a paradigm of the exact, or deductive, sciences,

understand that there are divergencies in biological thought as to the applicability of deductive patterns to all levels of biological organization,

understand that some areas of biological investigation are currently more deductively fruitful (genetics, open systems analysis) than are some other areas of inquiry, and

understand that a system of classification is not a deductive system although it may provide suggestions as to relevant relationships.

The processes of scientific thought have been considered in rather broad perspective and some aspects of the constructionist nature of scientific knowledge have been considered. A more detailed analysis of these topics will now be developed in the hope of clarifying these general considerations.

THE CONSTRUCTIONAL NATURE OF SCIENTIFIC KNOWLEDGE

As has been indicated, the organization of thought in the physical sciences may be used as a paradigm of the model of the exact sciences. One way of illustrating this organization is proposed in Figure 1.

This circle of thought "begins," "ends," and "continues" in the area of observation and thus emphasizes the empirical roots of the physical sciences. But observations are not given in nature. They are selected by the scientist—selected against the background of contemporary theory, general and metaphysical principles, and pragmatic considerations. The level of sense observation has been designated as the P field in

144

Figure 1 and the area of verbal description, the conceptual or constructional area, as the C field.[2]

The exact sciences are characterized by inductions which include inventive, imaginative qualities going beyond the observations which generated their development. Such inductions have been variously referred to as "hypotheses," "concepts," or "constructs."[3] The statements constructed by inductions from sense observations are not produced at random but emerge under the constraints of the theory within which they are being formed. The logical, mathematical, and metaphysical constraints which function throughout the invention and development

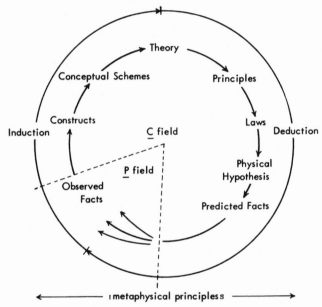

Figure 1. A schemata of the organization of thought in the physical sciences.

of constructs continue to function in the processes of verification to which constructs are subjected. They continue to function as the construct is tested further throughout the total area of discourse in which it is relevant. Metaphor and analogy often accompany the early phases of construction, but as testing proceeds, increasing the precision of terminology and reducing its ambiguity, removing metaphor and analogy become important parts of the formalization process.

Bridgman illustrates this use of analogy with the concept of light as a "thing traveling."

[2]The usage of "P field" and "C field" follows that developed by Margenau.
[3]The writer will follow Margenau's use of "construct."

145

There have been a number of different physical pictures of the nature of light, all of which have had the feature in common that light is to be regarded as in some way a 'thing travelling.' This statement obviously is applicable to the old corpuscular theory of light; it is true for the electromagnetic theory where the 'thing' is a phase in the electromagnetic field, which may be followed in thought as it moves, as in Einstein's special relativity; or finally we have the 'thing travelling' picture of the photons of quantum mechanics. . . . But we cannot see a photon in flight nor does it create a wind. [13]

These analogies (instrumental operations produce "things lighted," not "light traveling") are not currently capable of instrumental verification, but they do serve to stimulate experimentation.

Verification proceeds from the P field through operational definitions to the C field with its network of accepted constructs where it moves into what are generally referred to as deductive processes—the prediction of new and non-trivial observations in the P field. The predicted observations must fall within the probability prescribed by the theory of which they are a part. When this circuit is successfully completed, the entire set of constructs involved is said to be verified.

It is now possible to indicate that *an individual who is developing scientific literacy will increasingly*

understand that the relevance and validity of the constructs of a science are determined by the theoretical structure of the science, and

understand that no construct is considered valid until it can be fitted into an existing theory and function successfully in facilitating scientific prediction.

THE PROCESSES OF OBSERVATION

Newtonian mechanics accepted the premise of man as a unique discontinuity in a continuous and orderly universe. Man the spectator could independently observe the spectacle of this ordered universe; his removal from the scene was believed to be of no consequence. But events of the past fifty years have brought about a reexamination of this premise and a realization that Newton's laws were valid not absolutely but relative to the system of fixed stars.

The relationships of observer and observed is dramatically illustrated by the problems associated with establishing the "existence" of "empty space." The introduction of instruments to verify that the purportedly empty space is really empty precludes the possibility of its being "empty." In discussing this dilemma Bridgman states that:

. . . within the last few years we have the quantum mechanical concept of a fluctuating zero point electrostatic field in otherwise empty space.

146

If the theory is correct, it means that it will be found as a matter of experiment that it never occurs that there are places where all physical instruments give no readings, so that 'empty' space corresponds as little to the physical actuality as do the simultaneous position and momentum prohibited by the Heisenberg principle of interdetermination. In this denial of the legitimateness of the concept of empty space it seems to me that we have as dramatic a demonstration as can be imagined of the impossibility of divorcing our concepts from the operations by which they are generated and of the impossibility of speaking of things existing of themselves in their own right. [14]

With the physicists' invasion of the microscopic realm the effect of the investigator on what is observed could not be ignored. Man, the ordered observer, enters into the construction of scientific knowledge as he observes phenomena and *selects* those aspects of experience which may be constructed into the ordered formalisms which scientists consider to be explanatory. Such selection does not occur *in vacuo* but is guided by theory, for without theory the scientist does not know what to observe. Observations may generate hypotheses which may be extensions of existing theory or they may become generative of new experiments and hypotheses which may eventuate in the modification or replacement of the theory within which they had their origins.

Within the structure of science, the processes of induction and deduction are seen to enter in the form of a web-like rather than linear order. The scientist collects observations and then proceeds by induction to constructs (hypotheses). This creation, or construction, from observational material of a structure of "linguistic material" includes more than the observational material, for theories, conjectures, and thoughts play an essential role in induction, furnishing raw materials which may be shaped by imagination into new constructs.

The inductions which lead eventually to deductions within established theory have been distinguished from those inductive generalizations which summarize or describe but do not predict. This distinction is a crucial one which partly explains the difficulty of "discovery" in modern science, for discovery develops within accepted theory—discoveries come to the well prepared mind.

Correspondences between constructs and observations provide connections between the logical, rational areas of thought, and the empirical, observational areas which give substance to constructs. The establishment and formalization of these rules of correspondence, including operational definitions, is another important aspect of the inductive–deductive cycle. As scientists have probed into the microcosm, the relations between the operations used to produce observables and the nature of the observables produced have had to be more rigorously examined.

P. W. Bridgman has contributed greatly to the understanding of these relations by his analyses of the operations which are involved in the content, definitions, and extensions of some of our physical concepts. He states:

> The fundamental idea back of an operational analysis is simple enough; namely, that we do not know the meaning of a concept unless we specify the operations which were used by us or our neighbour in applying the concept in any concrete situation. [15]

Various kinds of operations—instrumental, verbal, and mathematical —are employed together in a way to mutually reinforce and supplement one another to produce the observable properties from which physical objects are constructed. A great deal of latitude is allowed to the verbal and mathematical operations but such freedom is restricted by the requirement that these operations must be capable of eventually making connections with instrumental operations. This requirement is based on the premise that:

> . . . the broadest basis on which we can hope for an eventual understanding is *invariable correlation between the results of instrumental operations.* Given invariable correlation, we can find how to predict, and prediction is perhaps the most searching criterion of understanding. [16]

As verification proceeds, correlation between constructs may result in relations expressible in the form of differential equations—the criterion for a law of nature as it is used in its most precise formulation.

The passage from data to constructs to the prediction of new facts within a formal system comprises the inductive–deductive cycle. However, for the verification of predictions, purely logical deductions are correlated with physical objects by means of rules of correspondence. Thus the goal of scientific explanation is seen to be the development of a coherent logico–mathematical system of relations between symbols, and rules of correspondence for those symbols, developed in such a way that the logical conclusions drawn from these statements become statements about observable facts that are confirmed by actual sense observations. The development of such a deductive system serves not only to predict new facts but it also serves to guide the knower in carrying out observations.

The acceptance of those deductive theories which correspond closely to data, *i.e.,* are more "concrete" than "abstract," is based primarily upon the logical, semantical, and empirical relations of the theory. As more abstract theories are formulated, acceptance is based upon more than scientific criteria; the psychological and sociological climate in which they are formulated become a part of the criteria for acceptance.

Accordingly, an individual who is developing scientific literacy will increasingly understand the distinctions in structure and development as between the inductive and deductive aspects of theory,

> understand that if it were not for both of these phases, all statements regarding a theory would be analytically equivalent,

> understand that all conceptual schemes are built up from inductions which in turn have been in part achieved through prior deductions from existing theories,

> understand that the working scientist invents his signs in order to make representations of phenomena—the relationship between these signs and symbols is the semantical component of science,

> understand that scientists have selected as their criteria for truth sense data which can be comprehended and checked by everybody with the appropriate training, and

> understand that the principles of physics can only be valid when they refer to a system, or systems, of reference;

understand the role of the ordered observer as a constructor of reality;

understand the relationship of theory to observation—without theory man does not know what to observe;

understand the role of operational analysis as it has come to be a part of the methodology of the physical sciences;

understand the function of operational definitions in prediction, for prediction is only possible when the terms within the principles of science have been given their operational definitions,

> understand the way in which different operations reinforce and supplement each other in many ways, and

> understand the critical role of instrumental operations in developing physical content in physical concepts;

understand the impossibility of divorcing physical concepts from the operations by which they are generated and of the impossibility of speaking of things existing by themselves in their own rights, and

> understand that no observation record is understandable without knowledge of the theory which underlies the instruments used in observation.

THE VERIFICATION AND ACCEPTANCE OF THEORIES

The search for sciences of increasingly precise predictability, rather than correlational or descriptive sciences, was evidenced in each of the works investigated. That prediction does not seek to merely call forth the original observation but must also have the power, the deductive fertility, to be extended to as yet unknown phenomena was stressed by those writers who delved deepest into its meanings. The difficulties of prediction in biology, where the unique event is of interest, brings additional difficulties to this field which are as yet unresolved through available mathematical and logical techniques. That the symbolization denoting the entities of complex systems and rules for manipulating these symbols provided by the Boole-Frege movement offer an as yet unexploited methodological system was illustrated by Woodger's axiomatization of Mendelian genetics. [17]

The validation of theories which predict involves a threefold process. First, the constructs within theories must undergo the imposition of certain metaphysical principles. Second, they must successfully complete the circuit of verification. The circuit of verification begins in the P field (see Fig. 1), the field of perception, proceeds by rules of correspondence in the C field, the constructional field, and then returns to the P field by a different pathway. Third, verification also includes the establishment of rules of correspondence which link data to constructs. Working always within theory, the linking of constructs to the P field and establishing relations among constructs assures the validation of constructs and theory. As Margeneau indicates, the processes of verification have enabled the exact sciences ". . . to develop *theories* furnishing criteria for the rejection of illusory data." [18] As illustrated in Figure 1 and as discussed throughout this paper, prediction involves both empirical and rational knowledge; neither is sufficient alone. Through the development of operational definitions, correspondence between the rational and the empirical is maintained; throughout this circuit, the observer is an integral part of both what is observed and constructed. One has only to recall the changes in man's conception of the universe which followed the Copernican Revolution to appreciate the importance of the constructional nature of science.

Theories of high generality such as relativity, quantum theory, Newton's theory of gravitation, etc., are not uniquely determined by their logical consistency, as developed through the circuit of verification and their agreement with observed fact. Sociological and psychological factors, C. S. Pierce's pragmatic component of science, [19] enter into acceptance when several theories may be valid. As Frank points out, Francis Bacon preferred the Ptolemaic theory over the Copernican theory ". . . because it is more in agreement with common sense." [20] This illustration helps further to clarify the influence of the pragmatic component for "common sense" is shaped by the climate of opinion which prevails at a particular time in history. Bridgman provides a further clarification of theory acceptance in discussing Ostwald's proposal of fifty years ago that the concept of atoms was superfluous when he observed that "it may well be, however, that one of two alternative points of view is so much more congenial to the common-sense way of looking at things, *the commonsense point of view itself being recognized as at bottom a construction* (italics mine), that we shall adopt it in preference to the other. [26] In this instance further experimental discoveries became so overwhelming that Ostwald's proposal has been discarded.

The currents of scientific thought which questioned the organismic universe of the Greeks and resulted in the Copernican revolution and the world machine of Newton took place over centuries within the fabric of the evolving society of western civilization. We may thus consider theories as being constructed, and their validity may be considered adequate so long as their predictions are confirmed in experiment. An understanding of the constructed nature of theories and of the interrelationships of scientific thought with the social milieu in which they are imbedded is a necessary part of education in the sciences. It also becomes essential that education in the sciences provide ways for individuals to learn that the very "seeing" and "recording" that man does have been influenced by his past.

Accordingly, an individual who is developing scientific literacy will increasingly

understand the inextricable relationship of the knower and the known, and

understand the way in which other areas of human thought or beliefs in religion, logic, mathematics, technology, etc., may influence his views in science;

understand that those aspects of experience of interest to science are those which satisfy the available procedures for rationalizing data;

understand that prediction is only possible when the terms within the principles of science have been given their operational definitions,

understand that a prediction to be of value and interest in science must be able to predict a large number of apparently unrelated observations,

understand that prediction is more difficult in biology and that appropriate logical, mathematical, and syntactical procedures will be needed to cope with deductive theories and processes concerning the living state; and understand the differences in criteria used for verifying and for accepting a theory.

A Summary of Additional
Understandings with Regard to the Nature of Science

Imbedded in the discussion of the four areas of concern to which the writer has devoted the largest measure of his attention in this article, and which were selected for emphasis because of his judgment as to their central importance to science curriculum, there have been stated central understandings which emerged from this study. These understandings were stated so as to characterize an individual who will be in process of growth toward a more mature conception of the nature and structure of science.

In this concluding section additional understandings will be presented without elaboration except in the last instance.[4] Four of the areas will deal further with the constraints within scientific reasoning which both serve to facilitate this reasoning and to characterize it as "scientific" when contrasted with other modes of thought. A brief discussion of intuition and discovery is included since much current writing in science education relates to these processes, and it is the judgment of the writer that the works studied in this dissertation cast thoughtful light on some essential distinctions with regard to these processes.

Constraints: Metaphysical Principles

Accordingly, an individual who is developing scientific literacy will increasingly

understand the continuing role that certain metaphysical principles have had in directing inquiry;

understand the relative longevity of metaphysical principles, theories, laws of nature, and constructs within the evolution of scientific knowledge;

understand that certain assumptions serve as constraints and guides in the evolution of scientific knowledge and thus become a part of the structure of science.

Constraints: Language

Accordingly, an individual who is developing scientific literacy will increasingly

[4]The reader is referred to the dissertation, or the individual works analyzed in it, for substantiation of the statements.

understand the indispensability of language as well as instruments in the development of scientific knowledge—that the recording of observations and the construction of hypotheses is impossible without each;

understand the decreasing utility of the natural language as science develops and understand the requirements for developing a more precise language, and

> understand the pitfalls into which one may fall in the use of natural language in science—dualistic thinking, unwarranted use of metaphor, elliptical expression;

understand the role of man as an interpreter of nature and that as a consequence, the study of language is as essential to the scientist as the study of observation, and

> understand the advantages of the extensional point of view in developing scientific statements;

understand the metaphysical and organismic interpretations which were a part of man's attempt to construct explanatory schemes and that the contemporary sciences still exhibit such reasoning, and

> understand that philosophical interpretations of theories grow out of analogies to daily life and are not uniquely determined by theory;

understand the use of metaphor and analogy when speaking of "directiveness" in organisms as being like "conscious purposing" in man, a yet to be clarified area of methodological concern in biology, and

> understand the use of analogy as a method of discovery, but also understand its lack of complete and unique correspondence.

Constraints: Logical and Mathematical

Accordingly, an individual who is developing scientific literacy will increasingly

understand that the essential relationships within all exact, or deductive, sciences are logical and mathematical, and

> understand that without the utilization of set theory the biologist is left with properties which he often treats as though they were entities;

understand the "haziness" of measurement and the logical hiatus between measurements and their mathematical expression in numbers;

understand the development of a natural law as a statement which

153

has evolved from a definition to a differential equation in which each term has independent instrumental significance.

CONSTRAINTS: MODELS AND VISUALIZATIONS

Accordingly, an individual who is developing scientific literacy will increasingly

understand that models may be used in science to represent various sets of relationships and may be mechanical, linguistic, mathematical, etc.;

understand that as the sciences have developed, models have become increasingly theoretical and abstract—physical models give way to mathematical models;

understand the use of models and visualizations by the scientist as a means of assisting him in organizing his relationships into a unified whole and to assist him in formulating hypotheses, and

understand that models are idealizations that are widely used as pedagogical devices but that models are not the physical reality itself;

understand the term "model" which may be used in the biological sciences in the phrase "a family of models" as defining a biological theory which serves to interrelate concepts at different levels of organization.

INTUITION AND DISCOVERY

The impossibility of separating intuition and discovery from the matrix of thought patterns and processes which characterize scientific reasoning has been apparent from the six writings investigated, for each works within the total fabric of thought. One becomes convinced from these writings that intuition and discovery in science are the fruit of imagination working with the well prepared mind. Both involve the ability to see relationships previously unseen, but both must work within the semantical, logical, and pragmatic constraints of scientific reasoning.

Intuition particularly functions in the inductive phases of inquiry when, as Woodger notes, [22] the particularity of observation records is transformed by the formulation of a newer, verifiable hypothesis which speaks of "all" in reference to a given set of phenomena.

Discovery, too, functions within the inductive phases of inquiry and

154

can, also, be an outgrowth of the deductive phases as whole new cosmologies may be constructed. Discovery is frequently aided in the inductive phase by analogy and metaphor as the scientist seeks to transcend his observations and achieve a more general statement.

> Every individual scientific discovery refers, beyond the factual circumstances in which it arises, to some universal for its *significance*. The difference between noting a fact and making a discovery centers precisely in this crucial condition: that a discovery suggests a fairly general postulational proposition which presses for tentative acceptance, while the fact allows mere inductive generalization. The postulate, when analyzed, is replete with deductive consequences, each of which says more than the original discovery; the inductive generalization as such can say nothing save what might happen when similar facts are inspected. [23]

In the last analysis, the insights gained from both intuition and discovery must be integrated and formalized into the accepted patterns of reasoning if they are in time to become a part of the deductive structure of a particular scientific discipline.

Accordingly, an individual who is developing scientific literacy will increasingly

understand the use of imagination, intuition, and construction which are essential characteristics of the processes of discovery in science,

understand the use of analogy as a method of discovery, but understand its lack of complete and unique correspondence, and

understand the relationship between discovery and the well prepared mind of the inquiring scientist.

SUMMARY

The necessary interrelationships as between structure and process as they emerge from the findings of this investigator are presented in Figure 2. This schemata attempts to represent the pervasive influences of the metaphysical principles and the circuit of verification as they have developed historically and are expressed in contemporary experimental inquiry.

This paper has reported selected findings from a doctoral dissertation concerned with the nature or structure of science. Four aspects of the emergent structure of science were briefly discussed and a statement of selected understandings which characterize an individual who is growing in scientific literacy have been presented. The dichotomy of products and processes of the scientific enterprise has been replaced by a unity in which the knower and the known are inextricably intertwined.

155

The writer proposes that the series of understandings may provide, after further investigation, a basis for the development of science curricula which makes the structure of science more explicit and provides for uniting the methods of inquiry with the knowledge produced—science curricula which would reflect the nature and organization of scientific knowledge as developed in this study.

REFERENCES

1. Margenau, Henry, *The Nature of Physical Reality: A Philosophy of Modern Physics*, McGraw-Hill, New York, 1950.
2. Frank, Philipp, *Philosophy of Science: The Link Between Science and Philosophy*, Prentice-Hall, Englewood Cliffs, New Jersey, 1957.
3. Bridgman, Percy W., *The Nature of Some of Our Physical Concepts*, Philosophical Library, New York, 1952.
4. Woodger, J. H., *Biology and Language*, Cambridge University Press, Cambridge, England, 1959.
5. Beckner, Morton, *The Biological Way of Thought*, Columbia University Press, New York, 1952.
6. "Concepts of Biology," Ralph W. Gerard, Ed., *Behavioral Science*, 3, 93–215 (1958).
7. Ref. 1, p. 28.
8. Ref. 6, pp. 168–169.
9. Ref. 6, p. 173.
10. Ref. 6, p. 157.
11. Ref. 6, pp. 93–215.
12. Ref. 1, p. 417.
13. Ref. 3, p. 20.
14. Ref. 3, p. 19.
15. Ref. 3, p. 7.
16. Ref. 3, pp. 17–18.
17. Ref. 4, pp. 95–218.
18. Ref. 1, p. 463.
19. Ref. 2, p. 349.
20. Ref. 2, p. 353.
21. Ref. 3, p. 22.
22. Ref. 4, p. 32.
23. Ref. 1, p. 249.
24. Robinson, James T., "An Investigation of Selected Frameworks of Science," unpublished Ed.D. dissertation, School of Education, Stanford University, 1964, p. 381.

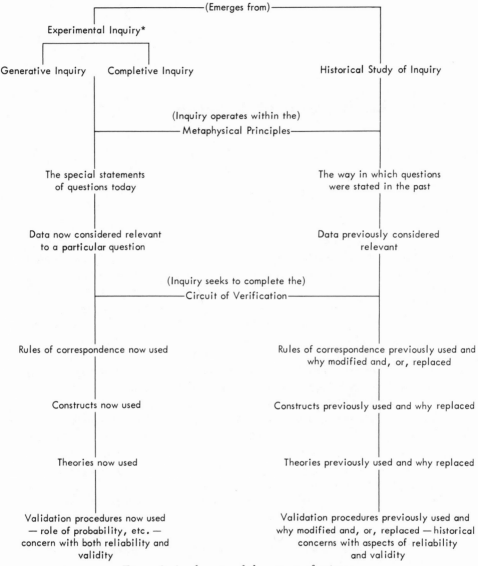

Figure 2. A schemata of the nature of science.

*J. J. Schwab made similar distinctions as to type of inquiry in a recent publication, "Education and the Structure of the Disciplines," a paper prepared for the Project on the Instructional Program of the Public Schools, National Education Association, Washington, D. C., 1961.

The writer uses the term "generative" in preference to Schwab's "fluid" and "completive" in preference to "stable" in the belief that these terms convey more of the findings of this study than do Schwab's terms. Schwab also uses "inquiry into inquiries" in a way somewhat parallel to "Historical Study of Inquiry."

The Nature of Discovery

Discovery has become a big word in science education. Most publishers realize that their advertising for new textbooks must contain liberal doses of this word. Failure to use it may quickly doom a new book. But what is discovery and how can students be expected to accomplish it? Is learning possible without an element of discovery? According to Jean Piaget, "Even in order to understand, we have to invent, or, that is, to reinvent, because we can't start from the beginning again . . . . anything is only understood to the extent that it is reinvented."[1]

In this book the author has been advocating finding ways of helping students to learn science through discovery in and outside of the classroom. The two articles in this section analyze briefly how discovery may occur. One important problem to consider is the role of facts in discovery. As Professor Farre points out, ordinary facts are neutral and point to neither one interpretation nor another; "they simply are." Discovering thus becomes primarily a matter of looking at old facts in a new way. There is as yet no simple logic for making discoveries, and yet discovery and rediscovery appear more and more to be essential elements of learning experiences in science.

[1]Frank Jennings, "Jean Piaget, Notes on Learning," *Saturday Review*, May 20, 1967, pp. 81–83.

158

The Act of Discovery*

Jerome S. Bruner

Maimonides, in his *Guide for the Perplexed*[1], speaks of four forms of perfection that men might seek. The first and lowest form is perfection in the acquisition of worldly goods. The great philosopher dismisses such perfection on the ground that the possessions one acquires bear no meaningful relation to the possessor: "A great king may one morning find that there is no difference between him and the lowest person." A second perfection is of the body, its conformation and skills. Its failing is that it does not reflect on what is uniquely human about man: "he could [in any case] not be as strong as a mule." Moral perfection is the third, "the highest degree of excellency in man's character." Of this perfection Maimonides says: "Imagine a person being alone, and having no connection whatever with any other person; all his good moral principles are at rest, they are not required and give man no perfection whatever. These principles are only necessary and useful when man comes in contact with others." "The fourth kind of perfection is the true perfection of man; the possession of the highest intellectual faculties. . . ." In justification of his assertion, this extraordinary Spanish-Judaic philosopher urges: "Examine the first three kinds of perfection; you will find that if you possess them, they are not your property, but the property of others. . . . But the last kind of perfection is exclusively yours; no one else owns any part of it."

It is a conjecture much like that of Maimonides that leads me to examine the act of discovery in man's intellectual life. For if man's intellectual excellence is the most his own among his perfections, it is also the case that the most uniquely personal of all that he knows is that

---

*Reprinted from *Harvard Ed. Rev.*, V. 31, pp. 21–32 (1961). ©, by permission.
[1]Maimonides, *Guide for the Perplexed* (New York: Dover Publications, 1956).

which he has discovered for himself. What difference does it make, then, that we encourage discovery in the learning of the young? (Does it, as Maimonides would say, create a special and unique relation between knowledge possessed and the possessor? And what may such a unique relation do for a man—or for a child, if you will, for our concern is with the education of the young?)

The immediate occasion for my concern with discovery—and I do not restrict discovery to the act of finding out something that before was unknown to mankind, but rather include all forms of obtaining knowledge for oneself by the use of one's own mind—the immediate occasion is the work of the various new curriculum projects that have grown up in America during the last six or seven years. For whether one speaks to mathematicians or physicists or historians, one encounters repeatedly an expression of faith in the powerful effects that come from permitting the student to put things together for himself, to be his own discoverer.

First, let it be clear what the act of discovery entails. It is rarely, on the frontier of knowledge or elsewhere, that new facts are "discovered" in the sense of being encountered as Newton suggested in the form of islands of truth in an uncharted sea of ignorance. Or if they appear to be discovered in this way, it is almost always thanks to some happy hypotheses about where to navigate. Discovery, like surprise, favors the well prepared mind. In playing bridge, one is surprised by a hand with no honors in it at all and also by hands that are all in one suit. Yet all hands in bridge are equiprobable: one must know to be surprised. So too in discovery. The history of science is studded with examples of men "finding out" something and not knowing it. I shall operate on the assumption that discovery, whether by a schoolboy going it on his own or by a scientist cultivating the growing edge of his field, is in its essence a matter of rearranging or transforming evidence in such a way that one is enabled to go beyond the evidence so reassembled to additional new insights. It may well be that an additional fact or shred of evidence makes this larger transformation of evidence possible. But it is often not even dependent on new information.

It goes without saying that, left to himself, the child will go about discovering things for himself within limits. It also goes without saying that there are certain forms of child rearing, certain home atmospheres that lead some children to be their own discoverers more than other children. These are both topics of great interest, but I shall not be discussing them. Rather, I should like to confine myself to the consideration of discovery and "finding-out-for-oneself" within an educational setting—specifically the school. Our aim as teachers is to give our student as firm a grasp of a subject as we can, and to make him as autonomous and self-propelled a thinker as we can—one who will go along on his own after formal schooling has ended. I shall return in the end to the question of the kind of classroom and the style of teaching that encourages an attitude of wanting to discover. For purposes of orienting the discussion, however, I would like to make an overly simplified distinction between teaching that takes place in the *expository mode* and teaching that utilizes the *hypothetical mode*. In the former, the decisions concerning the mode and pace and style of exposition are principally determined by the teacher as expositor; the student is the listener. If I can put the matter in terms of structural linguistics, the speaker has a quite different set of decisions to make than the listener: the former has a wide choice of alternatives for structuring, he is anticipating paragraph content while the listener is still intent on the words, he is manipulating the content of the material by various transformations, while the listener is quite unaware of these internal manipulations. In the hypothetical mode, the teacher and the student are in a more cooperative position with respect to what in linguistics would be called "speaker's decisions." The student is not a bench-bound listener, but is taking a part in the formulation and at times may play the principal role in it. He will be aware of alternatives and may even have an "as if" attitude toward these and, as he receives information he may evaluate it as it comes. One cannot describe the process in either mode with great precision as to detail, but I think the foregoing may serve to illustrate what is meant.

Consider now what benefit might be derived from the experience of learning through discoveries that one makes for oneself. I should like to discuss these under four headings: (1) The increase in intellectual potency, (2) the shift from extrinsic to intrinsic rewards, (3) learning the heuristics of discovering, and (4) the aid to memory processing.

1. *Intellectual potency.* If you will permit me, I would like to consider the difference between subjects in a highly constrained psychological experiment involving a two-choice apparatus. In order to win chips, they must depress a key either on the right or the left side of the machine. A pattern of payoff is designed such that, say, they will be paid off on the right side 70 per cent of the time, on the left 30 per cent, although this detail is not important. What is important is that the payoff sequence is arranged at random, and there is no pattern. I should like to contrast the behavior of subjects who think that there *is* some pattern to be found in the sequence—who think that regularities are discoverable —in contrast to subjects who think that things are happening quite by *chance*. The former group adopts what is called an "event-matching" strategy in which the number of responses given to each side is roughly equal to the proportion of times it pays off: in the present case R70:L30. The group that believes there is no pattern very soon reverts to a much more primitive strategy wherein *all* responses are allocated to the side that has the greater payoff. A little arithmetic will show you that the lazy

all-and-none strategy pays off more if indeed the environment is random: namely, they win seventy per cent of the time. The event-matching subjects win about 70% on the 70% payoff side (or 49% of the time there) and 30% of the time on the side that pays off 30% of the time (another 9% for a total take-home wage of 58% in return for their labors of decision). But the world is not always or not even frequently random, and if one analyzes carefully what the event-matchers are doing, it turns out that they are trying out hypotheses one after the other, all of them containing a term such that they distribute bets on the two sides with a frequency to match the actual occurence of events. If it should turn out that there is a pattern to be discovered, their payoff would become 100%. The other group would go on at the middling rate of 70%.

What has this to do with the subject at hand? For the person to search out and find regularities and relationships in his environment, he must be armed with an expectancy that there will be something to find and, once aroused by expectancy, he must devise ways of searching and finding. One of the chief enemies of such expectancy is the assumption that there is nothing one can find in the environment by way of regularity or relationship. In the experiment just cited, subjects often fall into a habitual attitude that there is either nothing to be found or that they can find a pattern by looking. There is an important sequel in behavior to the two attitudes, and to this I should like to turn now.

We have been conducting a series of experimental studies on a group of some seventy school children over the last four years. The studies have led us to distinguish an interesting dimension of cognitive activity that can be described as ranging from *episodic empiricism* at one end to *cumulative constructionism* at the other. The two attitudes in the choice experiments just cited are illustrative of the extremes of the dimension. I might mention some other illustrations. One of the experiments employs the game of Twenty Questions. A child—in this case he is between 10 and 12—is told that a car has gone off the road and hit a tree. He is to ask questions that can be answered by "yes" or "no" to discover the cause of the accident. After completing the problem, the same task is given him again, though he is told that the accident had a different cause this time. In all, the procedure is repeated four times. Children enjoy playing the game. They also differ quite markedly in the approach or strategy they bring to the task. There are various elements in the strategies employed. In the first place, one may distinguish clearly between two types of questions asked: the one is designed for locating constraints in the problem, constraints that will eventually give shape to an hypothesis; the other is the hypothesis as question. It is the difference between, "Was there anything wrong with the driver?" and "Was the driver rushing to the doctor's office for an appointment and the car got out of control?" There are children who precede hypotheses with efforts to

162

locate constraint and there are those who, to use our local slang, are "pot-shotters," who string out hypotheses non-cumulatively one after the other. A second element of strategy is its connectivity of information gathering: the extent to which questions asked utilize or ignore or violate information previously obtained. The questions asked by children tend to be organized in cycles, each cycle of questions usually being given over to the pursuit of some particular notion. Both within cycles and between cycles one can discern a marked difference on the connectivity of the child's performance. Needless to say, children who employ constraint location as a technique preliminary to the formulation of hypotheses tend to be far more connected in their harvesting of information. Persistence is another feature of strategy, a characteristic compounded of what appear to be two components: a sheer doggedness component, and a persistence that stems from the sequential organization that a child brings to the task. Doggedness is probably just animal spirits or the need for achievement —what has come to be called *n-ach*. Organized persistence is a maneuver for protecting our fragile cognitive apparatus from overload. The child who has flooded himself with disorganized information from unconnected hypotheses will become discouraged and confused sooner than the child who has shown a certain cunning in his strategy of getting information—a cunning whose principal component is the recognition that the value of information is not simply in getting it but in being able to carry it. The persistence of the organized child stems from his knowledge of how to organize questions in cycles, how to summarize things to himself, and the like.

Episodic empiricism is illustrated by information gathering that is unbound by prior constraints, that lacks connectivity, and that is deficient in organizational persistence. The opposite extreme is illustrated by an approach that is characterized by constraint sensitivity, by connective maneuvers, and by organized persistence. Brute persistence seems to be one of those gifts from the gods that make people more exaggeratedly what they are.[2]

Before returning to the issue of discovery and its role in the development of thinking, let me say a word more about the ways in which information may get transformed when the problem solver has actively processed it. There is first of all a pragmatic question: what does it take to get information processed into a form best designed to fit some future use? Take an experiment by Zajonc[3] as a case in point. He gives groups

[2]I should also remark in passing that the two extremes also characterize concept attainment strategies as reported in *A Study of Thinking* by J. S. Bruner *et al.* (New York: J. Wiley, 1956). Successive scanning illustrates well what is meant here by episodic empiricism; conservative focussing is an example of cumulative constructionism.

[3]R. B. Zajonc (Personal communication, 1957).

of subjects information of a controlled kind, some groups being told that their task is to transmit the information to others, others that it is merely to be kept in mind. In general, he finds more differentiation and organization of the information received with the intention of being transmitted than there is for information received passively. An active set leads to a transformation related to a task to be performed. The risk, to be sure, is in possible overspecialization of information processing that may lead to such a high degree of specific organization that information is lost for general use.

I would urge now in the spirit of an hypothesis that emphasis upon discovery in learning has precisely the effect upon the learner of leading him to be a constructionist, to organize what he is encountering in a manner not only designed to discover regularity and relatedness, but also to avoid the kind of information drift that fails to keep account of the uses to which information might have to be put. It is, if you will, a necessary condition for learning the variety of techniques of problem solving, of transforming information for better use, indeed for learning how to go about the very task of learning. Practice in discovering for oneself teaches one to acquire information in a way that makes that information more readily viable in problem solving. So goes the hypothesis. It is still in need of testing. But it is an hypothesis of such important human implications that we cannot afford not to test it—and testing will have to be in the schools.

2. *Intrinsic and extrinsic motives.* Much of the problem in leading a child to effective cognitive activity is to free him from the immediate control of environmental rewards and punishments. That is to say, learning that starts in response to the rewards of parental or teacher approval or the avoidance of failure can too readily develop a pattern in which the child is seeking cues as to how to conform to what is expected of him. We know from studies of children who tend to be early overachievers in school that they are likely to be seekers after the "right way to do it" and that their capacity for transforming their learning into viable thought structures tends to be lower than children merely achieving at levels predicted by intelligence tests. Our tests on such children show them to be lower in analytic ability than those who are not conspicuous in overachievement.[4] As we shall see later, they develop rote abilities and depend upon being able to "give back" what is expected rather than to make it into something that relates to the rest of their cognitive life. As Maimonides would say, their learning is not their own.

The hypothesis that I would propose here is that to the degree that one is able to approach learning as a task of discovering something rather

[4]J. S. Bruner and A. J. Caron, "Cognition, Anxiety, and Achievement in the Preadolescent," *Journal of Educational Psychology* (in press).

than "learning about" it, to that degree will there be a tendency for the child to carry out his learning activities with the autonomy of self-reward or, more properly by reward that is discovery itself.

To those of you familiar with the battles of the last half-century in the field of motivation, the above hypothesis will be recognized as controversial. For the classic view of motivation in learning has been, until very recently, couched in terms of a theory of drives and reinforcement: that learning occurred by virtue of the fact that a response produced by a stimulus was followed by the reduction in a primary drive state. The doctrine is greatly extended by the idea of secondary reinforcement: any state associated even remotely with the reduction of a primary drive could have the effect of producing learning. There has recently appeared a most searching and important criticism of this position, written by Professor Robert White,[5] reviewing the evidence of recently published animal studies, of work in the field of psychoanalysis, and of research on the development of cognitive processes in children. Professor White comes to the conclusion, quite rightly I think, that the drive-reduction model of learning runs counter to too many important phenomena of learning and development to be either regarded as general in its applicability or even correct in its general approach. Let me summarize some of his principal conclusions and explore their applicability to the hypothesis stated above.

> I now propose that we gather the various kinds of behavior just mentioned, all of which have to do with effective interaction with the environment, under the general heading of competence. According to Webster, competence means fitness or ability, and the suggested synonyms include capability, capacity, efficiency, proficiency, and skill. It is therefore a suitable word to describe such things as grasping and exploring, crawling and walking, attention and perception, language and thinking, manipulating and changing the surroundings, all of which promote an effective—a competent—interaction with the environment. It is true of course, that maturation plays a part in all these developments, but this part is heavily overshadowed by learning in all the more complex accomplishments like speech or skilled manipulation. I shall argue that it is necessary to make competence a motivational concept; there is *competence motivation* as well as competence in its more familiar sense of achieved capacity. The behavior that leads to the building up of effective grasping, handling, and letting go of objects, to take one example, is not random behavior that is produced by an overflow of energy. It is directed, selective, and persistent, and it continues not because it serves primary drives, which indeed it cannot serve until it is almost perfected, but because it satisfies an intrinsic need to deal with the environment.[6]

[5]R. W. White, "Motivation Reconsidered: The Concept of Competence," *Psychological Review*, LXVI (1959), 297–333.

[6]*Ibid.*, pp. 317–18.

I am suggesting that there are forms of activity that serve to enlist and develop the competence motive, that serve to make it the driving force behind behavior. I should like to add to White's general premise that the *exercise* of competence motives has the effect of strengthening the degree to which they gain control over behavior and thereby reduce the effects of extrinsic rewards or drive gratification.

The brilliant Russian psychologist Vigotsky[7] characterizes the growth of thought processes as starting with a dialogue of speech and gesture between child and parent; autonomous thinking begins at the stage when the child is first able to internalize these conversations and "run them off" himself. This is a typical sequence in the development of competence. So too in instruction. The narrative of teaching is of the order of the conversation. The next move in the development of competence is the internalization of the narrative and its "rules of generation" so that the child is now capable of running off the narrative on his own. The hypothetical mode in teaching by encouraging the child to participate in "speaker's decisions" speeds this process along. Once internalization has occurred, the child is in a vastly improved position from several obvious points of view—notably that he is able to go beyond the information he has been given to generate additional ideas that can either be checked immediately from experience or can, at least, be used as a basis for formulating reasonable hypotheses. But over and beyond that, the child is now in a position to experience success and failure not as reward and punishment, but as information. For when the task is his own rather than a matter of matching environmental demands, he becomes his own paymaster in a certain measure. Seeking to gain control over his environment, he can now treat success as indicating that he is on the right track, failure as indicating he is on the wrong one.

In the end, this development has the effect of freeing learning from immediate stimulus control. When learning in the short run leads only to pellets of this or that rather than to mastery in the long run, then behavior can be readily "shaped" by extrinsic rewards. When behavior becomes more long-range and competence-oriented, it comes under the control of more complex cognitive structures, plans and the like, and operates more from the inside out. It is interesting that even Pavlov, whose early account of the learning process was based entirely on a notion of stimulus control of behavior through the conditioning mechanism in which, through contiguity a new conditioned stimulus was substituted for an old unconditioned stimulus by the mechanism of stimulus substitution, that even Pavlov recognized his account as insufficient to deal with higher forms of learning. To supplement the account, he introduced the idea of the "second signalling system," with

[7]L. S. Vigotsky, *Thinking and Speech* (Moscow, 1934).

166

central importance placed on symbolic systems such as language in mediating and giving shape to mental life. Or as Luria[8] has put it, "the first signal system [is] concerned with directly perceived stimuli, the second with systems of verbal elaboration." Luria, commenting on the importance of the transition from first to second signal system, says: "It would be mistaken to suppose that verbal intercourse with adults merely changes the contents of the child's conscious activity without changing its form. . . . The word has a basic function not only because it indicates a corresponding object in the external world, but also because it abstracts, isolates the necessary signal, generalizes perceived signals and relates them to certain categories; it is this systematization of direct experience that makes the role of the word in the formation of mental processes so exceptionally important."[9, 10]

It is interesting that the final rejection of the universality of the doctrine of reinforcement in direct conditioning came from some of Pavlov's own students. Ivanov-Smolensky[11] and Krasnogorsky[12] published papers showing the manner in which symbolized linguistic messages could take over the place of the unconditioned stimulus and of the unconditioned response (gratification of hunger) in children. In all instances, they speak of these as *replacements* of lower, first-system mental or neural processes by higher order or second-system controls. A strange irony, then, that Russian psychology that gave us the notion of the conditioned response and the assumption that higher order activities are built up out of colligations or structurings of such primitive units, rejected this notion while much of American learning psychology has stayed until quite recently within the early Pavlovian fold (see, for example, a recent article by Spence[13] in the *Harvard Educational Review* or Skinner's treatment of language[14] and the attacks that have been made upon it by linguists such as Chomsky[15] who have become concerned with the relation of language and cognitive activity). What is the more interesting

[8]A. L. Luria, "The Directive Function of Speech in Development and Dissolution," *Word*, XV (1959), 341–464.

[9]*Ibid.*, p. 12.

[10]For an elaboration of the view expressed by Luria, the reader is referred to the forthcoming translation of L. S. Vigotsky's 1934 book being published by John Wiley and Sons and the Technology Press.

[11]A. G. Ivanov-Smolensky, "Concerning the Study of the Joint Activity of the First and Second Signal Systems," *Journal of Higher Nervous Activity*, I (1951), 1.

[12]N. D. Krasnogorsky, *Studies of Higher Nervous Activity in Animals and in Man*, Vol. I (Moscow, 1954).

[13]K. W. Spence, "The Relation of Learning Theory to the Technique of Education," *Harvard Educational Review*, XXIX (1959), 84–95.

[14]B. F. Skinner, *Verbal Behavior* (New York: Appleton-Century-Crofts, 1957).

[15]N. Chomsky, *Syntactic Structure* (The Hague, The Netherlands: Mouton & Co., 1957).

is that Russian pedagogical theory has become deeply influenced by this new trend and is now placing much stress upon the importance of building up a more active symbolical approach to problem solving among children.

To sum up the matter of the control of learning, then, I am proposing that the degree to which competence or mastery motives come to control behavior, to that degree the role of reinforcement or "extrinsic pleasure" wanes in shaping behavior. The child comes to manipulate his environment more actively and achieves his gratification from coping with problems. Symbolic modes of representing and transforming the environment arise and the importance of stimulus-response-reward sequences declines. To use the metaphor that David Riesman developed in a quite different context, mental life moves from a state of outer-directedness in which the fortuity of stimuli and reinforcement are crucial to a state of inner-directedness in which the growth and maintenance of mastery become central and dominant.

3. *Learning the heuristics of discovery.* Lincoln Steffens,[16] reflecting in his *Autobiography* on his undergraduate education at Berkeley, comments that his schooling was overly specialized on learning about the known and that too little attention was given to the task of finding out about what was not known. But how does one train a student in the techniques of discovery? Again I would like to offer some hypotheses. There are many ways of coming to the arts of inquiry. One of them is by careful study of its formalization in logic, statistics, mathematics, and the like. If a person is going to pursue inquiry as a way of life, particularly in the sciences, certainly such study is essential. Yet, whoever has taught kindergarten and the early primary grades or has had graduate students working with him on their theses—I choose the two extremes for they are both periods of intense inquiry—knows that an understanding of the formal aspect of inquiry is not sufficient. There appear to be, rather, a series of activities and attitudes, some directly related to a particular subject and some of them fairly generalized, that go with inquiry and research. These have to do with the *process* of trying to find out something and while they provide no guarantee that the *product* will be any *great* discovery, their absence is likely to lead to awkwardness or aridity of confusion. How difficult it is to describe these matters—the heuristics of inquiry. There is one set of attitudes or ways of doing that has to do with sensing the relevance of variables—how to avoid getting stuck with edge effects and getting instead to the big sources of variance. Partly this gift comes from intuitive familiarity with a range of phenomena, sheer "knowing the stuff." But it also comes out

[16]L. Steffens. *Autobiography of Lincoln Steffens* (New York: Harcourt, Brace, 1931).

of a sense of what things among an ensemble of things "smell right" in the sense of being of the right order of magnitude or scope or severity.

The English philosopher Weldon describes problem solving in an interesting and picturesque way. He distinguishes between difficulties, puzzles, and problems. We solve a problem or make a discovery when we impose a puzzle form on to a difficulty that converts it into a problem that can be solved in such a way that it gets us where we want to be. That is to say, we recast the difficulty into a form that we know how to work with, then work it. Much of what we speak of as discovery consists of knowing how to impose what kind of form on various kinds of difficulties. A small part but a crucial part of discovery of the highest order is to invent and develop models or "puzzle forms" that can be imposed on difficulties with good effect. It is in this area that the truly powerful mind shines. But it is interesting to what degree perfectly ordinary people can, given the benefit of instruction, construct quite interesting and what, a century ago, would have been considered greatly original models.

Now to the hypothesis. It is my hunch that it is only through the exercise of problem solving and the effort of discovery that one learns the working heuristic of discovery, and the more one has practice, the more likely is one to generalize what one has learned into a style of problem solving or inquiry that serves for any kind of task one may encounter— or almost any kind of task. I think the matter is self-evident, but what is unclear is what kinds of training and teaching produce the best effects. How do we teach a child to, say, cut his losses but at the same time be persistent in trying out an idea; to risk forming an early hunch without at the same time formulating one *so* early and with so little evidence as to be stuck with it waiting for appropriate evidence to materialize; to pose good testable guesses that are neither too brittle nor too sinuously incorrigible; etc., etc. Practice in inquiry, in trying to figure out things for oneself is indeed what is needed, but in what form? Of only one thing I am convinced. I have never seen anybody improve in the art and technique of inquiry by any means other than engaging in inquiry.

4. *Conservation of memory.* I should like to take what some psychologists might consider a rather drastic view of the memory process. It is a view that in large measure derives from the work of my colleague, Professor George Miller.[17] Its first premise is that the principal problem of human memory is not storage, but retrieval. In spite of the biological unlikeliness of it, we seem to be able to store a huge quantity of information—perhaps not a full tape recording, though at times it seems we even do that, but a great sufficiency of impressions. We may

[17]G. A. Miller, "The Magical Number Seven, Plus or Minus Two," *Psychological Review*, LXIII (1956), 81–97.

infer this from the fact that recognition (i.e., recall with the aid of maximum prompts) is so extraordinarily good in human beings—particularly in comparison with spontaneous recall where, so to speak, we must get out stored information without external aids or prompts. The key to retrieval is organization or, in even simpler terms, knowing where to find information and how to get there.

Let me illustrate the point with a simple experiment. We present pairs of words to twelve-year-old children. One group is simply told to remember the pairs, that they will be asked to repeat them later. Another is told to remember them by producing a word or idea that will tie the pair together in a way that will make sense to them. A third group is given the mediators used by the second group when presented with the pairs to aid them in tying the pairs into working units. The word pairs include such juxtapositions as "chair-forest," "sidewalk-square," and the like. One can distinguish three styles of mediators and children can be scaled in terms of their relative preference for each: *generic mediation* in which a pair is tied together by a superordinate idea: "chair and forest are both made of wood"; *thematic mediation* in which the two terms are imbedded in a theme or little story: "the lost child sat on a chair in the middle of the forest"; and *part-whole mediation* where "chairs are made from trees in the forest" is typical. Now, the chief result, as you would all predict, is that children who provide their own mediators do best—indeed, one time through a set of thirty pairs, they recover up to 95% of the second words when presented with the first ones of the pairs, whereas the uninstructed children reach a maximum of less than 50% recovered. Interestingly enough, children do best in recovering materials tied together by the form of mediator they most often use.

One can cite a myriad of findings to indicate that any organization of information that reduces the aggregate complexity of material by imbedding it into a cognitive structure a person has constructed will make that material more accessible for retrieval. In short, we may say that the process of memory, looked at from the retrieval side, is also a process of problem solving: how can material be "placed" in memory so that it can be got on demand?

We can take as a point of departure the example of the children who developed their own technique for relating the members of each word pair. You will recall that they did better than the children who were given by exposition the mediators they had developed. Let me suggest that in general, material that is organized in terms of a person's own interests and cognitive structures is material that has the best chance of being accessible in memory. That is to say, it is more likely to be placed along routes that are connected to one's own ways of intellectual travel.

In sum, the very attitudes and activities that characterize "figuring out" or "discovering" things for oneself also seem to have the effect of making material more readily accessible in memory.

On the Problem of
Scientific Discovery[*]

G. L. Farre

Like practically all forms of rational knowledge, science was born in ancient Greece. The first of these forms to be developed was mathematics, somewhere in the fifth or sixth century B.C. The young science was most rigorously studied among a group of brilliant thinkers, who formed a learned fellowship named after its founder, the Pythagoreans. The work they did was so fantastically good that in a little more than 200 years mathematics was in a well-developed form that was to be left virtually untouched until after the Renaissance. It was brought to that state of enduring perfection by such men as Euclid, Diophantos, and Archimedes.

It is interesting to observe what the Greeks did in this context. It is well known that they learned a great deal from the ancient Egyptians, as well as from the Chaldeans and Sumerians. The Pythagorean theorem, for instance, was known at least 1,500 years before Pythagoras.

Although the Ancients knew a great many propositions of geometry and of arithmetic, they knew them as (sorts of) empirical generalizations. The Egyptians, for example, had been faced with the problem of drawing the boundaries of the fields that each fellahin was to cultivate after the Nile returned to its bed following the annual flood. So important was this function that Pharaoh himself is represented on the murals and bas-reliefs with the tools of the harpedonapts or land surveyors. After the harvest, the fellahins came to the royal granaries where their grain was to be divided, one part going to the royal establishment as a sort of tax. And so, many of the problems found in the papyri are of the form: how to divide 10 bushels of wheat into three equal parts (with empirical means of solving them).

The inhabitants of the fertile valleys of the Tigris and the Euphrates,

*Reprinted from *The Science Teacher*, V. 33, No. 7, Oct., 1966, pp. 26–29.
©, by permission.

in what is now Iraq, were great traders who launched important cara-vans going to all parts of the known world, distributing and buying goods. Consequently, their mathematics had to do with what we would call bookkeeping and accounting, and they devised many techniques for the solutions of arithmetical problems, satisfied that such solutions worked in practice.

Furthermore, most of the early religions being astral, a great amount of work was expended in the determination of the relative positions of many stars, the planets, the moon, and the sun, and in the keeping of time.

Granted, then, that the early Greeks obtained most, if not all, of this mathematical information from the people of the Middle East, what did they do that so overshadows their inheritance? They did several things which have left a permanent imprint in our scientific posture. First, and perhaps most important, they made a fundamental distinction between *episteme* and *techne*, that is, between "pure" and "applied" science. The emphasis in the pure science being on demonstration; and in applied science, on problem solving. For example, they distinguished between *geometry*, dealing with extended figures, and *geodesy*, or geometry applied to practical problems, such as land surveying, or designing cylindrical wells, or altars and temples. Similarly, they made a distinction between *arithme*, the science of numbers, and *logistike*, the application of arithmetics to the solution of concrete problems, such as how to count cattle, or the yield of crops.

This distinction between the pure and the applied, so common today, marked a turning point in this history of our culture, for it made possible, among other things, the disciplining and the systematic development of speculative thought. This, I think, holds the key to the remarkable achievements of Western civilization.

Having distinguished clearly the domains of pure and applied knowl-edge, the Greeks were able to transform the empirical rules of thumb they got from the Ancients into scientific propositions. Not content to know that certain formulae were empirically true, i.e., useful in some applications—formulae such $3^2 + 4^2 = 5^2$—they also wanted to know *why* they were true at all. Once the question had been raised, the great merit of the Greeks is to have resisted the temptation of primitive people and to have shunned successfully all answers that smacked of the occult, the magical, or the mythical, and to have relied on rational processes, namely on deductive inferences, thereby introducing the theory of demonstration.

The Greeks seem to have recognized early the principal ele-ments of the theory of demonstration and to have paid due attention to them. For example, all demonstrations in geometrical discourse were to be done exclusively by means of the so-called "Euclidean tools"—the ungraduated straight edge and the compass with fixed opening. Furthermore, both the ruler and the compass had to remain on the plane of the figure at all times during construction. These requirements, which may seem to be unduly restrictive to the untrained, are in fact the rules of transformation, or deductive axioms of the system. These rules are responsible for the fact that the quadrature of the circle is insoluble on Euclidean terms. The Greeks, however, knew that it could be done otherwise; for example, by means of Archimedes' spiral, or by means of the earlier method of Hippias of Elis, that of the tetratrix (425 B.C.). Such was also the case with the trisection of an angle or of the doubling of the cube, which cannot be solved in Euclidean terms, but require, for their solution, transcendental, i.e., non-algebraic curves.

From the foregoing examples, it is clear that the "truth value" of the scientific proposition is, in some sense, relative to the means of "truth-determination." Another important feature of the theory of demonstration that the Greeks recognized early is that all deductive inferences are essentially conditionals—"if . . . then . . ." propositions. This means that all theorems (i.e., true propositions) are such relative to given assumptions or postulates which are, as it were, the foundations of the whole system.

This hypothetico-deductive conception of scientific discourse, inherited from the Hellenistic period, was seriously threatened by the discovery of the paradoxes that were implicit in the theory of sets as developed by Cantor, and the work of Richard, Frege, and others. The paradox is to deductive science what heresy is to dogmatic theology; that is, a catastrophe. The paradoxes presented a danger because they were contradictions that had been derived in orthodox ways from the premises or axioms of the system. The question that presented itself was this, "How do we know that all other branches of mathematical science, which up to now have been taken as models of scientific rigor and as patterns for scientific inferences, are not to yield self-contradictory theorems in the course of their development?"

The deductive method is seen to be operative between two kinds of propositions; namely, those that are descriptive of the empirical world—henceforward symbolized as "p," and those that are primitive to the deductive system, namely the postulates, axioms, and principles, that constitute, when collectively considered, the hypothesis (or theory) from which the empirical propositions p are derived. Let the hypothesis, so considered, be referred to, if need be, as H. Then the deductive method can be symbolized as $H \Longrightarrow p$.

Because of its inherent simplicity due in large part to the logical mechanism underlying it, the hypothetico-deductive aspects of scientific discourse were early discovered, long understood, and widely applied.

174

One of the most important tests of scientific theories has always been their predictive (and retrodictive) powers; the possibility they gave to infer deductive propositions descriptive of new or anticipated states of affairs (and past ones as well). In the first type of prediction, one could include, for example, the bending of light rays in gravitational fields, the increase of mass with velocity, or the dilatation of time as velocity increases, which served as tests of the Theory of Relativity. Of the second kind of prediction—anticipation—the best test is no doubt provided by the ever-increasing success of applied science in general and of technology in particular.

There is, however, another significant aspect of scientific activity that is not accounted for by the deductive method and that is best brought out by contrast with it. Granted that H and p are connected deductively, the questions present themselves: How do we get p in the first place, and, having found p, how do we get to H, the hypothesis that justifies p theoretically? For instance, having made numerous observations on the position of Mars at various times—such as were made by Tycho Brahe —how does one come to formulate a proposition descriptive of the orbit of Mars around the sun as elliptical? And having got it, as Kepler did, how does one get to the formulation of a theory—such as that of a central force field of the inverse square type that will account for the motion of Mars, and of planets in general? These two questions, that are in some ways related, are usually grouped together under the heading of the problem of discovery. It is to this, then, that I shall now turn my attention.

That the problem is an important one is evident to even the most casual observer. Francis Bacon, one of the modern founders of empirical philosophy, saw it well when he set out to develop a new kind of logic of an inductive sort that would render the art of discovery of empirical propositions as independent of the wits of man as the compass had made the drawing of a circle independent of his drafting skills. Even now, attempts are being made, to at least describe, if not prescribe, the way in which discoveries are made. N. R. Hanson, in this country, is probably the best known of the advocates of a retroductive inference pattern. If such a logic could be found, we would be in the (supposedly enviable) position to "program" discoveries and breakthroughs the way we now program problems in computers. Then scientific research could be considerably simplified, as well as made cheaper, and, more important perhaps, made predictable. It is not too difficult to imagine the far-reaching consequences, social and political among them, that such a logic would entail.

Despite these attempts, the fact remains that a logic of discovery is still in the domain of fancy and is likely to remain there until some prior problems are successfully analysed into simpler questions amenable to scientific treatment. I should like to indicate briefly the nature of these prior problems.

The best way to do this, perhaps, is to take some paradigmatic case that I hope will point to the salient features of the problem of discovery. First, let us consider some of the significant characteristics of so-called scientific facts. Let us imagine, for a moment, that on a hilltop watching the sun rise one bright morning, stand Kepler and his master, Tycho Brahe. Imagine further that, seeing them there, you ascend the hill and, upon joining the two astronomers, you inquire of them what it is they are seeing that so enthralls them. Tycho Brahe might answer something like "I am watching the rise of the Earth's largest satellite." Kepler, for his part, might say that "the earth, having completed one full rotation since yesterday morning," he is "watching the sinking eastern horizon bring the sun back into view"! On hearing such conflicting reports, you may wonder aloud, "How is it, gentlemen, that observing the same sun over the same horizon at the same time, you claim to see different things, so that, if one were so inclined, one could, with little effort, exhibit the contradiction of your two statements. Surely one of you, at the least, must be in error. Do tell me, what evidence do you take as warrant for what you say you see?" To this Tycho might reply by noting that any one who is not hopelessly blind will observe the increasing distance between the line of horizon and the solar disk, as well as the continued ascension of the sun, till it reaches zenith overhead, and its subsequent decline in the occident, and ultimate disappearance beyond the western horizon; and that the "facts" speak for themselves, most eloquently to the unprejudiced mind. And that, furthermore, the motion of the stars in the night sky, as well as that of the moon, and the observed stability of the earth, all go to support the reasonableness, nay, the self-evidence of his statement about the sunrise.

It then being the turn of Kepler, he will no doubt appeal to the same "facts," these being the only ones available, to support the reasonableness of *his* view, and the error of his teacher's, not to mention his stubborn refusal to see the world as it really is. I think it is evident, that so long as the discussion remains confined to "facts," meaning to what is the case, no resolution of this divergence is to be expected.

The point of this imaginary dialogue is threefold. First, it shows that "ordinary facts," or data, such as those appealed to above by the protagonists, do not "speak for themselves," as a naive realism bids us believe. Ordinary facts are quite neutral, they point neither to this nor to that interpretation, they simply are. Second, it shows that scientific facts, such as those asserted by Brahe and Kepler, are really interpretations of the data, that is, of the ordinary facts available to all. Third, it shows that the interpretation of the data reflects a certain way of looking at the world, that is, a perspective that orders the givens of experience in one way rather than in some other. The scientific facts are perspectival, reflecting, as it were, the light of intelligence that illuminates them. The disagreement between Brahe and Kepler is not of what the givens of experience are (presumably, their eyes *see* the same things, the solar disk, the line of horizon, the increasing distance between the two). Rather, the disagreement is on the ordering principle for these givens, that is, ultimately, on the perspective in which they are viewed. Brahe looking at the sun rise as a geocentrist, and Kepler as a heliocentrist. The difference between the two astronomers is not centered on what they see in a physiological sense, but rather on what they *see* it *as*.

This perspectival aspect of scientific facts is central to the problem of discovery, as it is to the whole theory of empirical knowledge. The most fundamental discoveries have been those of new points of view, or perspectives, in which the world appears in a new light. Newton somewhere remarks that, if he saw farther than others, it was because he stood on the shoulders of giants. This statement I take as an indication of intellectual modesty rather than as descriptive of his most noteworthy achievement. For the greatness of Newton is not that he saw more facts, but that he saw new kinds of facts· indeed, that he taught us to look at the world in new ways that revealed unsuspected features. Lots of people had seen the proverbial apple fall in the innumerable orchards that have dotted the face of the earth up to Newton's time, but when he exclaimed, in the presence of that falling fruit, "Gravity strikes again," he revealed not so much a fact, as a new way of looking at the world. What I said about Newton can be said, with equal justice, about Darwin, Mendel, Planck, Einstein, Freud, and others, for after them, science could no longer be done in the same way as it was before. Something radical had changed, and it was not the world (which I don't think worries over much about what we think of it) but rather our conception of it.

It is clear, I think, from what I have said so far, that our perspective determines to a large extent what we see the world as, and therefore, what the scientific facts are. Indirectly, it also determines what are our theories that account for those facts. Consequently, a logic of discovery, to be of real use, should give the means to discover a multiplicity of viewpoints that would reveal many new aspects of our experience. Unfortunately, we are very far from understanding the mechanism that is responsible for these perspectival mutations, although we understand some of the factors that enter into them. Assuming the time to be ripe for such a mutation, what is responsible for an Einstein? Why is it, for example, that Einstein, and not Lorentz, or Poincaré, originated the Theory of Relativity, and, more important, the idea of it. After all, the fundamental equations are due in large part to Lorentz, but he didn't see them in that light. Perhaps, as K. R. Popper has suggested, we should not raise the question of a logic of discovery in the context of perspective, but rather, should inquire into the psychology of discovery. But to seek an answer in psychology is, I feel, to seek an explication of *obscurum per obscuris*. Be this as it may, the problem is at present insuperable.

Let us now return to the "facts." The perspective is manifested in the facts that it reveals. The discovery of new facts will then be a question of looking, and ultimately, of the means of observation.

There was a time not so long ago when it was customary to make a distinction between observation and experimentation, the former being a sort of passive way of looking, while the latter was conceived as a sort of active probing, a forcing of nature into "unnatural" postures. What was simply observed was thought to be the case independently of the observer, the facts were taken to have a sort of reality of their own, which required, for their discovery, that the scientist be merely observant.

After the advent of relativity, which underlined the determining role of the observer in the form that the observables take, it became clear that the observables themselves were not only conditioned in some way by the means of observation, but actually generated by them. In other words, it was found that observables are relative to the means of observation, both in form and content, and that it makes no sense to talk as if they led a sort of private life, independently of the apparatus. Thus, the alleged difference between observation and experimentation ceased to have any significance.

From this fact of the dependence of observables upon the means of observation—for example, of spectra on spectroscopes—it follows that new facts may be discovered in two ways. Either there are devised some new means of observation that yield new facts (such as a synchrocyclotron, yielding a beam of polarized antiprotons), or else existing means of observation yield unexpected results (such as the finding of the spectrum of some new element). Such discoveries are obviously bound up ultimately with the development of theories and hypotheses. This linkage has been recognized very early, and we have a logic of sorts that describes it—the so-called scientific method. However, and this is important, the scientific method—or the logic of science, as it is sometimes called—does not provide us with a logic of discovery of either facts or theories, although it gives us the methodological criteria that such discoveries, once made, must satisfy.

This brings us to the last aspect of discovery that I wish to discuss; namely, the framing of hypotheses and the concomitant problem of the design of experimental set-ups that are circumscribed by such hypotheses. It is clear that hypotheses are framed within the general perspective that defines the facts, since the purpose of theories is to describe the facts as well as to correlate and order their descriptions in such a way as to obtain an organic unity for the multiplicity of empirical descriptions. Without going into details, which would take us too far afield, I shall simply outline a few points that are relevant to the question at hand.

1. New theories or hypotheses, in the context of a given perspective, are largely determined by old theories that have ceased to be satisfactory. This is due, in large part, to the fact that we always approach the unknown with what is familiar. This is borne out by the history of science, which presents an evolutionary, rather than a revolutionary, picture of the development of theories, leaving aside the discontinuities presented by the occasional change of perspective.

2. The form of the theories is largely determined by a series of *a priori* notions, which are often of a cultural rather than of a scientific nature. For example, we assume that nature is essentially thrifty, or economical, and that, of several ways of achieving a given effect, the cheapest one, energetically speaking, is to be realized. Such assumptions find expression in the so-called minima principles, which are really extrema principles, such as Hamilton's and Fermat's. Such considerations of economy led Gell-Mann, for instance, to postulate the "strangeness quantum number" to account for the fact that in π ion proton interactions, certain "expensive" reactions took place, instead of cheaper ones.

3. Last, but most importantly, a new theory will be conditioned, if not actually determined, by the availability of an adequate formalism to express it. Even if Galileo had had the idea of universal gravitation, he couldn't have discovered the Gravitational Theory, because the only mathematics at his disposal was the geometry of Euclid. Even Newton couldn't have invented his calculus of fluxions if he hadn't had at his disposal the analytical geometry of Descartes, in addition to the more ancient forms of mathematics.

These few points are not, of course, the outline of a logic of discovery for hypotheses. There is no such logic in existence. But they point to some of the problems that must be faced prior to the development of such a logic, assuming it to be possible.

Educational Objectives
and the Development of Curricula

There may be teachers who can walk into a classroom and intuitively, without needing formally to state any objectives, lead their students to understand and apply the processes of science. These people would be the born teachers we sometimes hear about. I cannot think of many teachers I have seen who fall into this category. Generally speaking, teachers need to plan carefully and to state precisely how they expect their students to perform when a lesson or unit of study has been completed. Careful statement of objectives has been made a major theme of this book, and the articles in the following section will serve to amplify, illustrate, and supplement some of the things I have suggested in Part One.

The detailed planning of curricula may seem to the ordinary teacher to be out of his hands. Yet most of the modern experimental science curricula have involved large numbers of ordinary classroom teachers. More local schools systems are recognizing the importance of including local teachers in curriculum planning. Furthermore, the open, relatively unstructured nature of many of the new national science curricula (BSCS biology, PSSC physics, CBA and CHEMStudy chemistry, ESCP earth science, etc.) require much creative day-to-day curriculum planning on the part of the teacher who wishes to use the materials effectively. Every teacher should think of himself as a curriculum planner and should develop firm ideas of his own on both science content and skills that should be learned at all levels within his local system. If he has such ideas and can state his objectives in convincing terms, he will find that creative curriculum supervisors will begin to listen to him and use his ideas.

Learning and Motivation: Implications for the Teaching of Science*

Walter B. Waetjen

Educators find it difficult to talk about learning. What makes it difficult is that we do not know whether school learning is the same as nonschool learning; nor do we know whether problem solving in tests is the same as problem solving in nontest situations. In like manner, we have little knowledge as to whether learning in one curriculum area is similar to, or different from, learning in another curriculum area. Nevertheless, every person who is a teacher, using the word in a broad sense, goes about his daily activities trying to help individuals to learn. But the educator is interested not only in learning, he is equally interested in motivation.

When a teacher asks himself the question, "What motivated this pupil's behavior," he is asking to have identified one or several of three different things. The first of these is an *environmental determinant* which caused the behavior to occur. This could be the pressure of a parent to have his child learn, a provocative bulletin board display in the classroom, or a well-presented demonstration by the teacher. Second, it may be an *internal instinct*, want, desire, aspiration, plan, motive, purpose, urge, feeling, wish, or drive which precipitated the behavior. Third, it may be the *goal* which either attracted the learner or repelled him. Thus, we can see that when we raise questions about the motivation of pupils, we are not asking easy questions. The complexity of the questions has given rise to a number of theories of motivation. It is unfortunate that teachers and curriculum developers seem to subscribe to none. In order that this discourse not fall into the same trap, a theory of motivation will be presented; but prior to that we shall make explicit our use of the term "motivation."

For the purposes of this paper we shall define motivation as the

*Reprinted from *The Science Teacher*, V. 32, No. 5, May, 1965, pp. 22–26. ©, by permission.

process of arousing action, sustaining the activity in progress, and regulating the pattern of activity. This definition makes it clear that there must be some mobilization of energy, and there must be continuous flow of activity in order to assure attainment of the goal.

Fortunately, the picture is not wholly bleak, for there are some principles of learning and motivation that may be used by teachers in the organization of content and in their teaching. These principles have been derived from research on pupils in classroom settings and not from subhumans in laboratories.

THE SEX OF THE LEARNER
IS A DETERMINANT OF HIS LEARNING

It would be a rare educator who owned up to the fact that he did not believe in individual differences in learning. Strangely, these same educators are prone to overlook as a factor in learning one of the most basic differences in people—their sex. A thesis of this paper is that one's sex is a powerful determinant of both learning and motivation. The evidence is eloquent in support of this thesis.

It is patently clear that among the underachievers there are two to three times as many boys as there are girls; that there are at least four times as many boys as girls who are poor readers; and, that the general school progress of girls at all levels is superior to that of boys. These facts alone suggest that there be some effort made to ensure that school becomes a more significant experience for boys. Research studies indicate that even though boys and girls have identical scores on standardized biology tests, the teachers of those students in biology gave higher grades to the girls. This study has been replicated a number of times, and the findings may be generalized as follows: Even though male and female students have identical levels of achievement on standardized tests, teachers give higher grades to girls. [6] The sex composition of honor rolls and principals' lists are mute testimony to the generalization.

When one examines the skills possessed by pupils, it is obvious that girls have marked superiority over boys in the language area. Since school is essentially a verbal, symbolic, linguistic experience, it's small wonder that girls do better than boys. On the other side of the ledger it can be reported that boys are *somewhat* better than girls in math and science. This slight superiority can be attributed to the fact that analytical thinking is the cognitive skill that undergirds math and science. The skill in analytical thinking is associated with the greater aggressiveness of males. It is here that science teachers may play a significant role in the learning of all pupils, but especially boys by *consciously* structuring the teaching-learning situation so that analytical thinking is

182

brought into play. Butts demonstrated this when he used fourth-, fifth-, and sixth-grade children to determine whether they could combine discrete percepts into concepts without teacher help. [5] Clearly, this called for analytical thinking on the part of the learners. The finding of the study was that even when children are given free opportunity to experience certain science perceptions, meaningful concept development did not result.

Finally, we are constrained to point out that males are superior to females in transfer of training. A study [9] investigating transfer of training gave evidence that previous experience, maturity, reading ability, and intelligence could not account for boys' superior ability to transfer elements of one situation to a new situation. Presumably this superior transfer ability should enable males to perform at high levels, but yet, they do not. Transfer is seeing relationships, a skill which may be developed with great facility in science classrooms if teachers provide opportunities.

EPISTEMIC MOTIVATION

In rather simple terms, epistemic motivation can be described as the drive individuals have to seek knowledge. For generations, teachers have described such knowledge-seeking pupils as "inquisitive" or "curious." We prefer to use the term curiosity not only because it has been used by those who research this motive but because its simplicity communicates well.

It is worth noting that the study of curiosity is in its relative infancy, but we are reassured by the fact that some of the investigations of curiosity have been done with school-age children in school situations. [11]

Many investigations of curiosity, novelty, or uncertainty focus on the degree to which ambiguity is tolerable to the individual. This is reflected in the research done to determine the relation between qualitatively different types of environmental novelty and curiosity in children [12]. One could say on the basis of findings that novelty generally evoked positive approach behavior. There was also a significant difference between the boys' and girls' performance. The girls were found to be more rigid and less curious than the boys. Apparently, rigidity and curiosity are negatively associated.

A skeptic might raise the question as to whether children with high curiosity retain their knowledge after it has once been learned. Maw and Maw [10] addressed themselves to such a question in a study using approximately 800 fifth-grade children as subjects. In this study, it was hypothesized that retention is related, at least in part, to the level of curiosity children have about their environment. Children high and low in curiosity were identified, using teacher and peer judgments. The children were given copies of a story which was a collection of strange but true facts, mostly about animal subjects. As far as the children were concerned the experience ended with the experimentor asking if they had liked the story and the one thing they liked best about it. Seven days later, a 40-item true-false test was given the pupils. Tests of significance showed that in every case the difference between the means of the groups was highly significant and always favored the high curiosity group.

The evidence from this study seems to indicate that children with a high level of curiosity either learn more in a given period of time, or, they retain more of what they experience. It matters little whether there was more learning or greater retention. What is important is that children of comparable intelligence, but differing in curiosity, performed differently in the learning situation.

The research on curiosity does not have immediate recommendations as to how the teacher may improve his instruction; but, certain techniques used in the conduct of research sometimes suggest ways in which teaching might be altered so as to improve learning of students. One such suggestion emerges from a study [4] which sought to determine the effects of prequestioning on learning and curiosity. An experimental group of 24 high school biology students received a questionnaire about invertebrate animals, prior to any other information about the animals. A control group did not receive the same forequestionnaire. The 12 animals consisted of 8 familiar and 4 unfamiliar, of which 2 of the latter were fictitious. Following this, both the experimental and control groups were given 120-word paragraphs describing the animals (information input). After the word paragraphs had been read, a 48-item test was given each subject. The test was constructed in such a way that the subjects answered either that they were certain of the answer from previous knowledge or that they were surprised.

It was hypothesized that the experimental group would learn more effectively and would recall more answers than would the control group, because their curiosity would be aroused by the forequestionnaire. The findings support this hypothesis inasmuch as the experimental group made 32.41 correct responses on the post-test and the control group made 27.15 correct responses. The difference in these was significant at the .01 level of probability. Apparently, the prequestions did arouse curiosity, and the surprising statements were more likely to be recalled as answers in the post-test than were other statements. The prequestioning apparently "tuned" the organism by arousing curiosity which, in turn, predisposed it toward acquisition of information.

It is not beside the point to raise the question as to whether pupils who have formulated "hypotheses" in their cognitive structure are not also seekers of knowledge, i.e., they have epistemic motivation. Atkin's [1] analysis of the development of selected aspects of problem solving revealed that elementary school children tend to express hypotheses of their own after science learning experiences. The study was based on an analysis of tape recordings of children in grades 1, 3, and 6. Atkin found that children in the lower grades relied more on their own experience in formulating hypotheses, while those in the upper grades depended more on authority. Children in lower grades suggested more tests and indicated more needed data for their hypotheses than did upper grade children. Children in "permissive" classrooms (more freedom to seek knowledge?) tended to suggest more hypotheses than did children in less permissive classrooms. In short, knowledge-seeking skills are intimately related to the type of classroom situation the teacher creates.

LEARNING AND TEACHING

In the process of growing-up and experiencing, a child has many contacts with varied aspects of his environment. These "contacts" become incorporated into the cognitive structure that the teacher tries to develop by teaching the curriculum content. When a teacher gives a demonstration, has youngsters work on projects, shows a film, or gives a lecture, he is attempting to introduce information into the cognitive structure of the youngsters. It seems clear, then, that teachers must be knowledgeable about the functioning of the cognitive structure since this strikes at the heart of the dynamics of learning and motivation.

A person uses his cognitive map to make predictions from the past to the present. For example, a pupil uses his previous experience with teachers and classrooms to make predictions about the classroom which he has just entered. In so doing he assumes the present environment to be identical to, or highly similar to, what it was in the past. Ordinarily, this is a good assumption and benefits the pupil since his expectancies permit him to make optimal use of both time and intellectual resources. What must be emphasized is that the pupil is actually making hypotheses about the stimuli he will be receiving. Sometimes the environment has changed in relatively important ways and hypotheses are not fulfilled.

It is entirely probable that the learner doesn't expect or anticipate that the present situation will be *identical* to those of the past. A young child may make such predictions from his cognitive structure, but with increased experience he would anticipate some difference. Thus, the anticipation of change is partially an *experiential* matter. The pupil faces the present situation, then, with two anticipations: [1] the environment will be, in the main, comparable to what it was in the past, and

185

[2] there will be change in the environment. As experience accumulates, it is probable that the child savors the novelty of change in the environment and this becomes the basis for epistemic behavior.

It is not too uncommon to find teachers who assume that they are able to transmit curriculum content to the cognitive structure of a pupil. This assumption means that we can teach directly, that nothing intervenes beween what the teacher teaches and what the learner learns. It is believed that if the teacher makes the curriculum content "interesting" by a few audiovisual devices or by introducing a note of excitement into his voice, the students will be motivated to learn. To make such assumptions means that we minimize strategic individual differences as factors in learning rather than maximize them.

If the material to be taught to youngsters is already similar to, or contained in, their existing cognitive structure, learning is not facilitated. This is portrayed in Figure 1. Curriculum content and the instructional

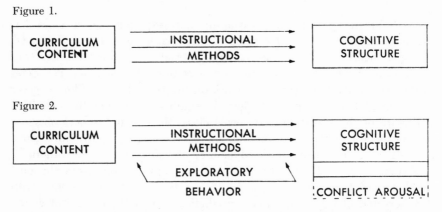

Figure 1.

| CURRICULUM CONTENT | INSTRUCTIONAL METHODS | COGNITIVE STRUCTURE |

Figure 2.

| CURRICULUM CONTENT | INSTRUCTIONAL METHODS / EXPLORATORY BEHAVIOR | COGNITIVE STRUCTURE / CONFLICT AROUSAL |

methods (indicated by the arrows) are designed to communicate to the youngster. In the event the curriculum content is already known to the youngster or is inconsequential to him, there is little behavior elicited from the learner himself. For the learner, such a situation is extremely lacking and probably devoid of meaningful content. Instead of engaging in learning activity, it is more likely that nonproductive verbal behavior will increase, that motor activity of a random nature will increase, and that the person will become increasingly unable to give attention to specific ideas or tasks.

In this instance, there is practically 100 per cent match between what the teacher is attempting to teach and the pre-existing content of the cognitive map. In such situations, learning is not enhanced. As a matter of fact, that situation which we shall call the *100 per cent match situation* is indeed an enemy to learning. The type of behavior elicited from

186

the learner is not learning behavior but is random and nonproductive in nature.

Figure 2 portrays a different state of affairs in which there is, for the most part, a match between the curriculum content (including the instructional procedures) and the cognitive structure of the learners. Since there is a generous portion of match between these two elements, it means that the youngster is familiar with the material or the situation because it fits into his predictions. On the other hand, there is also some degree of "mismatch," meaning there are some elements of either the content or the instructional procedure which the learner does not know and did not predict. This is a dissonant situation which results in arousal of conflict with a consequent need for the learner to assimilate or articulate the unknown, incongruous, or unfamiliar material into his cognitive structure. [7] To do this, he engages in exploratory behavior. Exploratory behavior, as it is being used here, means that the learner scans the classroom looking for new experiences and materials. Likewise, it means that the learner avoids the more familiar aspects of the classroom. There is an increase in the type of verbal activity which evokes information from other people. In this condition the learner is a *seeker* of knowledge. It would be improper to believe that all youngsters who are in the motivated condition engage in similar exploratory behaviors. We must recognize that the modes or strategies by which youngsters seek information and by which they process it into the cognitive structure are unique.

We emphasize that this is an individual difference in learning.

One implication of this discussion is: Teachers can begin to reexamine the matter of *who* asks questions in the classroom and the *type* of questions asked.

Occasionally a teacher will attempt to get pupils to learn something by presenting them with a vast array of entirely new and different kinds of material. Literally, the learners are bombarded with new stimuli. The teacher is rather chagrined to find that the learners do not respond as anticipated and may even resist this seemingly rich learning environment. In this instance there is great mismatch between the learners' predictions and the material with which they came in contact. Figure 3 portrays the two things which eventuate when a great amount of mismatch occurs. In either case, the information is unassimilated and usually is held in a context of anxiety. The learner is aware that he should be able to articulate the curriculum content with his present knowledge, but he is equally sensitive to the fact that he cannot do so; and, therefore, he becomes anxious about the matter. To cope with this situation, the learner may engage in a variety of withdrawing behaviors. He may withdraw from the conceptual material by being a gross dilettante in work production or by daydreaming to excess. On the other

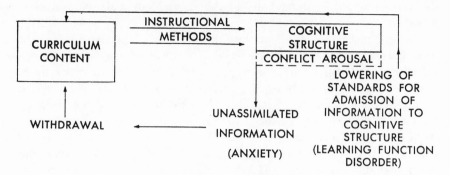

Figure 3.

hand, he may physically withdraw by virtue of cutting classes or being a truant.

The second way of handling unassimilated information is more insidious and should cause teachers to be introspective. In this instance the learner abandons his usual strategies for admitting information to his cognitive domain. In abandoning these strategies, he lowers his standards for admission of information into the cognitive structure. Instead of integrating simple facts into higher levels of organization, the individual holds them at a lower level. This person can be thought of as having a learning disability, for good learning involves orchestrating simple acts or relatively simple ideas into higher and more complex acts or ideas. What is unfortunate about this type of learner is that he is often judged to be at least an adequate and possibly a good learner, because he is able to retain facts even though not able to integrate them within the cognitive structure. When tests measure only the student's ability to retrieve data at the factual level, these students are erroneously perceived as progressing well even though they cannot be said to be effective learners. By lowering the standards for admission of information to their cognitive structure, they have at once put themselves in a position where they are functioning at a much lower level in their learning.

If the cognitive structure were unorganized, it would be a veritable psychological junkyard or collection of facts. While in certain cases this may indeed be true, in the majority of cases it is untrue. A recent theory of learning [2] indicates that the cognitive structure is organized in terms of highly generalized concepts under which are subsumed concepts of a less generalized nature as well as individual or specific facts. This is sometimes referred to as the subsumption theory of learning. It draws on the learner's past experience and mobilizes existing knowledge to facilitate learning of new material. The major organizational principle of the cognitive structure, in other words, is that of progressive differentiation of a body of knowledge from areas of greater generality to lesser generality. However, each area is linked to the next higher step in a hierarchy through a process of subsumption. These levels or areas are not necessarily deductively related, that is, one is not necessarily derivable from the other. The relationship is rather similar to a filing system or an outline in that one concept is included within another more general one.

If this theory does indeed describe the way in which a student learns new material, then teachers have reason to organize their teaching in such a way that they are confident their students possess in their cognitive structures highly general concepts under which they may include or subsume new material. These so-called general elements or concepts may be referred to as "advance organizers." An advance organizer is introductory material that is structured at a higher level of generality, abstraction, and inclusiveness, than the learning material it introduces. In a recent experiment there was used as an advance organizer, for a lesson dealing with metallurgical properties of carbon steel, a passage placing emphasis on the major differences and similarities between metals and alloys. It was found that this material was effective in anchoring the content of the lesson. [3] According to this theory, advance organizers are of two types. An *expository* organizer is used to introduce totally unfamiliar material. Its function is simply, but importantly, that of providing an anchorage for the learning material that is to be presented to the learner. It is here that we must come back to Figure 3 in which there was described the way in which some learners lower the standards for admission of material into the cognitive structure. If a learner has no anchorage in his cognitive structure for new learning material, then he tends to admit the new material at a straight and discretely factual level. That is to say, he has no ideational anchor or point to which the new material may be related.

The second kind of organizer might be called *comparative* in nature. A comparative organizer is used to introduce material that can be related to previously learned material. Not only does it provide anchorage for the material to be learned but it attempts to increase the discriminability between the new ideas to be learned and previously learned ideas. It does this by explicitly delineating at a higher level of abstraction, generality, and inclusiveness the principal similarities and differences between the two sets of ideas. It can thus be seen that the comparative organizer enables a person to use his cognitive structure dynamically. He can develop new organizations and new hierarchies by virtue of exercising the comparative organizing capacity. This is in contrast to the expository organizer wherein a person might well say that if this were the only type of organizer, the resulting cognitive structure would be rather static in its organization. Both expository and comparative organizers are formulated in terms of concepts and propositions that are familiar to the learner.

A study by Fonsworth [8] illustrates the way in which reflection or mediation organizes the cognitive domain. The "reflective thinking" approach in chemistry was compared with teaching procedures that emphasized acquisition of facts and principles.

It was concluded that the reflective thinking approach resulted in significant gains by students with regard to (a) growth in mental ability, (b) application of abilities required in critical thinking, and (c) use of scientific method in solving chemistry problems. Students in both experimental and control groups made significant gains in the acquisition of facts and principles.

Summary and Implications

Science is a strategic curriculum area in terms of the learning of all pupils, for science content gives children a "lever" on manipulating and understanding their environment. It can be an especially strategic area of learning for boy students since science subjects afford boys the opportunity to use their skills in analytical thinking. However, there is no inherent use of analytical thinking skills in science except to the degree that the teacher provides the opportunity. The burden of responsibility falls upon the teacher for understanding the differing ways in which the sexes learn and on these bases to differentiate his instruction accordingly.

Evidence indicates that we can create epistemic motivation (curiosity) by a variety of techniques. One of these is to employ prequestioning before a unit of instruction is begun. The prequestioning apparently "tunes" the pupil so that he is searching for further information when the unit is ultimately introduced. The *type* question which is used is important and will be discussed later.

Effective learning occurs when the classroom situation is one which, in the main, is predictable and familiar to the learner but which contains a slight amount of mismatch or dissonance. This causes the learner to seek information which allows him to fit the dissonant ideas or concepts into his cognitive structure. Thus, a teacher needs to be skilled in knowing how much novelty or dissonance is necessary and how much is too much. But structures of any kind can only be built if some things are dependent upon other things; if some elements are tied into other elements. The cognitive structure is no exception. The teacher can help learners to build this structure by advancing organizers, i.e., elucidating or presenting a concept before its subsumed facts are taught. Equally as important is that the learners need opportunity to *reflect* on the relationship between organizer and facts.

The types of questions teachers use to structure the teaching skills play an important role in (1) the kinds of thinking skills learners employ, (2) the range of information to be covered, and (3) the thinking skills they may learn. The following are types of questions that may focus, extend or lift the thinking skills of pupils.

Questions that develop memory skills. These questions call for the lowest level of cognition or thinking. Unfortunately, most questions asked by teachers are of this type. A good example is, "What is the speed of light?" Such questions give focus since they require students to state, describe, report, or define.

Questions that develop grouping or categorizing skills. These questions require a student to use higher cognitive skills such as classifying, comparing, contrasting, or substituting. In this respect they *extend* the subject under consideration. Example: "What is a property of 2 of the following 4 that is not a property of the other 2?"

Nitrogen—nitric acid—helium—hydrochloric acid

Questions that develop skills in interpreting information and making inferences. A higher level of thinking skill is required when one engages in a transformation of information from one situation to another. Questions of that type *lift* the level of cognition required for treating the subject being considered. Example: "What position might Herbert Hoover take with respect to federal aid to education were he now President?" Aspects of one situation are transformed to another.

Questions that develop skills in predicting consequences. With this type question the pupil is given an independent variable, a situation, and is then asked to predict the dependent variable or consequence. Example: "*If* sulfuric acid is a dehydrating agent, *then* what elements will it remove from wood?" It is important that the pupil repeat the "if" part of the question and then give the correct "then" portion. This type question lifts the level of cognition.

Unless a teacher is consciously aware of the impact of his questions on students of science he is not unlike the hunter who fires his gun into the dark, he knows not where the target is nor does he know where his shots fall.

REFERENCES

1. J. Myron Atkin. "Analysis of the Development of Elementary School Children in Certain Selected Aspects of Problem-Solving Ability." Unpublished doctoral dissertation, New York University, 1956.
2. David Ausubel. *The Psychology of Meaningful Verbal Learning.* Grune and Stratton, New York, 1963.
3. David Ausubel. "The Use of Advance Organizers in the Learning and Retention of Meaningful Verbal Material." *Journal of Educational Psychology,* 51:267–72. October 1960.
4. Daniel Berlyne. "An Experimental Study of Human Curiosity." *British Journal of Psychology,* 45:256–65. 1954.

5. David Butts. "The Degree to Which Children Conceptualize from Science Experience." *Journal of Research in Science Teaching*, 1:135–43, No. 2, 1963.

6. Robert Carter. "How Invalid are Marks Assigned by Teachers?" *Journal of Educational Psychology*, 43:218–28. April 1952.

7. Leon Festinger. *A Theory of Cognitive Dissonance*. Stanford University Press, Stanford, California. 1957.

8. Emile Fonsworth. "The Use of the Reflective Thinking Approach in the Teaching of High School Chemistry." Unpublished doctoral dissertation, The Ohio State University, 1957.

9. M. M. Kostick. "A Study of Transfer: Sex Differences in the Reasoning Process." *Journal of Educational Psychology*, 45:449–58. December 1954.

10. Wallace Maw and E. W. Maw. "Information Recognition by Children with High and Low Curiosity." *Educational Research Bulletin*, 40:197–201. November 1961.

11. Leon Mittman and Glenn Terrell. "An Experimental Study of Curiosity in Children." Unpublished paper read at Society for Research in Child Development, 1963.

12. C. D. Smock and B. G. Holt. "Children's Reactions to Novelty: An Experimental Study of Curiosity Motivation." *Child Development*, 33:631–42. September 1962.

Levels of Performance in Teaching*

Fred W. Fox

New developments in science programs are being received generally with enthusiasm. Teachers feel that good science is being taught, and in addition there is the satisfaction to students and teachers alike that the courses are intellectually stimulating. One is taught to think as well as to learn about the world of nature. Even apart from "the new programs" any teacher gains satisfaction from moving his teaching from the end of the spectrum which demands rote learning, imitation, or repetition of facts presented, to the other end which promotes critical thought and analysis, discovery, or creativity.

At which end of the spectrum do we as teachers perform or expect our students to perform? Are we satisfied to teach as we were taught, or do we use our teaching abilities uniquely and imaginatively according to our personal and community resources and the special needs of our students? Do students sit at their desks day in and day out simply giving back to us what is in their texts, or are they investigating with materials and equipment, testing, gathering data, making judgments, predicting, and discovering? What is the level of performance in our classes?

One of the most imaginative and striking analyses by which we may quickly judge our teaching has been devised by James M. Bradfield and H. Stewart Moredock.[1] It is titled "Levels of Performance" for this discussion. Look at the outline on page 194 and ask yourself: At which level do I expect my students to perform?

It has been the writer's experience that both practicing teachers and teachers in training have been caught up by Bradfield and Moredock's

*Reprinted from *The Science Teacher*, V. 32, No. 4, April, 1965, pp. 31–32. ©, by permission.
[1]James M. Bradfield and H. Stewart Moredock. *Measurement and Evaluation in Education.* The Macmillan Company, New York. 1957. p. 204. Quoted by permission.

LEVELS OF PERFORMANCE

LEVEL   PERFORMANCE

I. Imitating, duplicating, repeating.

This is the level of initial contact. Student can repeat or duplicate what has just been said, done, or read. Indicates that student is at least conscious or aware of contact with a particular concept or process.

II. Level I, plus recognizing, identifying, remembering, recalling, classifying.

To perform on this level, the student must be able to recognize or identify the concept or process when encountered later, or to remember or recall the essential features of the concept or process.

III. Levels I and II, plus comparing, relating, discriminating, reformulating, illustrating.

Here the student can compare and relate this concept or process with other concepts or processes and make discriminations. He can formulate in his own words a definition, and he can illustrate or give examples.

IV. Levels I, II, and III, plus explaining, justifying, predicting, estimating, interpreting, making critical judgments, drawing inferences.

On the basis of his understanding of a concept or process, he can make explanations, give reasons, make predictions, interpret, estimate, or make critical judgments. This performance represents a high level of understanding.

V. Levels I, II, III, and IV, plus creating, discovering, reorganizing, formulating new hypotheses, new questions and problems.

This is the level of original and productive thinking. The student's understanding has developed to such a point that he can make discoveries that are new to him and can restructure and reorganize his knowledge on the basis of his new discoveries and new insights.

---

imaginative ordering of potential classroom experiences. Science teachers who have studied the analysis have suggested a variety of implications for their teaching. Some of these follow:

"LEVELS OF PERFORMANCE"
USES FOR THE ANALYSIS

1. *Evaluation.* The original authors entitled the outline as "Performances Indicating Different Levels of Understanding of a Given Subject." Thus the "levels" were to be considered as standards or criteria against which to judge the work of our students. It is probably safe to say that our tests and examinations usually measure our students' abilities at Levels I and II. Bradfield and Moredock, of course, suggest that we evaluate student performance on more data than are accumulated

through tests, quizzes, and examinations.[2] Our students work in the laboratory, enter discussions, prepare reports, read, and engage in a variety of activities beyond mere recitation (usually a Level I performance) and test-taking. In using the "Levels of Performance" analysis in evaluation, key questions become: What sources of evidence of student performance are there for rendering teacher judgments, and how do I make a record of such evidence of student behavior?

2. *Goals for science teaching.* It is quite apparent that we cannot evaluate student effort at the upper levels of performance if we never arrange for our students to operate there. Converting these levels of performance to teaching goals is a distortion of the original authors' intent. Science teaching objectives should be in a context of the field of science knowledge, the means of deriving it, its social implications, and its application to the solution of our daily problems. But many of us could improve our teaching simply by stating and living up to such a statement as: "I am going to teach science in such a manner that students have to explain, justify, predict, estimate, interpret, and make critical judgments."

3. *Method of teaching.* The tremendous implication of raising the level of performance in our classroom is that we must change our method of teaching. Obviously it would be unfair to evaluate student behavior at the upper levels if students had not been permitted to develop skills at those levels. Evaluation apart, the significance of the "levels" is that laboratory work must become more vital, challenging, stimulating. Demonstrations can no longer be routine. Students will have to be given opportunity to solve problems for which there are no simple solutions. They will have to read, discuss, investigate, try out, argue, take trips, look at, listen to, improvise, succeed, fail. Only by changed methods in most of our classes will students have opportunity to compare, discriminate, reformulate, interpret, predict, discover, create—that is, to perform at a "higher level."

4. *Finding satisfaction in teaching.* No teacher likes to be accused of teaching as he was taught, nor does he like to believe that he teaches in a dull and perfunctory manner. The teacher who is gaining personal satisfaction from his teaching, who talks enthusiastically to his colleagues about his work, or who has a reputation among his students as a top teacher in the school, is exactly the same teacher who is himself teaching at a high level of performance. He compares the variety of

[2]For an additional discussion of sources of evidence for judging student work, see John S. Richardson, *Science Teaching in Secondary Schools.* Prentice-Hall, Englewood Cliffs, New Jersey. 1957. Chapter 7.

teaching techniques he knows are available for his use and with discrimination selects those most suitable for his students and his experience and resources. He critically judges the content of the many science courses he may choose for his students. At his best, the teacher resourcefully departs from the traditional and the routine and creates new and imaginative approaches to both content and method in teaching. He critically questions the commonplace teaching doctrines of his time (and even the not-so-commonplace) and searches for unique ways to solve teaching problems. And in this spirit of his own creativity he finds at the same time poise and confidence that his profession is worthy of his energy and devotion and that education under his direction is serving its proper ends.

What is your "level of performance"?

Science Curriculum Evaluation: Observations on a Position*

Henry H. Walbesser

Two of the fundamental positions concerning the purposes, conduct, and expected outcomes of evaluation, which are currently assumed in the assessment of experimental curriculum materials, are: the content position and the behavior position. It is the intention of this paper to point out the differences between these two conceptions of curriculum assessment and to describe the model, based upon the behavior position, which is being used by the AAAS Commission on Science Education in its curriculum project.

CONTENT

It would doubtless be valuable to explore the content position in depth, but that will not be done here. Our chief concern is with the behavior position. We need say only enough about the content position to help distinguish those aspects which are specific to it and those peculiar to the behavior position. In brief—as "content" suggests—those who adopt this view build a curriculum or develop instructional materials as a content-organizing enterprise. They use instructional materials which appeal to a logical, or rational, or historical presentation of a particular discipline or combination of disciplines. Choice of materials is considered in terms of the nature of the items which should be sampled from the content domains and relates to such questions as:

> What big ideas from this discipline should be chosen?
> What particular topics are fundamental to an understanding of the discipline?

*Reprinted from *The Science Teacher*, V. 33, No. 2, Feb., 1966, pp. 34–39. ©, by permission.

How can certain concepts be best presented?

What particular facts must an individual know if he is to appreciate the significance of this discipline?

Naturally, in the assessment of the instructional materials developed from such a curriculum orientation, the units of achievement are taken to be content items.

The primary measurement is most often a sequence of content items or content situations, and the measurement is made almost exclusively in terms of paper and pencil performances. Among those who adopt this content position there are some who use subjective "expert" evaluation, particularly among those who contend that the measurement field has not yet achieved the necessary technology so as to be able to provide useful or constructive information about the effects of the curriculum. However, assessment of instruction materials by means of a rigorous research design *is* possible within the content-directed framework.

BEHAVIOR POSITION

The second group of curriculum designers reflect what might be termed the behavior position. The AAAS Commission on Science Education subscribes to this position. The "behavioral" group focuses upon the creation of instructional sequences of material which supposedly assist the learner in the acquisition of a particular collection of behaviors rather than a particular collection of content. Unlike those who favor evaluation of content, the curriculum organization which appeals to a behavioral interpretation approaches the development of instructional materials by asking one question: *What do we want the learner to be able to do after instruction that he was unable to do before instruction?*

Then the curriculum designer proceeds to develop materials related to the answers given to this question.

The existence of each curriculum project is dependent upon being able to demonstrate that it accomplishes something. Whether this accomplishment is content assimilation or performance acquisition is of no real consequence. What is important, however, is the recognition and acceptance of the principle that every curriculum project has the honest and inescapable obligation to supply *objective evidence of accomplishment.* Furthermore, the evidence presented by the project must be able to satisfy the criterion that it was obtained by defensible research procedures and that these procedures can be replicated if someone should desire to do so.

For the behavior-oriented group of curriculum designers, reliably observable performance plays the same role as a content item does for

198

the content-oriented group. As a consequence of the behavior-oriented point of view, the evaluation of a collection of instructional materials becomes the assessment of the presence or absence of specific behaviors or specific sets of behaviors. The accomplishment of these objectives of the instructional materials for the behavior-oriented group is determined by observing the learner performing his specified task and thereby exhibiting the desired behavior. Such an assessment obviously demands that the behaviors under observation be clearly stated, the criterion for their presence be explicitly stated, and that the conditions under which the evidence of presence or absence is collected be described in such a way that the procedure used to obtain the evidence can be replicated by others. This investigator has adopted the position that the behavioral view of curriculum development possesses advantages sufficiently unique and productive to the design, development, and evaluation of instructional materials so as to make behavioral description of the objectives of instructional materials an unavoidable partner of content selection. The remainder of this paper is an explanation of this position.

PRACTICES FOR EVALUATION

What is the purpose of any collection of instructional materials? One response which has a high probability of acceptance by most, if not all, curriculum designers, is that the purpose of a collection of instructional materials is to effect learning. An appeal to this all-encompassing goal of learning leads one quite naturally to ask two questions: What is to be learned? and, Who is to learn it? The question of who is to learn relates, in this instance, to the population of elementary school children. Upon first consideration, one might argue that "what is to be learned" is exclusively within the domain of content selection. However, this view is soon replaced by the more basic behavioral orientation when one considers that the recognition of whether an individual possesses "knowledge of a particular collection of content" is only possible through some observable response on his part.

Does confinement of statements of what is to be learned to statements of observable performance restrict the nature of the content area or the general character of possible objectives of the curriculum? The constraints imposed by behavioral objectives for curriculum description are amazingly few. Consider, for example, the physicist who might set the goal for his curriculum to be that the student will understand Newton's First Law of Motion. How will the physicist distinguish those students who understand from those students who do not understand? Perhaps someone would wish to contend that the physicist is never certain of when the student understands. This position is indefensible for a writer who intends others to adopt an instructional procedure which will teach "an understanding of that concept." Furthermore, how can any author make a selection of instructional procedures, or decide upon an order, or include or exclude instructions from his discussion if he possesses no indicator of when he has succeeded? How can a writer make any decision under these circumstances? It is quite possible, however, that the physicist may not be able to verbalize the class of learner responses with which he is concerned, but the physicist, nevertheless, does possess them. The problem is merely to help the creator of the instructional sequence verbalize a description of the desired behaviors. From this standpoint one may contend that even the comfortable, ambiguous objectives such as understanding, appreciation, and knowing—so commonplace as objectives for contemporary curriculum projects—are potentially able to yield to a behavioral description.

The content selection and organization made by the writing efforts of the past decade are not under question by this discussion, but rather the lack of evidence to support or describe what these programs accomplish is the focus of attention. What is already available by way of instructional materials is not the central issue either, for this material is part of the past development and should remain part of the past. It is not sensible that one propose taking existing materials and attempting to provide a set of behavioral objectives to describe each program. What is important is that curriculum projects learn from these errors so that current activity improves upon past efforts.

Curriculum designers seldom possess professional interest in the problems associated with the clarification and specification of objectives in terms of a behavioral description. It is the obligation of the behavioral researcher to provide the guidelines which will enable the curriculum writer to make the statements of performance.

How will the project proceed after it has adopted the principle that statements of objectives be statements of observable performance? One procedure is to attempt an adaptation of the "Bloom Taxonomy." [1] However, lack of specification within, as well as between, Bloom's taxonomic classifications and their relationship to test development rather than instructional development make them somewhat unacceptable for the present purpose. Since the behavioral point of view focuses upon the ability of a learner to perform a specific task, the work of Miller [3] in the area of task analysis, and that of Gagné [2] and Walbesser [4] in the construction and interpretation of behavioral hierarchies, offer an alternative to the Bloom adaptation. It is this alternative strategy which has been adopted by the Commission on Science Education of the American Association for the Advancement of Science in the description and evaluation of the elementary science curriculum, *Science—A Process Approach*. The model of curriculum evaluation developed in this discussion is illustrated by the evaluation program of *Science—A Process Approach.*

STATEMENTS OF BEHAVIOR

Can scientists be persuaded to write behavioral objectives? The experiences with the science curriculum effort of the AAAS Commission on Science Education strongly suggest that the physical, biological, and social scientists can be persuaded to adopt this position, without interfering with their creation of instructional materials for science. The first requirement is a firm commitment on the part of the project decision-making body to have behavioral objectives.

Each instructional segment should clearly state the objectives of instruction—what the child will be able to do or say (observable performance) after instruction with the material that he was unable to do or say before instruction. The objectives must be statements of reliably observable behavior, written by the author of the instructional segment, and stated in terms of observable performances which the scientist feels are necessary as well as sufficient indicators of success.

If this procedure is to be effective, each writer will need to be provided with a description of what is desired by way of statements which are acceptable as statements of objectives and those statements which are unacceptable. One example of such a description is contained in the subsequent paragraphs. The description is meant to be illustrative of this one effort and nothing more.

CRITERIA TO BE USED IN THE CONSTRUCTION OF STATEMENTS OF BEHAVIORAL OBJECTIVES

The statement of objectives should include all of the individual performances one expects the learner to have acquired during the exercise. When conceived as immediately observable performances, these may be thought of as minimal objectives; but as such, none should be omitted from the statement.

Many authors tend to include some goals such as "increasing understanding," "developing appreciation," and so on. A statement of an objective must be considered unacceptable if it includes this kind of statement. The question to be faced is, what specific things is the learner expected to acquire which can be seen when immediate observations of his performance are made?

A major criterion should be clarity, the avoidance of ambiguity. For example, a statement like this is ambiguous: "The child should be able to recognize that some objects can be folded to produce matching parts, that is, are symmetrical." This statement might mean several different things:

A. The child recognizes symmetrical parts when they are folded to produce matching parts.
B. The child can verbally answer the question about what makes the object symmetrical by saying, "A figure is symmetrical if it can be folded to produce matching parts."
C. The child can demonstrate whether or not a figure is symmetrical by pointing out its matching (or nonmatching) parts.

These are not the same things. While the child is unlikely to be able to do C without being able to do A, he could certainly do A without doing C, C without doing B, and B without either A or C.

It is imperative to use words which are as unambiguous as possible. Some examples are:

A. *Identify*, also recognize, distinguish. These mean point to, choose, pick out, or otherwise respond to several stimuli differentially.
B. *Name*, also *state*. These imply that a verbal statement is required. "What color is this ball?" is naming.
C. *Describe*. Means a verbal statement and also that the categories stated are self-generated. "How do you describe this ball?" is describing.
D. *Order*, or *place in sequence*.
E. *Construct, print*, or *draw*.
F. *Demonstrate*. Means that the learner is applying a principle to a specific situation. For example, he may be asked to demonstrate symmetry for a figure by folding or matching halves.

Why the emphasis on performance in words implying behavior? The major reason is to stay away from "mere" verbalization. If one says the child "understands that such and such is true," this might be taken to imply merely that the child can repeat a verbal statement. Much better to have him *identify* something, *construct* something, or *demonstrate* something. Under these circumstances, we know that he "knows."

What does one hope to gain from this procedure? By requesting each author to specify the expected behavioral outcomes for the particular material he has written, we require him to specify what he considers success with this particular piece of instruction. Once this specification is made, any observer—whether he is a scientist, teacher, or interested individual—is able to distinguish those who have successfully achieved the objectives of the exercise from those who have not. Under these circumstances, all that is called for is that individuals making the judgment read the description of the desired performances and then determine whether they are present in the learner being observed.

If a scientist specified the performances one is examining, it can be argued that the scientist should also specify how one goes about the task of determining whether the learner does or does not possess a particular behavior. As an aid to the scientist in the construction of these performance measures, it is helpful to provide him with guidelines which describe the necessary characteristics of such measures.

The guidelines for constructing each of these performance assessments, or competency measures as they are called by the AAAS Commission on Science Education elementary science curriculum project, require that they meet the following criteria:

A. Each objective of the exercise should be represented by at least one task. Hopefully, these tasks should be suggested by the statements of the objectives; but in any case, behaviors proposed as instructional objectives should be measured.

B. The tasks need to be designed to elicit behaviors of the sort described in the objectives. If an objective calls for the construction of something, the task might begin "draw a _____." If the learner is being asked to name something, the task might be "What do we call this?"

C. The description accompanying each task should tell the instructor clearly what to do (not just imply it). For example, an accompanying instruction might be: "Place in front of the child a dittoed sheet containing drawings of an equilateral triangle and a circle." Or, "Give the child the meterstick."

D. The kind of performances that are acceptable should be clearly described so that a correct judgment can be made concerning the presence or absence of a particular behavior.

The collection of behavioral objectives for the entire instructional program provides a behavioral map (or bank of descriptions of behavior) which may be used to characterize the entire collection of instructional materials. In short, this totality of behaviors represents a measurable description of what this particular instructional program attempts to accomplish. Such a collection of behaviors is at least one means of providing a lower bound on what the curriculum is to accomplish.

A behavorial map such as the one provided by these procedures will in turn yield to analysis by behavioral hierarchies such as those of Gagné [2] and Walbesser [4], thereby providing the vehicle through which to obtain an assessment of the instructional program's effect far beyond that identified by this lower bound. Assessment of the long-term behavorial acquisition by the children exposed to *Science—A Process Approach* is determined by The Science Process Test or The Science Process Instrument which is administered on an annual basis. The Science Process Test is a performance measure administered individually and based upon the behavioral description provided by the behavorial hierarchies which describe each of the simple science processes. The results of this instrument provide an individual profile of the developmental progress of each child within each of the simple processes. The current version of this instrument, The Science Process Test, covers the kindergarten and first, second, and third grades.

INTEREST MEASUREMENTS

Up to this point, the evaluation has concerned itself with assessment within the cognitive domain. One might reasonably ask, what measures should or can be taken of the affective domain. That is, most science curriculum projects are interested in the investigation of the student's attitude toward science as well as the teacher's attitude toward science. The following remarks are directed at the question of student interests. Since the investigation of student interest in science has just been initiated by the *Science—A Process Approach* curriculum, it is only possible to describe the nature of the strategies being used.

The first of the three instruments intended to measure the child's interest in science is called the "Extra-School General Information Inventory." The strategy of development calls for the construction of a measure which samples general information from four broad areas: science, fine arts, sports, and literature. The assumption is that the interests of a child will be reflected by his fund of information on topics or in areas to which he is not ordinarily exposed in the formal school environment. Therefore, if the youngster demonstrates that he has a sizable collection of facts, which are miscellaneous from a standpoint of his formal schooling, but all the facts are science related, then one might reasonably infer that this is a reflection of his reading or activity pursued outside of the classroom—that is, a reflection of his interests. The general information categories which were selected as components for the Inventory are intended to reflect divergent interest areas. By appealing to these rather diverse categories, the science interest is not as visible to the child; that is, the child is not able to guess easily that you are interested in his science interests. With such a less visible indirect measure of interest, one works from the assumption that he has improved his probability of sampling the true interests of the child.

The second form of interest measure which is under development is one in which one employs duration of looking time as the measure of interest. Various levels of complexity in pictures depicting several kinds of activities are employed in this procedure. One obtains measures of the length of time which an individual will look at pictures related to four areas: science, fine arts, sports, and literature. The pictures are equated with regard to complexity. The intention is to develop a Looking Time Interest Inventory.

The third interest measure is a Structured Interview of Science Interests in which the interviewer guides the conversation with the child so as to sample the child's recent activities outside of school. It is much too early at this point to decide whether any or all of these interest inventories will be effective with children at this age level. However, they do represent three forms which may be logically supported as possible measures of science interest.

SUMMARY

By way of summary, then, the evaluation begins with the specification of behavioral objectives for each instructional unit, proceeds to assess the success of each instructional unit in terms of measuring the behaviors acquired by each child as set forth in the objectives, and assesses the annual progress of each child in terms of his acquisition of the behaviors identified in the behavioral hierarchies for each of the processes. Finally, the science interests of children exposed to the instructional program may be included within the evaluation design, but by indirect rather than direct measurement.

The case for the behavioral description of a set of instructional material is not a case against the content-oriented curriculum efforts. Rather, the behavioral view of curriculum is merely a recognition of the fundamental role which behavior and its specification as observable performance must play in a description of what a content-organized curriculum does accomplish. In this context, a content-oriented view of curriculum represents one plausible extension of the behavioral view. The acceptance of the need for the behavioral description of objectives will enable curriculum projects to carry out comparative studies on a basis which does yield to scientific investigation. Hence the benefits to content-oriented curricula would be clarification of the aims of the instructional materials, the existence of a vehicle for assessing a success or failure of the materials, and a technique for conducting comparative studies of curricula as defensible research investigations. Obviously the same benefits are present for behavior-oriented curricula with one additional possibility. Without stretching the point out of all perspective, one could readily imagine the existence of a curriculum development project which first specifies the tasks all learners successful with the curriculum will be able to accomplish, then describes the behavioral sequence in observable performance language so as to identify the behaviors which are prerequisite to the ability to perform each task, and finally develops the instructional materials which would shape the behaviors identified by each entry in the behavioral sequence. The instructional revolution implicit in such a curriculum development project has the potential of reshaping all educational enterprises, since one would finally direct his attention to the potentials of the learner, rather than the appropriateness of content selections.

The importance of a performance-based evaluation to the adoption of an instructional program by the classroom teacher also yields to a most fascinating behavioral assessment. Imagine the impact teachers could have on the curriculum if they demanded behavioral objectives and supporting evidence of accomplishment in terms of acquired behaviors. Why shouldn't every teacher demand statements of the behaviors their students can be expected to acquire as a result of exposure to every instructional program they are asked to use?

REFERENCES

1. Benjamin S. Bloom. *Taxonomy of Educational Objectives:* Handbook 1: *Cognitive Domain.* David McKay Company, Inc., New York. 1956.
2. R. M. Gagné. "The Acquisition of Knowledge." *Psychological Review.* 69:355–356. 1962.
   ———. *The Conditions of Learning.* Holt, Rinehart and Winston, Inc., New York. 1965.
   ———. "The Implications of Instructional Objectives for Learning." In C. M. Lindvall, Editor. *Defining Educational Objectives.* University of Pittsburgh Press, Pittsburgh, Pennsylvania. 1964.
   ———. *The Psychological Basis of Science—A Process Approach.* American Association for the Advancement of Science. AAAS Miscellaneous Publication 65–8. 1965.
   ——— and O. C. Bassler. "Study of Retention of Some Topics of Elementary Non-metric Geometry." *Journal of Educational Psychology.* 54:123–131. 1963.
   ———, J. R. Mayor, H. L. Garstens, and N. E. Paradise. "Factors in Acquiring Knowledge of a Mathematical Task." *Psychological Monographs.* 76: No. 7 (Whole No. 526). 1962.
   ———, and Staff, University of Maryland Mathematics Project. "Some Factors in Learning Non-metric Geometry." *Society for Research in Child Development.* 30: No. 1, Serial 99. 1965.
3. R. B. Miller. *Handbook on Training and Training Equipment Design.* Wright Air Development Center, Wright-Patterson Air Force Base, Ohio. Technical Report 53–136. 1953.
   ———. *A Method for Man-Machine Task Analysis.* Wright Air Development Center, Wright-Patterson Air Force Base, Ohio. Technical Report 53–137. 1953.
   ———. *Some Working Concepts of Systems Analysis.* American Institute for Research, Pittsburgh, Pennsylvania. 1954.
   ———. *Task and Part-Task Trainers.* Wright Air Development Center, Wright-Patterson Air Force Base, Ohio. Technical Report 60–469; ASTIA No. AD 245652. 1960.

―― and H. P. Van Cott. *The Determination of Knowledge Content for Complex Man-Machine Jobs.* American Institute for Research, Pittsburgh, Pennsylvania. 1955.

4. H. H. Walbesser. "Curriculum Evaluation by Means of Behavioral Objectives." *Journal of Research in Science Teaching.* 1:296–301. 1963.

―――. *An Evaluation Model and Its Application.* American Association for the Advancement of Science, AAAS Miscellaneous Publication 65–9. 1965.

Process Patterns and Structural Themes in Science*

Donald Lundstrom

Lawrence Lowery

"SCIENCE IS THE TOPOGRAPHY OF IGNORANCE"[1]

Science is concerned with man's knowledge of his physical environment and with the methods he has developed to control it. Consequently, science must concern itself with a way of thinking and doing (modes of inquiry) and with a conceptual structure.

In order to meet these concerns, school systems have developed a variety of programs. Yet the objectives of present science programs are often not clear to the teacher, and we still hear these familiar plaints: Science is all-too-often taught as an accumulation of information grouped into isolated segments. Textbooks may be loosely constructed or built upon isolated, dead-end topics. Secondary school science is as isolated from elementary school science as biology, chemistry, and physics are isolated from each other.

To avoid these common pitfalls in science education, one must look at four interwoven dimensions before planning a complete science program: (See Figure 1).

The following discussion will be concerned with two of these dimensions: the processes of science (taking into consideration how children learn) and the conceptual structure. Within this framework science course content should:

1. Illustrate the many different processes in a pattern that lead to the conclusions of science

2. Provide a comprehensive picture of the generalizations and theories

*Reprinted from *The Science Teacher*, V. 31, No. 5, Sept., 1964, pp. 16–19. ©, by permission.

[1]O. W. Holmes. *The New Dictionary of Thoughts*. The Standard Book Company, New York. 1955. p. 569.

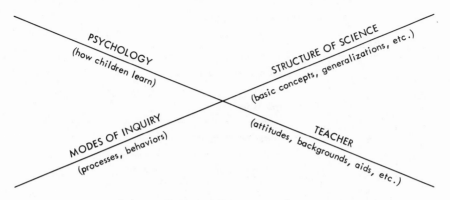

Figure 1. Diagram of interwoven dimensions.

that are the logical bases of modern science (the pattern of structure)

3. Provide the student with an opportunity to encounter the uncertainty of the frontier of knowledge

Secondary school content should be integrated with, articulated with, and dependent upon the elementary school curriculum.

We propose a pattern to the processes which are a part of the scientific enterprise. These processes are the avenues through which the principles and concepts of science can be taught. There seems to be a natural sequential order to the development of these processes. They are never independent of each other. However, there is an optimum period where an emphasis can be made of each process. The following chart is suggested as a plan to introduce and develop the processes of science, remembering that there is a continual extension of each process at each succeeding grade level (See Figure 2).

We also propose structural themes to represent the structure of science rather than the structure of each field. These themes should eliminate the isolated, dead-end topics in science. The themes selected are: Variation and Pattern; Interaction and Dependence; Change and Continuity.

If these three themes are set into a complementary pattern with children's growth, and placed alongside the process pattern, one finds that the first theme (Variation and Pattern) is best emphasized in grades K–3, Interaction and Dependence in grades 4–6, Change and Continuity in 7–9. Grades 10–12 would make equal use of all three themes simultaneously to allow students to see and utilize interrelationships. At all levels there will be a blend between the structures of chemistry, biology, and physics.

Now let us look at how the process pattern and structural themes blend into a meaningful vertical unit. The following outline of the sci-

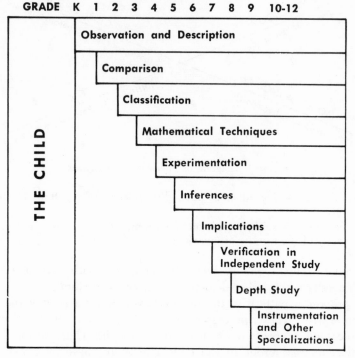

Figure 2. Processes of science related to grade level.

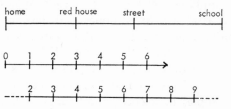

Figures 3, 4, and 5, top to bottom. Development of a number line concept.

entifically useful number line concept is presented as an example of the type of material possible in the elementary grades:

1. Kindergarten children can understand the observable distances that they relate to on a home-to-school journey. They can begin to describe certain guide signs that they encounter. (See Figure 3.) The teacher can take the children on a nature walk. They can begin to develop some concept of distance while observing. It might mean a definite number of steps between certain guide signs. Their starting point is usually a fixed one (e.g., the beginning), in many cases zero.

2. In the first grade the children are able to go beyond their immediate environment, observing and describing the number line concept as an extension of their earlier work. Comparison of distances can be an integral part of this development. A new look at the number line enables the student to see not only the concept of number (See Figure 4) but also that the starting point may be different. It does not have to be zero. (See Figure 5.)

3. Clocks are an important part of the work in grade two. Children begin to see the number line concept in a different relationship. The number line is broken into two parts, thus building a new dimension to the original concept. (See Figure 6.)

4. Further math techniques in the development of the number line concept can be made in grade three with the temperature scale. This introduces the number line in a vertical position. Positive and negative numbers become more comprehensible when the child sees that his number line now runs in two directions from a common beginning. (See Figure 7.)

5. In grade four an experiment on the burning time of a candle takes the number line another step—into a horizontal and a vertical direction. The charting of a constant rate develops the predictive ability of a straight-line graph. (See Figure 8.)

6. At the fifth-grade level curved line graphs and their interpretations are introduced. Water is boiled, hard crack candy is made, and the resulting curved line graphs are interpreted in terms of the knowledges the children have developed previously. Other inferences can be generalized.

7. A sixth-grade unit can build possible implications upon constant or predictable rates developed from number lines coupled with various independent observations of scientific phenomena. The use of four quadrants would also build upon the conceptual structure.

8. Developing a conceptual structure through slopes, vertical intercepts, vectors, and equations, students will reach the stage of apparatus that extends man's senses. The oscilloscope, as a regular piece of high school apparatus, makes further use of the number line concepts and may be used to measure pulse variations in a study of physiology or to develop the resultant equations from the pattern of falling bodies while studying physics.

Such conceptual structure development should lead to a systematic program for all students—one that develops logically yet scientifically.

How does the pattern and structure blend into a meaningful horizontal unit? If the fifth-grade level is selected, one can see that children in our program will have had extensive experience in observation, classification, mathematics, and experimentation. The fifth-grade level adds the dimension of inference. The children have also had several years' experience within the structural theme Variation and Pattern and some instruction in Interaction and Dependence. Keeping in mind that we believe there should be an intermixing or parallel set of experiences in biology, chemistry, and physics whenever possible, let us see how the processes and structural themes blend at the fifth-grade level.

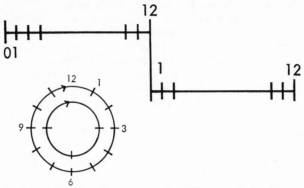

Figure 6. Number line concept in different relationships.

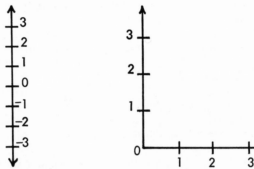

Figure 7. Number line concept showing positive and negative numbers.

Figure 8. Number lines showing horizontal and vertical directions.

The children may be asked to find out which evaporates faster— alcohol or water (They have had other experiences with evaporation). To find out whether their answers are correct or not, the children use their previous knowledge to design an experiment. They put equal quantities of alcohol and water in dishes and place them so that room conditions will be the same for each. They then table the data they collect day by day (See sample sheet in Figure 9). The processes utilized at this stage will be observation, mathematics, and experimentation. The children will be seeking variation and pattern in their data. Without finishing the experiment, but when enough data are gathered, they are asked to predict when the alcohol or water will be completely gone. Thus, the idea of inference will be developed, and their predictions can be easily checked by continuing the experiment. Data can be plotted on a graph showing liquid measure and evaporating time.

Another experiment, in the area of chemistry, will build upon the previous one. The children are asked how much salt it takes to saturate a certain quantity of water (They have had some previous experience

EVAPORATION

Equal Measure of Liquids: _____

TABLE

Time of Day	Evaporating Time	Remaining Water	Remaining Alcohol	Remarks
	minutes			

Figure 9. Sheet for recording day-by-day data for evaporation experiment.

in solubility). The children test to find out. After obtaining results, the children are asked what would happen if the temperature of the water were increased. Through further experimentation the children will discover the NaCl solubility curve (See sample sheet Figure 10). From

SODIUM CHLORIDE SOLUBILITY

TABLE

Temperature	Grams NaCl/100 g H_2O	Remarks
degrees centigrade [a]		
0		
10		
20		
30		
40		
50		
60		
70		
80		
90		
100		

[a] suggested temperatures

Figure 10. Sheet for recording data on sodium chloride solubility.

this, it is hoped that they can discover the saltwater-temperature ratio. This then takes them into the simple ideas of interaction and dependence. Comparison of a graph of the data can be made with other graphs (such as that of a hypo solubility curve) to look for patterns and variations and to help children interpret and make inferences.

In the area of biology the students will encounter a less directive continuation of this experiment. Each child will grow his own plant or plants from seeds. He will be seeking to answer any question he wants concerning the growth of the seeds (See sample sheet, Figure 11).

PLANT GROWTH

Problem:_____

_____

What I Have Done to Solve My Problem:_____

_____

_____

What I Think Will Happen: _____

_____

Table of Observations: _____

Figure 11. Pupil's outline for plant growth experiment.

Preferably he will be limited to one variable: e.g., Does a plant grow differently in the dark than in the light? Does freezing a seed change its pattern of growth? Do radish seeds grow differently than do bean seeds? In this experiment the children will be utilizing concepts from our first theme, Variation and Pattern to new concepts from our second theme, Interaction and Dependence. All the processes must be used effectively to draw conclusions.

By using the processes of science pattern and the conceptual structural themes, a school system should be able to eliminate the isolated, dead-end topics in science. The program would grow from kindergarten through grade 12 instead of the usual textbook's grade 1 through 6 or 8. The program should bring about a closer articulation between the elementary and secondary levels. Scope and sequence should become clearer to the teacher, and science as an accumulation of information should become a fossil of the past.

Experimentation with
Teaching Methods and Styles

Throughout this book you have been encouraged to experiment with various teaching methods in order to develop a personal style of teaching that takes maximum advantage of your personal qualities. The author has asked you to perform a number of activities all related to developing a personal style, but he has purposely given you few direct statements about specific techniques to use. The articles within this section will help to acquaint you with some ways in which several different investigators have gone about experimenting with teaching styles and techniques.

Experiment
in Learning Discovery Techniques*

Thomas E. Tinsley, Jr.

When science teachers in Greenwich decided to revise the junior high school science curriculum, many previously accepted educational objectives had to be discarded, because we felt science should fill a more functional need. Our group set as our primary general aim to give students knowledge and skills necessary for effective citizenship by developing their powers of rational thinking. Among the observations which led us to this conclusion were the facts that eighth-grade science is a required course; that most of our students would not pursue science as a career; and that scientific knowledge is developing so rapidly that the facts we teach today may be outmoded or found untrue tomorrow.

We compiled a list of objectives that would contribute to our aim, as well as help students gain confidence in their own observations and statements. Fostering intelligent skepticism, teaching students to analyze, compile, and use data both to draw logical conclusions and to predict results, and instilling scientific methods of inquiry were prime objectives. We hoped to teach students to recognize the tentativeness of scientific facts, the place of chance in science, and the importance of approaching problems from as many directions as possible. We hoped also to increase the students' ability to communicate their ideas clearly and precisely.

We chose the properties of matter as the subject of our new program and began selecting laboratory experiences to "springboard" our students into the realm of scientific investigation. Each experience included a pre-lab (introduction of vocabulary, equipment, and procedure), the lab itself, and a postlab (analysis and discussion of data and drawing conclusions).

Developing concepts took longer this way, but the rewards were worth it. Students began to open up. They discussed problems freely,

*Reprinted from *The Science Teacher*, V. 33, No. 7, Oct., 1966, pp. 45–47. ©, by permission.

criticized each other's data, and drew their own conclusions—all without fear of giving a wrong answer. We teachers often found it difficult to keep quiet or ask questions rather than give answers.

By the end of the year we had found that students could handle a process learning situation. Their enthusiasm was evident from the constant spirited debates and discussions we had witnessed. However, even though we had eliminated a large amount of usable material, we found that we had included too much. The result had been a high-powered chemistry course with no apparent unifying thread the students could follow with ease. The labs seemed isolated from one another, and there was little flexibility to accommodate creativity and different ability levels.

For the second year of our "experiment in learning," we kept the same basic format, but cut and reorganized materials, introducing as much color and dramatic effect as possible. We began with highly structured labs which stressed observation and familiarization with new equipment. Succeeding labs became less and less structured, so that students eventually began to design their own procedures. A teacher's guide was prepared which suggested questions and possible avenues to explore and gave leads from the postlab to the next prelab.

The curriculum was left wide open for both teachers and students to create and investigate on their own at any point. The basic thread of the curriculum can easily be picked up again without disrupting the sequential conceptual theme of exploring the properties of matter. Allowances are made for the students to experience frustration as well as success. Traps are set along the path, and students seem to derive great satisfaction from working their own way out.

A brief look at our basic outline, explaining a few of the lab experiences, will give the reader an idea of the discovery techniques we use.

Experience 1: On the first day of class we meet students with a demonstration designed as an attention-getting device which will sharpen the students' powers of observation. The class is shown three beakers containing clear liquids and asked if these solutions are water. Do they look like water? If they are mixed, will anything happen?

The solutions are mixed, and they remain clear. In two minutes this mixture flashes bright orange. Just about the time the students gain the attention of the teacher, the mixture has flashed purple. While the students are buzzing about the "magic" that has just occurred, a sheet is passed out on which are such questions as: How many liquids were mixed? In what order did the colors appear? In what order were the solutions mixed? The remainder of the period is spent discussing these questions.

Experience 2 is also an observation lab. At this point the class is introduced to the use of the Bunsen burner and the balance. Ammonium dichromate is burned, *after the students are warned* of the dangers of the dusts and oxides that will be formed. The teacher asks:

1. What was the material like before burning?
2. What was the material like at the end of the lab?
3. Describe what you observed as the change took place.

We do not at this point stress the chemical reaction that has occurred.

Experience 3: We try to point out that people will experience things differently even though exposed to the same media or phenomena. PTC taste-test paper is passed to each student with instructions to taste it and record his observations. In the discussion that follows, we try to bring out the fact that two people observing the same phenomenon may respond with two different versions of it and we can not say that either is wrong.

Experience 4: By now the students are becoming very sure of themselves when it comes to observing. In this lab the class is confronted with four unknown white compounds and asked to group or (if possible) name them, but not to taste the compounds. At the end of the postlab, students admit that they have been able to do nothing but describe the compounds. Are there other ways in which we can distinguish these materials? Eventually someone will suggest, "Let's put them in water."

Experience 5: The compounds used in experience 4 were chosen for their solubility—very soluble, soluble, slightly soluble, and not soluble. The students dissolve three grams of each in 20 ml of water. Two (in test tubes 1 and 2) seemingly dissolve; two (in test tubes 3 and 4) do not. The teacher asks, "Where did the powders go?"

Experience 5-1: A beaker is filled with marbles, and the class is asked whether it is full. Then sand is poured in, then water, and finally alcohol, and each time the same question is asked. This demonstrates the possibility of our powders fitting between the water molecules. Question: If the compounds are there, can we get them back?

Experience 5-2: At this point the students are introduced to the water bath and evaporation technique to get the material back from the solutions.

Experience 5-3: The teacher asks the class, "If the material in test tubes 1 and 2 dissolved, can we be sure that some of the material in 3 and 4 did not also dissolve?" Another technique is introduced—filtering. Once students have filtered and evaporated the two so-called insolubles, they find that one has left a residue. Here they begin to wonder. If some of the material dissolved, is there a way to dissolve the rest? Ah! Add more water. (*Experience 5-4*)

Experience 5-4 leads the class to the conclusion that it is possible to

218

dissolve more of one material than of another in the same amount of water. (*Experience 6*)

At this point students begin to develop their own labs, covering such topics as whether material will dissolve more completely in hot water than in cold. We eventually lead the students to the development of solubility curves.

Other subjects for lab experiences are crystals, density, interaction of chemical compounds, and the forming of new materials with different properties from the ones with which the students started. Our final goal is to develop the concept of the atom and the interaction of atoms to produce compounds with particular characteristics. To help explain this phenomenon we make use of the periodic chart. Supplementary readings are suggested, and vocabulary and equipment terminology are subtly introduced and used constantly in classroom discussion so that there is no need for a formal vocabulary list.

There are many ways in which a science teacher can use open-ended experiences such as these as a point of departure for developing new concepts and techniques. We wholeheartedly encourage teachers to be creative—only then can teacher and student alike truly sense the pleasures of discovery.

A Comparison of the Performance of Ninth-grade and College Students in an Earth Science Laboratory Activity*

William D. Romey

John H. Merrill

"Educators who are concerned with giving nonscientists an education in science that will be both lasting and useful are apt to believe that a sense of understanding *what science is* and *how scientists work* is more important than all the rest." [1]

In order to show what science is, teachers must develop in their science students the capacity to reason inductively. Inductive reasoning, which involves the development of generalizations from observations made by the investigator himself, has not been stressed in traditional science courses until students have become engaged in independent research. Students have normally gained no practical experience in scientific reasoning until they have begun work on a bachelor's or master's thesis. Many students have received bachelor's degrees from some of our best universities and colleges without ever having been faced with the problem of interpreting data they have gathered themselves.

In recent years, many scientists and science educators have become increasingly aware that an understanding of inductive reasoning processes should come at the very beginning rather than at the end of a student's scientific training. High school curricula prepared by the Physical Science Study Committee (PSSC), Chemical Bond Approach Project (CBA), Chemical Educational Material Study (CHEM Study), Biological Sciences Curriculum Study (BSCS), and others have been aimed at increasing comprehension of scientific processes by introducing a discovery approach to learning. In such programs, students discover fundamental generalizations and concepts through their own laboratory work rather than reading about them in textbooks or performing standard "experiments" designed to confirm a given principle.

The great increase in earth science teaching in the secondary schools since 1950 has made it apparent that training programs in earth science

*Reprinted from *The Science Teacher*, V. 31, No. 4, May, 1964, pp. 49–52. ©, by permission.

also must undergo a major reevaluation. The GEO-Study program [2] and the Earth Science Curriculum Project (ESCP) [3] have been established further to examine earth science curricula on the college and high school levels, respectively.

A few physical geology courses offered at various colleges and universities now incorporate laboratory activities designed to introduce inductive reasoning. Exercises of this type have been used at Syracuse University for several terms, and we recently introduced some of the same material to a ninth-grade earth science class at Fox Lane School, Bedford, New York, in order to compare the relative performance of high school and college groups. The purpose of this study was to see whether a rather complex series of related concepts could be developed in an experiential manner with equal success at the two levels.

PROCEDURE

The experiment chosen involved a study of the concepts of porosity, water retention, and permeability in unconsolidated sediments as related to aquifers and artesian water systems [4]. Students were first directed to measure the porosity of aggregates of spheres (lead shot) and of different natural sands, each consisting of uniform-size grains. Porosity was measured by pouring a measured volume of sand or spheres into a measured volume of water and calculating the maximum percentage of water that could be contained in the given volume of sand or spheres according to the relationship:

$$(a) \quad \frac{\text{volume of water}}{\text{volume of spheres or sand}} \times 100 = \% \text{ porosity}$$

By plotting a graph of grain size versus measured porosity (see Figure 1), students discovered for themselves that porosity is essentially independent of grain size.

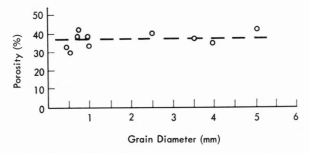

Figure 1. Graph of grain size vs. porosity, showing typical results obtained by students.

In the next step, students measured the volume of water which flowed out of the sands when a solid cork at the bottom of the containing tube was replaced by a perforated cork covered with wire gauze to prevent loss of sand. Then they calculated retentivity according to the relationship in (b) below.

$$\text{(b)} \quad \frac{\text{orig. vol. of water} - \text{vol. of water drained from aggregate}}{\text{original volume of water}} \times 100 = \% \text{ retentivity}$$

By examining the results, they found that the percentage of water retained increased as grain size decreased. Class discussion brought out that the total surface area of aggregates having small grain size is much greater than that of aggregates having large grain size. It was concluded that molecular attraction between grain surfaces and drops of water was much greater in aggregates of small grain size and that this accounted for the relationship observed.

The third major part of the experiment involved finding the relative permeability of the different sands and spheres by measuring the volume of water which flowed through them at a fixed pressure in a fixed time interval (sketch of apparatus given in Figure 2). Volume of flow per unit time (permeability) versus grain size was then graphed (Figure 3).

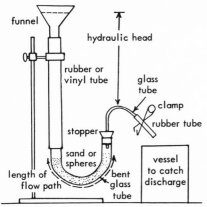

Figure 2. Sketch of permeability apparatus, redrawn from Gilbert and Christensen (4).

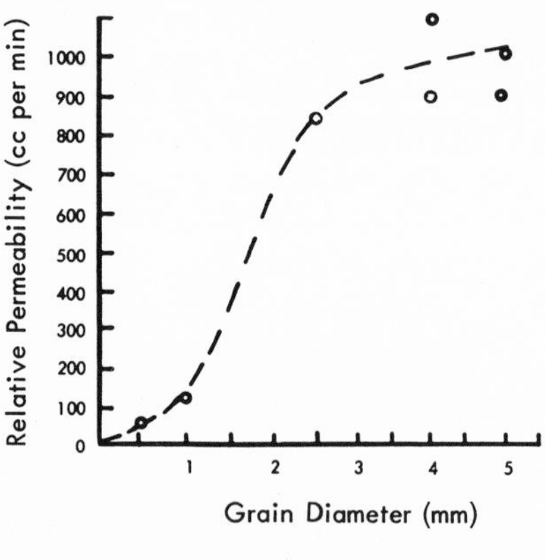

Figure 3. Graph of grain size vs. permeability, showing typical results obtained by students.

These concepts were related to aquifers and artesian well systems in a short discussion period that followed the activity.

At Fox Lane School, the secondary school group extended this activity during subsequent periods. Students had the opportunity to mix grain sizes and were able to discover the relationship between porosity, permeability, and sorting of aggregates. A comparison of the two age groups is shown in the accompanying chart.

During the last 15 minutes of each laboratory period, an un-announced quiz consisting of 15 multiple-choice statements was given. Statements were designed to test for understanding and transfer of the concepts being taught during the laboratory rather than for memorization of definitions or facts. The example below illustrates the type of multiple-choice statements which were used.

1. Porosity is:
    A. The total volume of open spaces in a rock times the total volume of the rock
    B. The total volume of open spaces in a rock divided by the total volume of the rock
    C. The grain size times the total volume of the rock
    D. The total volume of spaces in a rock
    E. None of these

2. A barrel full of marbles compared to a barrel full of baseballs would hold:
    A. Less water
    B. More water
    C. The same amount of water
    D. Not enough information given

3. In comparison to marbles alone, a mixture of marbles and baseballs would cause the porosity to:
    A. Increase
    B. Decrease
    C. Remain the same
    D. Not enough information given

4. Gravel compared with a sample of gravel mixed with clay would have:
    A. A higher relative permeability
    B. A lower relative permeability
    C. The same relative permeability
    D. Not enough information given

Results

The mean scores received by the two groups were nearly identical. The range of scores for the ninth-grade group was from 6 to 15,

223

COMPARISON OF GROUPS SELECTED FOR TESTING AND LABORATORY PROCEDURES

CHARACTERISTICS	COLLEGE GROUP	NINTH-GRADE GROUP
Composition	45 students from Syracuse University (26 freshmen, 6 sophomores, 3 juniors, 2 seniors, and 8 graduate students).	26 students from Fox Lane School (19 freshmen, 3 sophomores, 2 juniors, and 2 seniors).
Scholastic aptitude	College board examination (CEEB) scores available for about two thirds of the undergraduates: verbal range = 450 — 684, mean 552; math range = 505 — 737, mean 616	Range of scores on the California Mental Maturity (IQ test = 97 — 136. Average score (IQ) = 122
Previous training in science	All previously had had at least one term of either high school or college chemistry and physics.	All had had a limited exposure to science in the elementary school plus seventh- and eighth-grade general science. The 3 sophomores had had ninth-grade general science; the 2 juniors, ninth-grade general science and biology; the 2 seniors, ninth-grade general science, biology, and chemistry.
Number and size of participating laboratory groups	Students were divided into 3 groups of 15 students each. Within each group the students worked in twos or threes.	Students were divided into 2 groups of 13 each. Within each group the students worked in groups of 4 or 5.
Advance preparation	Students had been assigned advance reading on ground water which included a discussion of porosity and permeability.	Students had no advance preparation other than having previously been engaged in developing concepts by inductive reasoning.
Laboratory time spent in actual experimentation	90 minutes	75 minutes
Plotting of data	Students in both college and high school groups constructed curves to show their own data, and the instructor drew a summary curve on the blackboard.	
Advance knowledge of participation in instructional research	Neither the college nor the high school students were informed that they were participating in an instructional research experiment.	
Role of the instructor	The instructors in both groups set up the apparatus in advance of the class; carried on informal discussions with students during experimentation; drew summary curves on the blackboard; and led short, informal discussion periods at the end of the classes.	

and the mean score was 10.9. For the college group the range was 5 to 15, and the mean score was 11.1. It must be pointed out that division of the college group into graduate and undergraduate categories has an appreciable effect on the mean score. For the 37 undergraduate students the mean was 10.5, and for the 8 graduate students (mainly National Science Foundation Academic Year Institute science teachers) the mean was 13.3. Curves showing the distribution of scores are given in Figure 4.

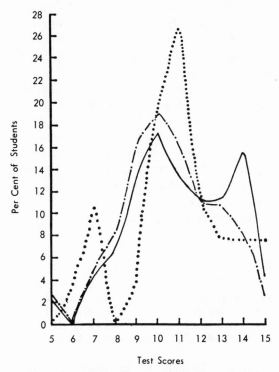

Figure 4. Graph showing test scores of ninth-grade and college groups. The solid line represents the college group, including graduate and undergraduate students. The intermittently dotted line represents college undergraduate students only. The dotted line represents the ninth-grade class.

CONCLUSIONS AND DISCUSSION

Our results show that the ninth-grade earth science class grasped the material presented as well as did the college undergraduate group. The bimodal nature of the curve showing college undergraduates and graduates combined reflects the more advanced scientific background

225

of the graduate students. We are not dealing with a case of presenting the college group with oversimplified material since we know from past experience that college groups consider the exercise used in this study both challenging and interesting. Instead, we are treating the ninth-grade students at a level of sophistication at which they should have been approached in the first place and which, unfortunately, is achieved in few high school or college courses. We feel that science students should be taught sound experimental techniques, careful treatment of data, the use of inductive reasoning to develop fundamental concepts, and the application of these experimentally derived generalizations to the explanation of natural phenomena at the earliest possible opportunity. The ninth-grade classroom is unquestionably a place where experimental work may be conducted.

We anticipate that this experiment will lead to further work on the level of material which can be successfully introduced in the secondary schools. Secondary school teachers should carefully examine some of the newer secondary and college manuals and resource books for material which can be used in their own classrooms. Conversely, teachers of college science courses must become aware of the growing competence of their entering students. More and more students entering colleges during the coming years will be "overprepared" for traditional approaches used in elementary college science courses.

REFERENCES

1. Eric M. Rodgers. "The Research Scientist Looks at the Purposes of Science Teaching" taken from chapter 2, "Science Education for Changing Times" in *Rethinking Science Education*, 59th yearbook of the National Society for the Study of Education Part I, University of Chicago Press. 1960, 344 pp.
2. William W. Hambleton. "The Status of Undergraduate Geological Education," *Geotimes*, 8:1–29 (No. 4, 1963).
3. "Earth Science Curriculum Project," *Geotimes*, 8:14–19 (No. 1, 1963).
4. Charles M. Gilbert and Mark N. Christensen. *Physical Geology Laboratory Course*. Laboratory 9, McGraw-Hill Book Co., New York. 1962. 96 pp. (An extension of this exercise is proposed by J. C. Brice and H. L. Levin in "Porosity and Permeability Experiments for General Geology Laboratory," *Journal of Geological Education*, 10:81–90 (No. 3, 1962).

Using History in Teaching Science[*]

Melvin Berger

An added touch of history now and then dramatizes the way science is built—piece by piece, brick on brick, scientist following scientist. The historical approach, consciously and skillfully used, has a valuable place in the teaching of science. To be sure, there is scarcely a textbook or individual teacher who does not present a certain amount of historical background when introducing a new subject; for example, Copernicus and the solar system in 1543, Mendeleev and the periodic table in 1869. But do these bits of history provide a feeling for the growth of science—or are they merely other facts to be memorized among the great number of facts that are thrown at the student in any science course?

The historical approach enables the student to stand alongside the scientists in their laboratories as they worked toward the great discoveries of science, to follow along with their experiments, guess at their thinking, catch their mistakes, and see how often they were able to turn accidents and unexpected results into significant new discoveries. If we can help the students, in effect, to rub shoulders with the scientists who created our modern science, we are providing an educational experience of the greatest value.

Let us look now at some of the particular ways that the history of science can contribute to the development of the basic concepts of science. How can the excitement of thus sharing a lab bench with some of the world's greatest scientists give the student a deeper insight into the science he is learning? If we look briefly at one specific discovery, the discovery of the first vitamin, for instance, perhaps we can see how this study of history provides a depth of understanding that is sometimes lacking from the more familiar presentations.

[*]Reprinted from *The Science Teacher*, V. 30, No. 7, Nov., 1963, pp. 24–26. ©, by permission.

The usual unit on vitamins starts with a few of the famous historical anecdotes. There is usually the one about the sailors on Columbus' voyage getting scurvy, being put on an island to die, and unexpectedly recovering. Then there is the story about why the British sailors are called limeys and why the London waterfront is called Limehouse. Finally, there is the story of Takaki and the barley rations he ordered for sailors of the Japanese Navy who were going on long voyages. Occasionally, other names are mentioned, the first to do this or that, and the dates involved.

Yet, how much more interesting to devote a little more time to history and follow along with the step-by-step scientific work that led to the discovery of vitamins. Not only can the student obtain a real understanding of vitamins, but he is able to trace the use of scientific method, not in a made-to-order lab experiment, but on the track of a major scientific triumph.

Let us now briefly retell the story of the discovery of vitamins and see how this material can be turned to educational advantage.

DISCOVERING VITAMINS

Christiaan Eijkman, a Dutch Army doctor, was part of a medical team sent in the 1890's to study beriberi in the Dutch East Indies. This dread disease was killing millions annually throughout the East. The medical group first set out to find a germ of some sort responsible for beriberi. After two years of work, they were unable to report any progress at all. (*How would you go about looking for an unknown germ that causes a known disease? What substances from the body of a victim of the disease might you check for infectivity? How?*)

Eijkman was working at a native prison on the island of Java. He noticed that the chickens in the prison yard were showing the symptoms of beriberi, the strange shuffling gait, the head held at an unnatural angle. He also knew that large numbers of prisoners were suffering from the disease. Yet, chickens outside the prison were just as healthy as chickens everywhere else. (*What might explain why more prison chickens were afflicted than were those outside? How might this be related to the large number of beriberi victims among the prisoners?*)

Eijkman suggested that this was a matter of diet. Chickens outside the prison ate a wide variety of foods, while the prison chickens ate only the rice left over from the prisoners' meals. (*What difference could this have made?*)

Eijkman knew that the rice eaten in the prison, as well as throughout the Orient, was polished rice, with the outer husk and inner silverskin removed. This prevented the rice from turning rancid in storage. Perhaps, Eijkman thought, the beriberi was somehow related to the fact that the rice was polished. (*How would you set up an experiment to determine whether beriberi is related to the polishing of rice?*)

Starting with some healthy chickens, Eijkman divided them into three groups. Group I was fed whole grain rice. Group II was fed rice with only the outer husk removed. Group III was fed polished rice, with both the outer husk and silverskin removed. The chickens in Groups I and II remained healthy, while those in Group III developed the symptoms of beriberi. Yet, when Eijkman fed the sick chickens the silverskins from the rice they quickly recovered. (*The beriberi cause is now isolated. Where?*)

However, after coming this far, Eijkman came to the wrong conclusion! He realized that the silverskin was significant; but he believed that it contained a substance which killed the beriberi germs that were in the rice. (*Even though we called this a wrong conclusion, is there any error in Eijkman's experiments or thinking?*)

The importance of Eijkman's work was that now the "cause" of beriberi had been isolated, and a way of experimentally causing and curing the disease had been found.

In 1906, Sir Frederick Gowland Hopkins carried vitamin research one step further with his famous experiment in which he took two groups of rats, fed one group all the known ingredients of milk but no whole milk, and fed the other group the same ingredients, plus a few drops of whole milk. At the end of 20 days, the rats in the first group had not gained any weight, while those in the second group had nearly doubled their weight. (*What does this tell you?*)

By 1925, the name vitamin had already been coined, and working at Eijkman's prison laboratory, B. C. P. Jansen and W. F. Donath started a search for the "anti beriberi" vitamin. They started with about 700 pounds of rice polishings and several hundred small rice-eating birds, called bondols. They found that the bondols would develop beriberi symptoms in 11 days if fed only polished rice. Then they chemically separated out different substances from the polishings and fed each one to the bondols, along with a regular diet of polished rice. If the bondols did not show the symptoms within 20 days, they knew that the substance for which they were searching was within that separation. (*What was the basic plan of their research?*)

They finally worked the 700 pounds of polishings down to 1/300th of an ounce of a powder that could either prevent or cure beriberi. We, of course, know this powder as thiamin, or vitamin B_1. Their experiment, just as Eijkman's, was important not only for what it taught us about vitamins, but for establishing a method for further vitamin research. Jansen and Donath set up the form that much subsequent vitamin research has taken. First, the laboratory animals are fed a deficient diet of some sort, while a close lookout is kept for the appearance of any symptoms. Then a food is sought that can cure the symptoms. Finally, the particular substance within the food is found that is responsible for relieving the symptoms. (*How is the Jansen-Donath experiment a specific example of this general pattern?*)

Let us pause now, and see what benefits this approach can bring to teaching about vitamins. First of all, the material is presented as an interesting, dramatic story. A skillful teacher can give the student an exciting, verbal picture of the native prison, with both the chickens and prisoners developing the strange walk and posture that are the first symptoms of beriberi, and then the research of Eijkman, followed 30 years later by the work of Jansen and Donath. Against this vivid background the entire story of vitamins can be told with much greater impact.

Moreover, vitamins are not presented as only names and numbers to be associated with certain foods and certain deficiency diseases. Rather, the student is led along with the scientists involved, to arrive himself at our present knowledge of vitamins. This is, of course, very much in line with the scientific ideal of not accepting facts on faith, but whenever possible, following through the steps that led to the acceptance of the fact.

Finally, this approach puts an emphasis on process, not only on result. The student is given valuable and vital insights into the process of science, as seen in the solution of a real problem of science. For instance, in the very brief outline we have given, he not only learns some of the important facts about vitamins, he also is learning how an experiment can be set up, how controls can be established, how the results can be checked. He can even follow a carefully planned experiment and see how it can be misinterpreted because of insufficient knowledge.

THE DETECTIVE APPROACH

Another manner in which the history of science can be used in the teaching of science might be called the detective story approach. In it, the experiments and discoveries become the clues, leading to a solution of the mystery. There is a very clear example of this approach in a completely different branch of science—the field of atomic structure.

The mystery with which we can start is the cathode ray, which various researchers had discovered in discharge tubes during the latter years of the 19th Century. Several explanations of the mystery had been offered, but none was found acceptable. Perhaps the most widely held belief was stated by Sir William Crookes, who said that the cathode rays were a fourth state of matter, adding luminous to solid, liquid, and gas.

Sir Joseph John Thomson was the detective who was finally able to track down a solution. He was Director of the Cavendish Laboratory at Cambridge University, which he built up to be, in effect, the Scotland Yard of atomic mysteries.

Let us stand alongside Thomson now as he "grills" the cathode rays, and amasses clues, until he reaches the only possible explanation of the mystery.

First, Thomson coats the anode in the Crookes tube with a fluorescent chemical and puts a small metal cross in the path of the cathode rays. He sees that the cross casts a clear shadow on the anode.

Some detective stories stop after all the clues have been discovered to ask if the reader has a solution to the mystery. We can stop our story after each clue, and ask what the clue tells us. (*What does this clue tell us?* It suggested to Thomson that the cathode rays traveled in straight lines, since the cross cast a clear image on the anode.)

Next, Thomson places a delicately balanced paddle wheel in the path of the cathode rays. He notes that the rays are actually able to turn the wheel. (*What does this tell us?* To Thomson it meant that the cathode rays consisted of particles that have mass and were able to exert a mechanical pressure on the wheel. He also realized that somehow these particles had to be coming from the trace of air that remained in the imperfect vacuum he had created in the tube.) For the third experiment Thomson sets up a magnetic field around the tube. The cathode ray, or rather the cathode particles, are deflected to the positive pole of the magnet. (*What does this tell us?* Thomson concluded that the particles had a negative electrical charge.)

Next, Thomson passes the rays between two electrically charged plates. By measuring the amount of current necessary to deflect the particles, Thomson is able to determine the mass of the particles—about 1/2,000 of the mass of an ion of hydrogen. (*What does this tell us?* Since Thomson already knew that hydrogen was the lightest element, and his particle was 2,000 times lighter, this led him to the belief that this particle was much smaller than an atom.)

Finally, Thomson introduces traces of various different gases into the tube. In each case the cathode ray particles seem identical, in charge, behavior, and weight. (*What does this tell us?* Thomson concluded that these particles can be found in many different elements, and were always the same.)

At this point, Thomson is ready to announce a solution to the mystery. Are we? We know that the cathode ray is made up of particles and that they travel in straight lines. We know that they have a negative electrical charge and a mass of 1/2,000 of the mass of a hydrogen ion. And we know the same particle can be found in different elements. (*What is the only explanation that can tie together all these clues?*) Thomson's explanation is familiar. He said that the cathode particles were electrons, particles of negative electricity coming from within the atom. Thus, not only was he able to solve the mystery of the cathode rays, but he made the first cut into the Dalton atom, which had lasted intact for nearly 100 years.

We have included two short examples of how history can be used to improve and enrich the teaching of science. There are literally hundreds of other examples and ways in which the history of science can be used. The learning can be focalized around a dramatic story. The student is given insight into how a conclusion was reached, without a full explanation. The student is led to a full awareness of process and scientific method. This can lead to clearer thinking and experimenting on the student's own projects, both in the laboratory and in other situations. It also makes it easier, as the student continues his science studies, to grasp in greater and greater depth the new information he is given. And finally, it enables him to accept, and put into perspective, the new discoveries in science that are coming from today's laboratories. If he knows and understands the thinking and experimenting that led to the older information, it is an easy task for him to build on that foundation, and assimilate the new findings.

Teaching from Research Papers[*]

Howard B. Baumel

J. Joel Berger

In the past 30 years, leaders in the field of science education have continually called attention to the need for, and importance of, emphasizing scientific methods and attitudes in teaching procedures. Brandwein, Watson, and Blackwood[1] report that a survey of 42 syllabuses, from 37 states for all secondary school science courses, reveals one common element—all propose to teach scientific methods.

Many definitions of the objectives related to scientific methods and attitudes have been developed. It appears that all of the definitions have a great deal in common.[2] Recently, however, the idea of the existence of any single, definable scientific method has been questioned and viewed as a gross oversimplification and distortion of the methods of scientific inquiry.

Thus, while there is a genuine concern on the part of scientists, science educators, and science teachers that students develop insights into methods of science, it is generally believed that the presentation of the "scientific method" as the well-known sequence of steps is an approach that is all too often completely unsuccessful in inculcating a conception of what science is about, how science works, and what the real character of the scientific enterprise is.

An approach that attempts to combine the character of science with its content through the involvement of students with the research papers of scientists appears to have great potential in teaching science as a

[*]Reprinted from *The Science Teacher*, V. 32, No. 4, April, 1965, pp. 29–30. ©, by permission.

[1]Paul F. Brandwein, Fletcher G. Watson, and Paul E. Blackwood, *Teaching High School Science: A Book of Methods.* Harcourt, Brace and World, Inc., New York, 1958. p. 11.

[2]National Society for the Study of Education, Fifty-ninth Yearbook, Part One, *Rethinking Science Education.* University of Chicago Press, Chicago, Illinois. 1960. p. 47.

process. Among the many rewards to be gained from the student's first-hand contact with original scientific writings are the genuine excitement in seeing fundamental discoveries through the eyes of their discoverers, the humanizing enrichment in becoming acquainted with the personalities of great scientists, and the possibility that youngsters will "catch" the climate of accuracy, the carefully detailed work, and the essential honesty of their scientific efforts.

The authors have been using this approach in their respective science classes for the past four years. Only those research papers which involved content similar to that studied at the time, which could easily be understood by the students, and which reflected significant contributions to the development of scientific knowledge were selected. There are many sources available from which suitable research papers may be chosen. The selected papers were duplicated for distribution to the students. Explanations were included for any terms which might not have been clear.

A series of questions which attempted to focus student attention upon important aspects of scientists and experimentation was prepared for each selected research paper. These questions required the students to:

1. Recognize and state problems.
2. Select, evaluate, and apply information in relation to problems.
3. Recognize and state hypotheses.
4. Recognize and evaluate conclusions, assumptions, and generalizations.
5. Identify remarks, attitudes, procedures, or conclusions in the research paper that involve or illustrate aspects of scientists or experimentation.

The following sample questions may serve as a guide to any paper selected:

1. What problem was the scientist studying?
2. What information did the scientist have at hand when he investigated the problem?
3. What hypothesis did the scientist probably have in mind as he planned his investigation?
4. What was the outcome of the experiment
   a. Observationally?
   b. In relation to hypothesis?
5. What conclusion was reached?
6. Is the conclusion justified?
7. What simple experiments could you plan that make it possible to confirm the scientist's conclusions?
8. What have you used in your experimental plan that was not available to the scientist?

234

In addition, questions which involved an understanding of the specific science content in the paper were also included in the guide.

The students received copies of the papers to be considered and the accompanying questions approximately two days prior to class discussion. In class the students had before them both the paper and the completed questions. The teacher then gave a brief description of the historical background pertinent to the paper being analyzed. The answers of individual students to each of the questions served as the framework around which discussion of the significant aspects of the papers proceeded.

The regular use of these research papers does not diminish student achievement in terms of subject matter. Baumel[3] found that students who studied biology in classes where research papers were used performed as well, on a standardized biology achievement test, as did students who had spent full time in covering the usual course content.

Those students who read and analyzed the research papers were invited to express their reactions anonymously to this technique in a free response type of questionnaire. Many of the students believed that their conceptions of science and scientists had changed as had some aspects of their behavior. A typical comment was "I got to feel as if I was in the scientist's shoes, making all the experiments and decisions."

The experiences of the authors in using research papers in secondary school biology and chemistry classes indicate that this is an approach which appears to be on the right track toward the development in students of the attitudes, appreciations, and understandings inherent in the ways scientists work.

[3]Howard B. Baumel. "The Effects of a Method of Teaching Secondary School Biology Which Involves the Critical Analysis of Research Papers of Scientists on Selected Science Education Objectives." Doctor's Thesis. New York University, New York, New York. 1963.

Teaching Science
by What Authority?*

Warren L. Strickland

Do you recall from your professional education courses this most simple behavioral definition of education: "To teach students to do better that which they will do anyway"? Recently I asked various subject-matter teachers at the high school level what it is they believe *their* students are learning to *do* better. The English teachers replied that their students learn to read, write, and speak—in short, to communicate better. The industrial arts teachers said that their students learned to use tools and make things in better ways. Mathematics teachers suggested that their students learned how to apply mathematics better in our technical and industrial society. Social studies teachers indicated their students learned to do those things that made them better voters and citizens. Business teachers suggested that their students learn to do better processes (like typing, for example) that help them to perform in the business world.

When science teachers were asked what *their* students learn to do better, most initially mentioned such things as manipulating equipment, understanding scientific words, understanding what a scientist does, and understanding facts and principles. When each was reminded that the question explicitly involved what it is that their students learn to *do* better, most, but not all, indicated that *critical thinking* and *problem solving* were the important things their youngsters learned to do.

However, it was difficult to see how most of these teachers accomplished this in their classroom lectures, discussions, laboratory activities, or the use of their textbooks. Nor, with few exceptions, could the teachers present an organized program for helping their students think critically and solve problems that was congruous with actual procedures in their classrooms.

*Reprinted from *The Science Teacher*, V. 31, No. 6, Oct., 1964, pp. 23–25. ©, by permission.

My thesis is that much of our difficulty in teaching for critical thinking and scientific problem solving lies in the all-too-general acceptance by the teacher of himself and the textbook as the primary authority for learning science. *A way out of this difficulty might well be to re-orient the classroom activities so that the authority for learning science becomes nature itself.*

How would classroom procedures change if nature becomes the authority for learning? To best illustrate this, we shall refer to a stereotype of teaching in which the teacher and the text are the authority for learning. This stereotype will be compared to the type of teaching that might follow when nature is used as the authority for learning. The following chart has been spaced after the various components so that the discussion can immediately follow each aspect.

TEACHING-LEARNING COMPONENTS	AUTHORITY	
	THE TEACHER—THE TEXT	NATURE
Principal technique of teacher	Telling	Creating experiences (laboratory)
Principal technique of student	Memorizing, doing type problems	Experiencing nature

When the teacher is the authority for learning, he need only impart his knowledge to his students, and they will have "learned science." Applying this concept, the teacher's primary function is to tell. When the technique of the teacher includes use of a text as the authority or an alternate authority, the students read and discuss, and thus again they have "learned science." It is somehow difficult to justify using the procedure of "telling" as a method of helping young people to think critically. However, with nature as the authority for learning, a teacher's primary activity is helping the students to come to grips with nature itself in a purposeful organization of laboratory experiences.

We cannot say without qualification that memorization of scientific facts is of little consequence to the science student. We can say, however, that memorization is not of itself conducive to critical thinking or to scientific problem solving. Memorization of teacher- and text-given

TEACHING-LEARNING COMPONENTS	THE TEACHER—THE TEXT	NATURE
Problem solving	Deductive	Inductive and deductive

principles may lead the teacher to devise problems where the student must use these principles to explain phenomena not previously studied. This is the *deductive method.* "Why does a gun 'kick'?" (The student applies Newton's action-reaction law.) "What might the cross between a dominant white- and a recessive red-flowered plant produce?" (Student applies Mendel's laws of heredity.) However, the student may also be given a technique for solving certain kinds of problems, Mendelian boxes for heredity problems, or perhaps, parallelograms for doing vector force problems. His ability to use these techniques in "type problems" is too often interpreted as the student's ability to do scientific problem solving and to think critically.

On the other hand, when nature is the authority for learning, the teacher has the opportunity to provide experiences where the student can generalize from his observations and form the principles himself. This is the *inductive method*. For example, the teacher can select for the students a variety of experiments in which nature exhibits the properties that Newton described as "action and reaction." If the students have *not been told* this generalization previously, they can indeed generalize to the principle itself.

Some teachers call this inductive process "discovery," actually re-discovery, and encourage their students to "discover" most generalizations for themselves. Mendel's laws can be discovered inductively by encouraging the students to generalize from actual plantings and through mounted specimens of the parent and offspring organisms.

Teachers who have used this rediscovery approach to encourage critical thinking and problem solving from nature, have been happily surprised by the sophistication and ability to generalize by almost all of their students, regardless of apparent academic ability. This is not unexpected, however, since our students have been employing the in-ductive method intuitively much of their lives. In their adjustment to family and community, they generalize on what is acceptable behavior. Very early we all generalized on the law of gravity after spilling milk, falling, and other experiences. Youngsters early generalize on stability, and they place irregular objects on their broadest bases. All students have made many such scientific generalizations from their own observations of the way nature works.

Teaching-Learning Components	Teacher—Text	Nature
Laboratory activities	Verifying	Generalizing

It is all too easy to find laboratory manuals of the stereotype shown in the illustrations. In this kind of presentation, the manual itself is the authority, and what the student seeks in nature is merely a verification of what the manual says nature is like. No wonder that students say, "This experiment (nature) didn't work out the way it was supposed to work!" There is little room for inductive reasoning when a student must

Dr. G. S. Ohm (1787-1854) investigated and stated the relationship of current, voltage, and resistance in an electrical circuit. This relationship, now known as Ohm's law, is one of the most useful tools in designing and maintaining circuits using electrical energy.

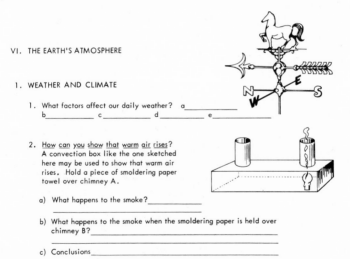

Object: To show that the strength of an electric current depends on the amount of voltage in the circuit and thus to clarify Ohm's Law:

$$\text{Ohms} = \frac{\text{Volts}}{\text{Amperes}}$$

Materials needed: 25-ohm, 10-watt, wire-wound resistor, DC ammeter 0-0.5 range, DC voltmeter 0-10 volt range, 6-volt battery, 1 1/2-volt battery, porcelain switch, and wire.

Procedure:
1. Build a circuit like the one diagramed above. Check the circuit carefully and then throw the switch momentarily noticing whether the pointers on the meters read up scale. If they read down scale, reverse the connections on the battery.
2. Vary the voltage using the 6-volt battery and the 1 1/2-volt battery. What happens to the amperage?_____
How does this verify Ohm's Law? _____
_____

VI. THE EARTH'S ATMOSPHERE

1. WEATHER AND CLIMATE

1. What factors affect our daily weather? a_____
   b_____ c_____ d_____ e_____

2. How can you show that warm air rises?
   A convection box like the one sketched here may be used to show that warm air rises. Hold a piece of smoldering paper towel over chimney A.

   a) What happens to the smoke?_____
   _____

   b) What happens to the smoke when the smoldering paper is held over chimney B?_____
   _____

   c) Conclusions_____
   _____

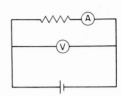

seek to have nature work in such a way that it will verify a statement in a book.

TEACHING-LEARNING COMPONENTS	TEACHER—TEXT	NATURE
Basis for testing	Verifying, memory	Applying generalizations

Stereotype tests require that the student recall an appropriate response previously given to him by the teacher or the text. Such test items are

239

easily constructed and do provide a means of testing a student's acquaintance with the facts of science. However, there is little opportunity in such tests for the student to evaluate a situation and respond to it, nor is there any opportunity to solve problems other than "type problems." But when nature is the authority for learning, testing can be based upon whether a student is able to explain new phenomena with the generalizations he has reached through his laboratory experiences. For example, a student may be asked to show in his own words understanding of such phenomena as: "A man has the wheels of his car balanced." The student applies his own generalizations learned in the laboratory about the center of gravity. He may respond, "The center of gravity is moved to the center of the wheel and thus the weight (mass) will be distributed equally. The wheel is balanced and will spin without vibration." "Two dominant brown-haired parents give birth to a blonde-haired child." The student may apply his previously discovered generalizations about heredity and respond, "The parents were probably hybrid for brown and blonde hair traits."

In the life sciences, teachers may have their students apply their generalizations to superstitions. For example, the old belief that the "hairworms" found in water troughs where horses drink come from horse hairs. (The student essentially describes the concept that life comes from life, and these "hairworms" might have come from eggs carried by the horse's mouth from some other place.)

TEACHING-LEARNING COMPONENTS	TEACHER—TEXT	NATURE
Measurement	Nature and type problems Little compromise with text Deals in ABSOLUTES	Nature and statistical compromise Tends to be SPECULATIVE

When the teacher or the text is accepted as the authority for learning, there is usually only one answer that is acceptable for each problem. That answer is the one provided by the teacher or the text. When nature is the authority there is no "answer," only the results from measuring and remeasuring. These results provide a statistical average, tendency, mean, or some other composite measurement. An average, for example, does not describe a particular event, rather it is a speculative statistical compromise. Whether averaging the white and dark kernels on an ear of hybrid corn to arrive at a Mendelian generalization or averaging the periods of a pendulum to arrive at generalizations about a pendulum, the student, like the scientist, is making statistical compromises.

"Explaining more and more (phenomena) with fewer and fewer

Teaching-Learning Components		Teacher—Text	Nature
Evalua-tion	Assets	May cover much information, primarily as facts and principles	Science is process—explaining more and more with fewer and fewer generalizations
	Liabili-ties	Science becomes a body of knowledge that should be memorized	Frequently general-izing and from too few experiences and too few sets of conditions

generalizations" is indeed the very essence of the modern scientific enterprise. If our students are to learn what science is all about and if they are to do scientific problem solving, they might well be given the opportunity to seek generalizations from nature in the high school science classrooms.

There is an old Chinese proverb which may be roughly translated, "If I hear, I forget; if I see, I remember; if I do, I know!" By using nature as the authority in your classroom your students will *do*, and they will know, and as a result they will learn to practice critical thinking and scientific problem solving, and to do better much that they will have to do anyway.

The Study of Teaching
and the New Science Curricula*

Maurice Belanger

Persons involved in the teaching of science would probably characterize the past decade by the extensive activity in curricula development. The same period has also been a time of considerable fruitful work in another area, no less important but perhaps less well known—the study of the classroom behavior of teachers.

About ten years ago a quiet revolution began to be reflected in various educational journals when critical review papers scanned the history and status of the study of classroom teaching. (Levin 1954, Rabinowitz and Travers 1953, and Symonds 1950 [6, 8, 11]). Two general criticisms were prevalent:

First, researchers had sought to find a simple factor, either of the act of teaching or of the teacher as a person, to account for the learning of pupils. Despite the hundreds of studies conducted over a 50-year span, THE factor of teaching or of the teacher had not been found, and moreover, said the critics, such endeavors were likely to continue to be unproductive. The simple styles of one-to-one correlation so successful during the 18th and 19th centuries in studying the physical world, are insufficiently powerful to deal with the varied and complex acts of teaching.

A *second criticism* centered about the premature attempts, brought about in large measure by the merit-rating movement, to evaluate teaching. Various studies and merit-rating programs, utilizing evaluation devices based on ad hoc global criteria of teaching, not only failed to add to our knowledge of teaching, but tended to alienate teachers toward classroom observation when such observations were associated with retention, increase in pay, or promotion.

These two criticisms are of interest today, for there appears to be

*Reprinted from *The Science Teacher,* V. 31, No. 7, Nov., 1964, pp. 31–35. ©, by permission.

doubt that methods can be devised and used profitably in an attempt to find orderly patterns in such a multifaceted phenomenon as teaching. There is still a question of whether the acts of teaching can be studied dispassionately in their own right as behavioral phenomena without passing judgment on an individual teacher.

It might be expected that science educators would be receptive to viewing classroom teaching as a unit of experience susceptive to analysis by carefully designed observational procedures. Indeed, a number of observational devices had been designed in the 1930's and 1940's by persons in science education. However, these methods do not appear to have been taken up by others, and what research was conducted using particular procedures tended to be one-shot studies. Moreover, the collection of classroom data is a laborious affair in its own right, and, without a sound rationale to guide in the selection and interpretation of masses of data, tended to result in scattered inferences that were difficult to relate in the absence of a conceptual framework.

Two changes appear to have taken place in the past decade concerning the study of teaching. Admittedly teaching is complex, like other expressions of human behavior. However, this complexity can be reduced to manageable proportions by a judicious selection of particular behavioral acts of teaching. These particular acts render it highly probable that their analysis will shed light on a problem within a general framework.

The first change, then, has been a more careful consideration of what selected aspects of teaching to study, what data to collect, and what to do with the data once it has been collected. A general framework for the study of teaching does not yet exist, and studies still tend to deal with a variety of factors difficult to relate. For theoretical discussions see Biddle and Ellena (1964 [2], and Silberman (1963 [10]). A second change is largely a change of purpose. The study of teaching is not aimed directly at administrative evaluation, but is aimed at increasing our knowledge about teaching.

It is important to realize that recently developed methods for studying teaching represent, at best, work in progress. There is no single factor of teaching, and similarly there is no single method for studying teaching. A few procedures, however, appear to offer promising leads for dealing with a matter associated with the new science curricula. It is to the latter consideration we turn first.

MODIFICATION OF STYLE

There is a fair amount of evidence to suggest that after a few years of teaching a teacher develops a personal style of teaching that

243

remains relatively stable over time. Very little is known about what happens to a teacher's classroom performance when new knowledge or new situational factors are introduced to the teacher. Factors would include, for example, further study in science, psychology, or education, changes in physical facilities, new arrangements of school organization, and new curricula. Modification in classroom performance of a teacher, after or during experience with such matters, is very likely not an "all or nothing" change. For no change in classroom performance to occur is painful to speculate, and for a dramatic change to occur is too altruistic in view of the stability of human behavior. It is plausible that for some teachers little or no change occurs, for others a major modification may take place. For the majority, however, two speculative hypotheses are suggested: (1) change by "hybridization," and (2) change by "successive approximation to maximum tolerance."

MR. SMITH INVITES ENQUIRY

Perhaps a hypothetical example would be helpful before offering a further discussion of these speculations. Let us assume that Mr. Smith has been teaching a traditional biology course for ten years. During a summer he attends a science institute. As a part of this institute he learns about Schwab's "Invitations to Enquiry." He reads material in the BSCS Handbook, the instructor demonstrates an exercise with the adult students, and Mr. Smith is intrigued. Although BSCS Biology will not be introduced in his school for another year, Mr. Smith sees the opportunity to try out the "Invitations to Enquiry" with his students. If we had observed Mr. Smith's classroom teaching over a period of several classes prior to the institute, a few patterns of Mr. Smith's teaching style would have emerged. He is very much in control of his class, control not simply in the sense of discipline, but more broadly conceived. Mr. Smith asks almost all of the questions, he answers the students' questions, he passes judgment, he makes evaluations, and he raises critical points. He is, in fact, a master of the directive style of teaching, and his students consider him to be a magnificent teacher.

Some time after the institute, Mr. Smith introduces Schwab's "Invitations to Enquiry." (Whether or not this is appropriate is not the point.) We again visit Mr. Smith and observe that he asks all of the questions for the first quarter of the lesson. The students then begin to raise questions, and Mr. Smith answers these, he makes judgments, evaluations, and raises critical points. In short, he is in full directive control. Over successive lessons we note that gradually Mr. Smith turns over more of the question asking to students, student questions are more frequently turned back to students, a few times he asks the

244

students to make judgments, and students raise critical points which are followed up by Mr. Smith's questions. In these lessons a new pattern begins to emerge, still highly directive teaching, but more indirective patterns are apparent. The old pattern is changing form, a hybrid of new and old. In further exercises, more change to an indirect pattern takes place, and by successive approximations Mr. Smith's style is gradually changing into a DIRECTIVE-INDIRECTIVE style.

During one exercise Mr. Smith raises a few questions, and he is flooded by student questions. Students begin to suggest hypotheses and question one another in an orderly fashion. (Mr. Smith seems pleased.) A student makes a suggestion which is eagerly accepted by the others, and they pursue this avenue of discussion. Mr. Smith sees a new point to introduce in the discussion. The students ignore this and pursue the student question. Mr. Smith asks a question, which is quickly answered, and students return to the point under discussion. (The teacher appears uneasy.) Two students begin to argue about the interpretation of a set of data. Mr. Smith interrupts and offers an evaluation. The students return to their argument. The pattern in this class is almost totally indirective, and for Mr. Smith at this particular time, the point of maximum tolerance for indirect teaching has been passed. He stops the discussion, states the argument is not a fruitful one, and asks a question to start a new track of discussion. The class continues characterized by the hybrid style, more directive than indirective, at a level which the teacher can tolerate.

New Curricula as Change Factors

This pat and oversimplified example may serve to illustrate one form of hybrid style along a dimension, of directive-indirective style, and the intent of the phrase "successive approximation to maximum tolerance." By hybrid style is meant the emergence of new patterns among old patterns of teaching resulting in a new characterization. The illustration above dealt with a pattern of indirect-direct, but numerous other dimensions exist obviously. As the pattern of teaching changes gradually over time, it is hypothesized that point of maximum change and tolerance for change occurs, and this point will vary from teacher to teacher. For some it will be low, for others high.

The introduction of new science curricula appears to be a dramatic change factor in the teacher's experience. Presumably it necessitates an alteration in the classroom performance of many teachers. The two tacit assumptions concerning hybrid styles and successive approximation (in reality still hypotheses about teaching), should become operative as teachers undertake the teachings of these materials. Curriculum designers seem to be well aware that teachers may face problems in changing styles, for many teacher guides contain at particular points such suggestions as delaying the answering of student questions, expecting and valuing student confusion at times, and in some cases go so far as specifying in some detail a new role for the teacher.

OBSERVABLE BEHAVIOR

One of the major difficulties an individual faces in attempting to establish new teaching patterns is to secure data based on one's teaching performance. These data are needed to assess how well the actual performance approaches one's own criteria. It is in this area of data collection that current research on teaching behavior is suggestive of systematic observation techniques that may be used to obtain information for analysis. The first step in designing or using an established observation technique is a careful analysis of specific observable teacher behavior that can be reliably recorded by an observer, and which is considered as an important dimension of teaching in the particular context. We do not know with any certainty what those important teaching dimensions are, and many of the current research efforts are attempts to investigate what these dimensions might be. Embedded in the documents of contemporary science curricula are a variety of teaching behavior factors which are valued as important dimensions of science teaching. However, no systematic analysis and classification of these teaching behaviors exist. Consequently, to construct an observational schema one either invents dimensions of teaching behavior by intelligent guesswork, constructs dimensions from an analysis of a psychological or sociological theory, or accepts the dimensions suggested by current workers in the field, which may or may not be anchored in theory.

VERBAL BEHAVIOR

One dimension that has received considerable attention is the interaction of teacher talk and student talk. Here only the verbal behavior of teacher and pupils is selected, and nonverbal behavior, such as gestures or postures, is ignored. To classify classroom verbal behavior in the categories of teacher talk and student talk would not provide much useful information, and hence a further classification must be devised which does provide useful information. Medley and Mitzel (1963 [7]) have reviewed some of the major categories and attendant observation instruments that have been developed based on these categories.

246

One of the most interesting and useful categories and observational techniques has been devised by Flanders. Flanders uses ten categories. Seven represent teacher talk. Of these seven, four categories reflect the indirect influence of the teacher, (1—accepts feeling, 2—praises or encourages, 3—accepts or uses ideas of students, 4—asks questions), and three categories reflect the direct influence of the teacher (5—lecturing, 6—giving directions, 7—criticizing or justifying authority). Student talk is divided into two categories (8—talk by students in response to teacher, and 9—talk initiated by the students). The last category, 10, is silence or confusion.

Using these categories, an observer notes in three-second intervals the category that best represents the ongoing verbal behavior in a classroom. Flanders has devised an ingenious method for summarizing the data in a matrix that allows selected cells or groups of cells to represent patterns of influence in the classroom. Furthermore, indirect-direct ratio, computed as number of tallies in categories 1 to 3 to the number of tallies in categories 5 to 7, can be used to compare teachers, or the same teacher in different situations. Complete descriptions of this system are contained in Amidon and Flanders (1963 [1]), and research conducted with the system has been reported by Flanders (1961, 1964 [3, 4].)

DATA FOR SELF-ANALYSIS

It would appear that the Flanders' "System of Interaction Analysis" would be extremely useful as a research tool for studying the behavior of teachers teaching the new science curricula since superficial analysis of the new science curricula tends to indicate the desirability of greater use of indirect teacher influence in classroom interactions. Teachers might find the system very helpful as a way of obtaining data for a self-analysis of their own teaching. In collaboration with another teacher or with a science supervisor, successive periods of data collection and self-analysis might reveal patterns of direct-indirect influence and aid in successive approximations to the teacher's own criteria.

As another possibility, teachers could construct their own categories of teaching behavior which are particularly appropriate to specific science curricula or to certain areas of a curriculum, and devise methods for securing data based on these categories. For example, most of the teacher guides to new curricula contain suggestions to "discuss" certain aspects of the materials with the pupils. It would be helpful to know what are the categorical dimensions of these "discussions" and whether they differ from the dimensions of "discussion" associated with more traditional materials.

Science education researchers now have available to them excellent published materials to serve as guides to research in the area of teacher behavior. The reference, par excellence, is the recent *Handbook of Research on Teaching* edited by Gage (1963 [5]). Particularly relevant to matters touched on here is Chapter 6 by Medley and Mitzel. Research in progress, as well as discussions of methodological and conceptual problems in the area of teacher behavior research, have recently appeared in a report edited by Silberman (1963 [10]) and in a book edited by Biddle and Ellena (1964 [2]).

This brief survey is only intended to call attention to the importance of considering what events take place in the classroom between teachers and pupils, and to suggest a few avenues of study related to new science curricula. The enormous amount of input to the teacher from the new curricula is all directed at hopefully improving in some way learning by pupils. The important mediators between all these inputs and pupil learning are the acts between teacher and pupils. Science education efforts might profit if we knew more about these encounters.

REFERENCES

1. Edmund Amidon and Ned Flanders. *The Role of the Teacher in the Classroom.* Paul S. Amidon Associates, Minneapolis. 1963.
2. Bruce Biddle and William Ellena, Editors. *Contemporary Research on Teacher Effectiveness.* Holt, Rinehart & Winston, New York. 1964.
3. Ned Flanders. "Analyzing Teacher Behavior." *Educational Leadership,* 19:173–75, 178–80, 200. December 1961.
4. Ned Flanders. "Some Relationships Among Teacher Influence, Pupil Attitudes, and Achievements." In *Contemporary Research on Teacher Effectiveness.* Holt, Rinehart, and Winston, New York. 1964. pp. 196–231.
5. N. L. Gage, Editor. *Handbook of Research on Teaching.* Rand McNally and Company, Chicago. 1963.
6. Harry Levin. "A New Perspective on Teacher Competence Research." *Harvard Educational Review,* 24: 98–105. 1954.
7. Donald Medley and Harold Mitzel. "Measuring Classroom Behavior by Systematic Observation." In *Handbook of Research on Teaching.* Rand McNally and Company, Chicago. 1963. pp. 247–328.
8. William Rabinowitz and Robert Travers. "Problems of Defining and Assessing Teacher Effectiveness." *Educational Theory,* 3: 212–19. 1953.
9. David Ryans. "Research on Teacher Behavior in the Context of the Teacher Characteristics Study." In *Contemporary Research on Teacher Effectiveness.* Holt, Rinehart and Winston, New York. 1964.
10. Harry Silberman, Editor. "A Symposium on Current Research on Classroom Behavior of Teachers and Its Implications for Teacher Education." *The Journal of Teacher Education,* 16: 235–325. September 1963.
11. Percival Symonds. "Reflections on Observations of Teachers." *Journal of Educational Research,* 43: 688–96. May 1950.

Contrasting Techniques of Teaching

Many teachers who actually use mainly traditional, content-oriented methods are convinced that they are already employing techniques of teaching that require student inquiry, investigation, and discovery. This is largely because they do not know just exactly what inquiry really involves. The articles below by Samples, Fish and Goldmark, and Rutherford examine some different ways in which topics might be treated in truly inquiring and investigative fashion. Juxtaposed against these discussions, particularly in Samples' article, is a description of how some teachers think *they are successfully using inquiry techniques but are failing miserably instead.*

Death of an Investigation*

Robert E. Samples

This article illustrates the differences between two approaches to the problem of involving students in laboratory activities in the science classroom. The first approach is what may be called "authoritarian," whereas the second is often referred to as "investigative."

The setting is a ninth-grade classroom where students are supposedly determining the density of ice (ESCP Investigation P–2). The basic ideas, however, are applicable at all grade levels, from elementary to college.

As the class period opens the teacher instructs the students.

"The alcohol costs money, so don't waste it. The proper way to use it is to pour 25 ml. of alcohol into the beaker and place the ice cube in the alcohol. As you notice, the ice cube will sink. Add water slowly, mixing it until the ice cube just floats. Remove the ice cube, weigh the solution, and measure its volume. This will give you the information necessary to determine the density of the ice cube. All right, get your materials and get to work. Let's not have a mess; you're not third graders."

As the students silently proceed through the lab, one drops a beaker as it is being filled.

"All right, butterfingers, let's see you finish the lab without one of your beakers. Can't you people do this kind of thing without somebody holding your hand? You don't think science got this far without some discipline, do you?"

The rest of the "investigation" is explosively punctuated by outbursts from the teacher that follow the same pattern.

"I thought I told you to pour water into the alcohol. Can't you people listen?"

*Reprinted from the *Journal of Geological Education*, V. 14, No. 2, April, 1966, pp. 69–72. ©, by permission.

"I said, take the ice cube out of the solution after it starts to float. You know why?"

The students shake their heads.

"What's the temperature of the room?"

A chorus of "I dunnos" is interrupted by a scattering of "70 degrees."

"Right, it's 70. What is the temperature of the ice cube?"

"Thirty-two." It rings clear this time.

"Okay, so you don't want the ice to melt into the solution or it will change your results and the accuracy of the answer will be out the window. Hurry up, I want this place spotless before the bell rings. Watch your math and *follow the instructions* or you will never get the right answer which is .974 grams per milliliter."

The writer never actually heard this particular monologue, but it is typical of the sort of teaching in too many classrooms. At the end of a session like this, the teachers' lounge probably echos with complaints about the lack of quality to be found in junior high students, beakers, and curriculum writers. In all but the first instance, the teacher may be right. The junior high student is intrinsically a dynamic, highly inter- ested human being. In a learning environment such as the one described, he is almost superfluous.

First, the ritualistic recitation of the instructions had nothing to do with the investigation and little to do with the students, except, of course, the management of their actions. In a sense they form the chess board upon which the game is to be played. The students cannot leave the confines of the pattern without being ridiculed any more than a rook can move 25 spaces to the left without leaving the board. The teacher is the mover and by innuendo guides the course of action.

And the students? They are the mute pieces that mechanically shuffle through the constricting corridors created by the instructions. Like the chessmen, the students are different, but their motions are still governed by external rules.

Is this analogy preposterous? Unfortunately, it isn't. Things like this happen in classrooms and often the teacher feels that the orderliness of the action is a criterion for judging the quality of the "science." It would seem, by this view, that science is good if the students report their psychomotor obedience with an equally obedient communication effort. If you examined the total situation you would find that the "writeup" is an end in itself, and, being an end, the means to it should be subject to rigor.

However, any teacher, even the mythical one who provided the monologue, would cry heresy if it were suggested that there wasn't room for the students to think during an investigation. In reality the thoughts of the students were probably of a Darwinian survival type.

They recognized the teacher's stimulus and responded accordingly. The peripheral concepts that could have been achieved, the process of investigation, and the basic idea of intellectual honesty, are never made available to the student.

Let's be specific. The detailed instructions remove the "investigation" from the activity and make it a demonstration problem. The only difference between this and more traditional approaches is that the *student* baits the hook before fishing for the answer.

By being so specific in the instructions, "place the ice cube in the alcohol. As you notice, the ice cube will sink. Add water slowly, mixing it until the ice cube just floats," the teacher removes the exercise from the realm of science. The students should have been permitted to discover the need for controls such as "slowly mixing until the ice cube just floats." Such precisely phrased instructions may make the student wonder why it is necessary to mix the water with the alcohol. The teacher might answer that the densities of alcohol and water are different, so it is necessary to mix them. Since this is true, why not allow the students to establish the truth themselves?

The reason for the second instruction, "Remove the ice cube, weigh the solution and measure its volume," is provided when our mythical teacher says ". . . you don't want the ice to melt into the solution or it will change your results and the accuracy of the answer will go out the window."

Because equilibrium is a scientific concept of such stature, why not let the students discover it for themselves if at all possible? In the discourse, the teacher stresses the sanctity of the answer several times, even suggesting a value of .974 g/ml. It is highly probable that most of the students will manipulate their data until the lie .974 g/ml. appears on their papers. After all, the handwriting *is* on the wall. The bubbles that were in their ice cubes, and which *really* gave them a value of .914, will be ignored, as will the other variables that should have affected their results. The accuracy of their measurement of mass and volume of the solution may also be ignored if they interfere with getting the "right" answer.

In short, all the science involved in the investigation will have been sacrificed for adherence to the recipe. No one will have realized that more science went into writing the recipe than in following it.

This point of view might rightly be termed idealistic and dismissed with the comment, "that approach looks good on paper, but it's impossible in a real classroom." After all, the critics might add, junior high students are too immature to perform without rigorous guidance. And more certainly, they *must* be guided through the material to be covered.

There is little that can be said to a teacher whose attitude demands rigid adherence to the rules. The very foundations of such an attitude are rooted in two disputed notions. The first notion conceives of science as a veritable mountain of information over which novices must be guided by rigorous routes. The second conceives of scientific inquiry as a rigid methodological pattern of behavior. The precision of performance and adherence to "the routine" would be the criteria for evaluation under these concepts.

These notions project an image of science and inquiry that modern science curricula are attempting to erase. By modern educational standards, science must be presented as both inquiry and the knowledge gained by inquiry. The knowledge is never an end in itself, but a stepping stone to further inquiry.

How can a teacher participate in the investigation described earlier and sponsor inquiry in a more effective manner?

"What do you people see here on the table?"

"Two beakers of water." The class members at their places view these beakers at the teacher's demonstration table.

"What would happen if I put ice cubes in the beakers?"

"They would float."

The teacher then places an ice cube in each beaker. In one beaker it floats, and in the other it sinks. The excitement generated by this "anti-intuitive" event is at once apparent by the excited murmur throughout the room.

"What's wrong?" the teacher asks.

"One of those beakers contains some pretty silly water."

"One ice cube is heavier than the other."

"The cube that sank is not ice."

The responses of all the students are directly related to the nature of the materials that are viewed. They are mildly frustrated by being unable to touch and handle the materials. This kind of reaction is generally true of student response to demonstrations of any kind.

"What can I do that will allow you to check some of your ideas?" The teacher asks the question only after he is sure that the students have exhausted a good supply of possible explanations.

"Switch the cubes," one student challenges to a chorus of approval from his peers.

The teacher switches the cubes and the results are the same. The cube sinks in the same liquid in which it had sunk previously and floats in the same liquid in which it had floated before.

"The ice cubes are the same," a student offered, "so the liquids have to be different."

"I told you it was silly water," said the student who originally proposed this notion.

"Well, we *proved* it couldn't be the cubes," said others.

253

"Since you people have worked with calculating the densities of different materials, can we make some kind of a statement about the densities of these things we are viewing?"

After a bit of further discussion, the students decide that they can rank the density order of liquids on the basis of ice. The liquid in which the ice floats is denser than ice, and the liquid in which it sank is less dense than ice. The teacher writes these relationships on the board.

"Okay, here's your assignment: Using these liquids, which are, by the way, water and rubbing alcohol, you will measure the density of an ice cube. You will need scales, beakers and the liquids. Go to it."

From this point on, the teacher's role is to act as director of inquiry who turns student questions back on the results of the demonstration, their knowledge of the technique of measuring density, and their own ideas as to how the problem might be solved. Several groups decide on different ways of solving the problem; they are concerned at first about the differences in their approach. The teacher tells them that they should try what they proposed and evaluate the results. There is not, he assures them, an *only* way to reach the solution.

Throughout these multiple approaches the students "discover" the variables that might affect their results, such as the melting of ice in the alcohol-water solution mentioned by our first teacher. They also become aware of the change in volume of the ice while the mass is being measured on the scales. The materials themselves guarantee that these variables will become apparent.

What fundamentally was the difference in the two approaches? In both, the students were *doing* something. In both, they were manipulating materials. Both would be categorized by an outside observer as a laboratory approach to science. So again, let us ask what the difference in approach is.

In the first classroom, the students performed as the teacher told them to. In the second, they performed as they thought they should perform. In the first, science was being done by recipe; in the second, it was being done by inquiry. If the students gained confidence in anything in the first classroom, it was in the safety of following the teacher's instructions. In the second, it was likely that they gained confidence in using their own minds in the process of inquiry.

Perhaps the most discerning summary of discovery-type inquiry was stated by Bruner (1963). Bruner describes the advantages of discovery learning under four headings: (1) the increase in intellectual potency, (2) the shift from extrinsic to intrinsic rewards, (3) the learning of the heuristics of discovering, and (4) the aid of conserving memory.

Increased Intellectual Potency. Discovery learning increases intellectual potency by allowing students to recognize fundamental order and relationships through their own framework of perception and experience. Rather than receiving the order through the perception of the teacher, who in turn probably received it through the perception of scientists, the student perceives *real* order because it *happened* during his inquiry. The relationships perceived by direct inquiry will be much more relevant than any recipe-type order handed down in terms of content or process.

Shift from Extrinsic to Intrinsic Rewards. Quoting Bruner's introduction to this section, we find the essence of this advantage of discovery learning:

> "Much of the problem in leading a child to effective cognitive activity is to free him from the immediate control of environmental rewards and punishments" (p. 87).

In the first classroom the students were operating in an environment in which their observance of the teacher's rules provided the reward. In the second, the extent to which they used their minds was much more closely related to the reward pattern. In the first, the environment defined their course of action. In the second, their course of action defined their environment.

The Heuristics of Discovery. It is only through the process of making discoveries that a student will be able to learn how to make discoveries. If, through discovery, a student defines his particular style of inquiry, then it is probable that the style will become part of this thought process in the face of further inquiry.

Conservation of Memory. The body of information composed of facts that are "stored" in our memories is often considered to be the knowledge we possess. This view has retarded progress in science education more than most other notions. We are all alert to those things which we "memorized" dozens of times and promptly forgot. Certain facts have not been forgotten, and this is most often related to the use of these facts. In order to use information, it must be "retrieved from storage," to use Bruner's terminology. The retrieval process is enhanced by discovery-type inquiry and thus memory, as such, is similarly enhanced.

If as seems likely, these notions have validity and are the results of discovery-type inquiry, then what can be our role as teachers of science? It appears that to teach science we must retain the intellectual honesty of science in our teaching. If science is inquiry and its knowledge is the product of inquiry, then we must allow the students to inquire.

It is difficult to relinquish the role of alerting the students to the elegant logic of the teacher's mind. But we must, for what we really want is for the students to become confident in the use of their own minds. We want their minds to become facile enough to enjoy the tentative and adhere to the restrictions imposed by the nature of scientific inquiry, rather than the restrictions imposed by the recipes offered by authoritative teaching. The excuse that "there isn't enough time to teach this way" is not valid, for there is too little time *not* to teach this way.

REFERENCE CITED

Bruner, Jerome, 1963, *On Knowing: Essays for the Left Hand*: Harvard Univ. Press, 1963, 165 pp.

Inquiry Method: Three Interpretations

Alphoretta S. Fish

Bernice Goldmark

Inquiry is receiving considerable attention as a method of changing behavior and attitudes through elementary school science instruction. Many interpretations of how experiences with inquiry can function to change behavior have been made. Three of these interpretations in which a definition and method of inquiry have been structured were described at the National Science Teachers Association Southwest Regional Conference in Tucson, Arizona, October 28–30, 1965, by Arthur Costa, Director of Instructional Services, Sacramento, California; Ben Strasser, Consultant, Elementary Education-Science, Los Angeles County, California; and Alphoretta Fish.

SELF-DIRECTED INQUIRY

Arthur Costa, addressing himself to Suchman's inquiry training,[1] gave the following explanation of the techniques of inquiry:

J. Richard Suchman's inquiry program is designed to enable the learner to direct and control his own learning. To do this the teacher must provide the climate and conditions necessary, structure the process, organize the sequence, and assist the pupil in evaluating his own progress. Thus the teacher is seen as a facilitator, and the child as a "programer" of his own learning.

The conditions which Suchman describes as necessary for self-directed inquiry and which must be provided are: freedom and a responsive environment.

*Reprinted from *The Science Teacher*, V. 33, No. 2, Feb., 1966, pp. 13–15. ©, by permission.

[1]Dr. Suchman is Acting Director, Division of Elementary and Secondary Research, Office of Education, U.S. Department of Health, Education, and Welfare. He is on leave from the University of Illinois. Mr. Costa's remarks have been supplemented by material from Dr. Suchman.

Once the inquiry is initiated by the student, the teacher's task is to establish the conditions that will sustain the inquiry. The child must be free to decide for himself what data will be needed to find this new set of explainers. This means that no psychological pressures can be exerted on the child with teacher-questions. It also means that there be no competition among the children, no extrinsic rewards, no stress on grades. It is only when the child is free from pressures, when he has a favorable physical and social environment in which to work, that he can proceed with inquiry. When these pressure conditions are removed, the child can become involved in inquiry and excited by it, "caught up" in the process.

The teacher has the further task of providing a "responsive environment" for the child. He must make available data that the child might need for testing the theory with which he is operating. The process of inquiry which Suchman has structured is a process of formulating theories and testing them through experimenting and data gathering.

More than just creating the conditions to stimulate and support inquiry, the teacher helps the children to examine the inquiry process itself, to come to understand how knowledge comes into being, where theories come from, and how they can be appraised. By inquiring into inquiry, the learner becomes more aware of what he knows, how he knows it, and how to go about acquiring new knowledge for himself. In effect, inquiry training shifts the learner from a consumer of knowledge toward being a producer-consumer. This gives him more degrees of freedom as a learner since he can use and evaluate the theories and conclusions of others without being a slave to them, and he can generate his own theories and conclusions when this brings him more meaning.

The goals which Suchman sets for this program are: (1) stimulating and supporting the pursuit of meaning, (2) creating the conditions that make this pursuit possible and productive, and (3) bringing about inquiry into inquiry itself to help children become purposeful and effective inquirers.

INQUIRY INTO SCIENCE TEACHING

Ben Strasser described an approach related to inquiry into science teaching. His frame of reference was a teacher's self-examination of his own teaching behavior. One aspect of the examination is locating what it is learners do when they inquire. A second aspect of the teacher's inquiry is to become aware of the behaviors he exhibits that stimulate learners to do the kinds of things anyone does when he "sciences." Hence, the inquiry into science teaching involves a systematic examination of one's own teaching behavior in an attempt to extend

258

one's awareness of the range of and the consequences of one's behavior upon a given group of learners.

This approach views teaching as a truly dynamic process. According to this notion, the roles of the teacher include observing the learners, their actions and interactions; interpreting such data about the learners; making diagnoses in terms of the learner, the situation, and the goals; and behaving in terms of the diagnoses made. Thus, teaching is viewed as inquiring, though not inquiring *for* the learner, but rather *about* him. Of this approach, we might say it was inquiring into science teaching as inquiring!

Mr. Strasser suggested that one way we may begin our own self-examination is to focus attention, at first, on the way we use questions in the instructional situation. The kinds of questions we use determine the kinds of operations the children will perform. The questions we use outline the kinds of thinking, observing, and other behaving responses of the learners for which we, their teachers, search. Therefore, through looking at the various kinds of questions we ask, we can begin to build a picture of our own teaching behavior. Do we ask *only* questions which demand recall and then convince ourselves we are giving children opportunities to engage in higher level thinking? Do we ask *only* those questions which call for *our* answers and then convince ourselves we are stimulating divergent, creative behaviors in the children of our class? Do we often wait *after* our questions to give our students *time to think*, without jumping in to give them clues—just to keep the "noise" going? Over a period of several lessons, do we ask a *variety* of kinds of questions which stimulate the *range* of behaviors we may readily identify as aspects of sciencing in science education?

Strasser concluded his presentation with the idea that inquiring into science teaching is a never-ending process. As we begin to understand more about our own behaviors, the more new goals and ways of working we identify. And, looking at the *ways we use questions* as well as at *the questions we use* may be one way to begin inquiring into the complex, dynamic, interactive process we call science teaching.

INQUIRY TEACHING AS METHOD SELECTION

Alphoretta Fish indicated another level to which inquiry can be taken. In this model inquiry shifts from the level on which alternative methods of science inquiry are focal, to the level on which *decisions about which methods to select* are focal, as shown on the following diagram:

LEVEL II: Judgments about alternative methods of science inquiry
LEVEL I: Alternative methods of science inquiry

In this approach to inquiry *pupils make the decisions* about the method to use in their science inquiry, experience the consequences of their decision, and assess the consequences by inquiring into the science inquiry methods which produce the consequences.

Pupils are guided to expand experiences and reconstruct method by encountering a discrepancy in the *method* about which they have made a judgment.

Inquiry could be structured in the following way.

One. When the teacher gives the pupils magnets and asks, "How can the way in which magnets interact be described?" she allows the pupils to decide upon a method of describing. Suppose the pupils make a decision to describe what happens when magnets interact and discover that sometimes they "attract" and sometimes they "push away." When the teacher asks the pupils to predict what will happen if she brings a magnet toward a suspended magnet, she introduces a discrepancy which points up the inadequacy of the method selected. Pupils become dissatisfied with the method they selected, because they realize the possibilities for prediction are limited.

At this point the pupils experience a "dissatisfaction" and a "need" to reexamine the magnets to "see" them in a new way, to select another method of describing—in short, to inquire anew. Hence inquiry is continued, and pupils discover that there are *conditions* under which magnets attract and *conditions* under which magnets "push away."

Two. In the next phase of the lesson the teacher guides the pupils to inquire into the two experiences they have had with science inquiry. First, the components of each experience are organized as shown on Chart 1.

1. Organization of inquiry experiences

What Questions did we ask?	What Means did we use?	What Method did we select?	What Conclusions (ends) did we reach?
A. What happens when magnets interact with each other?	Random manipulation of magnets	Observation	Magnets attract and repel each other
B. Under what *conditions* do magnets interact?	Systematic manipulation of magnets	Recording conditions of change	Like poles of a magnet repel, unlike poles attract

By having the children "revisit" the questions, means, methods, and ends they used in each instance, the teacher enables the children to formulate relationships about which questions may be asked in the future. In this way children *expand* the relations they make with each new inquiry.

Three. Next, pupils are guided to *evaluate* their experiences. As shown on Chart 2, the judgment to select one type of question and one method rather than the other is made by assessing the consequences (or, more exactly, the means-ends-method) of the questions and methods used.

2. EVALUATION OF INQUIRY EXPERIENCES

EVALUATION QUESTION	EVALUATION MEANS	EVALUATION METHOD	EVALUATION ENDS
Which was the better method for describing how magnets interact with each other? (Which was the "better" science inquiry method?)	Revisit the two methods used, asking: 1. What did we do in each inquiry? (What were our science inquiry *means?*) 2. How did we do it? (What were our science inquiry *methods?*) 3. What did we conclude? (What were the *ends* of each science inquiry?) (Shown on Chart 1)	Inquiring into alternative science inquiry methods used (Comparing the means-ends-methods of each)	Building criteria for evaluating the two methods: 1. The method leading to a description of *conditions* gave us more information and therefore allowed for *greater prediction.* 2. Prediction can be used as a criterion for judging science inquiry methods.

This inquiry into the two science inquiry experiences is a second *level* of inquiry. Here the children are building criteria for judging alternative methods of inquiring in science. The inquiry can also be taken to a third level on which the children would then evaluate the criteria they have built. (An explanation of procedure at this level, however, was not included in the discussion at this conference.)

Four. The final task of the teacher in the *inquiry into inquiry method* phase of the lesson is to guide the pupils to "see" how the inquiry can be continued, to further expand "meaning," and to reconstruct method. By asking, "What other questions might we ask about magnets?" the teacher can guide pupils to ask some of the following questions: How do magnets interact with non-magnets? How do magnets interact with energy—for example, heat? How do magnets interact with the earth's magnetic poles? How do magnets interact with air and water? Here, pupils are also provided opportunity to "see" how alternative questions lead to the relating of alternative means-ends-methods in their inquiries. As they evaluate their methods of inquiring, they can build further criteria for judging methods of science inquiry, such as consistency and simplicity.

The point is that we should not be content with methods which result in the making of a *single* relation between (1) "object" or "event" and (2) "meaning." Obviously, the more relations pupils examine, the richer the "meanings" they develop. This method is designed to enable children to:

1. Expand "meanings" by expanding relations instituted
2. Examine the questions they ask and the methods they use for inquiring in science (by analyzing the means-ends-methods of each method selected)
3. Evaluate the questions and methods (by building criteria)
4. Reconstruct the questions and methods of science inquiry, and, finally, the step not illustrated here:
5. Evaluate and reconstruct the criteria.

This, it is believed, will help children develop responsibility for their own inquiry and commitment to ongoing inquiry and reconstruction of method.

Summary

Three alternative interpretations of inquiry were presented at this conference. How are these different, but related, approaches to inquiry to be assessed? Perhaps we can proceed with an inquiry into the three methods themselves, as shown in Chart 3.

If we examine the means-ends-method relations of the inquiries, we can see that the methods of inquiry proposed by both Suchman and Strasser are designed for the expansion and reconstruction of theories and methods. These are, however, theories and methods pertaining to the subject matter inquired into in the case of Suchman, and theories and methods pertaining to teaching and learning, in the case of Strasser. Both of these are first level, or substantive, theories and methods. Fish's inquiry is designed for the expansion and reconstruction not only of the substantive theories and methods, but also of the *methods of making judgments about theories and methods*. It is designed to provide a method for building criteria for selecting—for building criteria for "better" questions in science inquiry.

3. Inquiry into Three Alternative Inquiry Methods

Investigator	Question	Means	Method	Ends
Suchman	Can *pupils* examine and reconstruct theories?	1. Discrepant event introduced by teacher 2. Selection and organization of data by pupil 3. New theory constructed and tested by pupil	Inquiry into questions asked by pupils	1. Expansion of pupils' question-asking 2. Reconstruction of theories
Strasser	Can *teachers* examine and reconstruct their *teaching techniques*?	1. Teachers' questions and pupils' responses examined by teacher 2. Teachers' questions reconstructed to meet goals for pupil behavior	Inquiry into consequences of questions asked by teachers	1. Expansion of teacher's question-asking 2. Reconstruction of teaching-learning theory
Fish	Can *pupils* evaluate and reconstruct their *method* of evaluating and reconstructing science inquiry?	1. Discrepancy in method introduced by teacher 2. Criteria for judging alternative methods formulated by pupils 3. Methods of inquiring reconstructed	Inquiry into the method of inquiry	1. Expansion and reconstruction of science inquiry methods 2. Expansion and reconstruction of *methods* of evaluating and reconstructing science inquiry

The Role of Inquiry in Science Teaching*

F. James Rutherford

Inquiry and Content

When it comes to the teaching of science it is perfectly clear where we, as science teachers, science educators, or scientists, stand: we are unalterably opposed to the rote memorization of the mere facts and minutiae of science. By contrast, we stand foursquare for the teaching of the scientific method, critical thinking, the scientific attitude, the problem-solving approach, the discovery method, and, of special interest here, the inquiry method. In brief, we appear to agree upon the need to teach science as process or method rather than as content.

Judging, however, by what we can see taking place in many, if not most, classrooms and by the kinds of tests that teachers use, we might reasonably conclude that there is a large gap between our practices and our convictions. This may well be the result of many factors—the natural conservatism of science teachers, a failure of those who call for change and innovation to provide teachers with effective models and materials, and others. *One* of the contributing factors, it seems clear, has been a failure to recognize and take fully into account the close organic connection between process and content in science. It is here suggested that the effective teaching of the physical sciences as inquiry becomes possible in a particular and important sense once we understand that the conclusions of science are closely linked with the inquiry which produced them, and, conversely, that the nature of a given inquiry depends upon the topic under investigation. The choice is *neither* facts and laws *nor* inquiry and process; it is *both* facts and laws *and* inquiry and process.

*Reprinted from the *Journal of Research in Science Teaching*, V. 2, pp. 80–84 (1964). ©, by permission.

264

First, the designation "teaching science as inquiry" needs some clarification. It is currently being used in at least two general ways. Sometimes it is employed in a way which emphasizes that inquiry is really part of the science content itself. It acknowledges that there is a pattern of inquiry characteristic of a given science, or of a given field within a science, and that such patterns form an integral part of what science "is." At other times, the phrase "teaching science as inquiry" is used to refer to a particular technique or strategy for bringing about learning of some particular science content. This is the meaning associated with the term "inquiry *method*." The distinction here is between "inquiry as it appears in the scientific enterprise," on the one hand, and "using the method of scientific inquiry to learn some science," on the other. For purposes of brevity, I shall refer to the former as *inquiry as content* and to the latter as *inquiry as technique*.

One other matter of semantics needs attention: whether speaking of inquiry as content or inquiry as pedagogic technique, the modifier "scientific" is implied. It is *scientific* inquiry we are concerned with, not inquiry in general. Otherwise, if all that is intended by the inquiry method is that we should encourage a student to be inquisitive, curious, to ask questions, and to try to find answers for himself, then we are advocating no more than what good teachers have long believed in and practiced. Thus we must keep in mind that it is scientific inquiry that is being offered by some people as a paradigm on which to base a teaching strategy.

As a basis for discussion, two topics which might seem to lend themselves to the teaching of science as inquiry have been selected from the subject matter of physics. An examination of these two quite different cases gives substance to the following conclusions:

(1) It is possible to gain a worthwhile understanding of science as inquiry once we recognize the necessity for considering inquiry as content, and operate on the premise that the concepts of science are properly understood *only* in the context of how they were arrived at and of what further inquiry they initiated.

(2) As a corollary, it follows that it is possible to learn something of science as inquiry without the learning process itself having to follow precisely any one of the methods of inquiry used in science. That is, inquiry as technique is not absolutely necessary to an understanding of inquiry as content.

(3) While the laboratory can be used to provide the student experience with and knowledge of some aspects or components of the investigative techniques employed in a given science, it can effectively do so

only after the *content* of the experiments have been carefully analyzed for their usefulness in this regard.

UNIVERSAL GRAVITATION AS AN EXAMPLE EMPHASIZING CONTENT

The two examples to be used are those of universal gravitation and the law of reflection of light from surfaces. These topics are covered in all physics courses and in most physical science or general science courses. Let us turn first to the law of universal gravitation.

Science teachers surely wish to help each of their students acquire an "understanding" of universal gravitation. But when can they be satisfied that a student does in fact understand that concept? One cannot, of course, draw an absolute boundary between complete understanding and no understanding. Nevertheless, with a concept of the magnitude of universal gravitation, it seems reasonable that at least two conditions should be fulfilled before we could assume a student has acquired an acceptable understanding. The first is that the student become aware of the *range* of applicability of the theory. The second is that he have some knowledge of the network of inquiry, the sequence of investigations and thought, which led to the final formulation by Newton. Certainly we would all agree that the student does not understand universal gravitaton just because he can recite the equation $F = G\,m_1m_2/r^2$ and work simple problems using it.

As far as the range of the law of universal gravitation is concerned, the first step is to bring the student to an awareness of its magnificent successes. The brilliant way in which the Newtonian principle of universal gravitation explains so many diverse terrestrial and celestial phenomena—comets, tides, precession of the equinoxes, and geographical variations of g—and in which it was able to predict other phenomena— the existence of undiscovered planets being, of course, the most spectacular instance—are really part of the content of the concept itself. So in fact are the additional investigations which it instigated. In examining a wide array of phenomena to find out just how *universal* universal gravitation is and in studying the relationship between that formulation and the new inquiries stemming from it, the student will come to see that Newtonian mechanics does indeed have limitations. The interesting point for our purposes is not so much that relativistic and quantum mechanics were ultimately needed, but that the long series of investigations stimulated in great part by Newton's formulation of universal gravitation itself led to the kind of knowledge which would expose its own limitations. Thus in studying universal gravitation in the context just described, the student may gain the insight that an important attribute of scientific theory is that it generates new investigations even if in doing so its own conceptual weaknesses are mercilessly exposed. A good theory stems from successful inquiry and generates additional ones.

Turning to the other condition for "understanding," it has been claimed here that an acceptable understanding of the concept of universal gravitation implies a knowledge of the network of inquiry which led to it. The discovery, or the "invention," to use the terminology of Atkin and Karplus, [1] of universal gravitation was the outcome of inquiry on the grand scale, involving, as it did, the investigations and insights of many people in many places over a substantial span of time. The giants upon whose shoulders Newton admitted standing were practitioners of the art of inquiry into the nature of the physical world. Each practiced his art in his own characteristic way. No one of them can serve as the perfect model of how a contemporary investigator should proceed, but their work taken as a whole illuminates beautifully many facets of the scientific enterprise. If one wishes to study science as process, it is surely wiser to look at the work of several scientists in the context of a significant scientific problem than to concentrate upon the work of a single scientist or to settle for some abstract formulation of inquiry divorced from science content. By noting the contributions and modes of operation of the men whose work led to the law of universal gravitation, the student learns his science as both content and inquiry.

If one looks upon the concept of universal gravitation as the culmination of a long series of investigations and the beginning of still another series, then a variety of insights on the complex nature of scientific inquiry may accrue. For purposes of illustration, only a few of these are cited:

(1) The power of indirect experimentation is dramatically demonstrated by Galileo's work with the pendulum and the inclined plane. Incidentally, the approach recognizes that these instruments have their main interest as experimental equipment rather than as objects to be understood for their own sake.

(2) The importance of being able to formulate experiments and ideas in the language of mathematics is shown in the work of Galileo, Kepler, and Newton himself.

(3) Both the necessity for and the limitation of accurate data in scientific inquiry are brought out by the use made of Tycho Brahe's magnificently precise planetary observations. In the hands of Kepler they played a key role in the overthrow of the two thousand year old conceptual reliance upon uniform circular motion. But these same facts were unable to lead Tycho himself to a correct interpretation, and indeed we know now that facts alone are never enough to provide us with understanding of nature.

(4) Kepler's speculations, fanciful and sometimes even bizarre, but always in the end put to the test of measured fact, present another facet of inquiry. Furthermore, the use of Kepler's laws made by Newton allows one to emphasize the difference between empirical laws and explanatory laws or principles, and the importance of one to the other.

(5) The significance of physical and metaphysical preconceptions in shaping a scientific investigation is illustrated by the reluctance of Copernicus, no less than Ptolemy, to abandon uniform circular motion.

One could add many more items to this list. But perhaps the point has been made: to understand the concept of universal gravitation, it is important that the student be made familiar with the key experimental and theoretical inquiries (and their interactions) which ultimately were synthesized by Newton so succinctly in a single equation. [2]

Now surely no one would advocate that the student be brought to this kind of an understanding by conducting his own investigations, that is, by the application of inquiry as technique. Anyone tempted to do so should reconsider the strong arguments put forward by Gagné. [3] But this is not to discourage the teaching of physics as inquiry; instead it is to suggest that if the nature of scientific inquiry is taken to be an integral part of the subject matter itself, then neither the conclusions of science (the facts, laws, principles, theories, conceptual schemes, etc.) nor the process of discovery and investigation which lead to those conclusions will be neglected. Content and inquiry will appear as the warp and woof of a single fabric, which is, after all, the way science really is.

LIGHT REFLECTION AS AN EXAMPLE EMPHASIZING PROCEDURE

Let us turn now to the second example, that of the law of reflection. Here is a relatively small topic upon which the student might be expected to conduct an investigation, that is, to learn about scientific inquiry at first hand rather than vicariously. At least that would seem so judging by the number of classrooms in high school and elementary school in which students "discover" the law of reflection. Typically, the student is given a plane mirror, some pins, a protractor, a straight edge, and instructions on how to locate the path of incoming and reflected light rays. He is then asked to find the relationship between the angle of incidence and the angle of reflection (after, of course, these have been defined for him). A little thought, however, suggests that whatever other value such an "experiment" may have, it has little merit as an honest exercise in scientific inquiry, even assuming that the student is not told the answer ahead of time. The following few points are offered merely to add substance to this claim. Any effort to devise a laboratory procedure which will enlarge the student's investigative skills while discovering the law of reflection must, surely, take these and similar criticisms into account:

(1) The concept of "light ray" is a fairly abstract one. In fact, as used in such experiments, a light ray is fictitious: its virtue is that it provides a useful way to talk about certain optical phenomena, in this case the regularity of image reflection. It is the invention of the light-ray as the physical analogue of the Euclidian straight line, and the related acceptance of the correspondence between plane geometry and optical phenomena (rather than the discovery of the rule of equal angles), that was the key step here. [4] This suggests, at the very least, a prior need for the student to consider evidence for the rectilinear propagation of light, and for working out an operational definition of "light ray."

(2) But if we admit that the student cannot uncover such an abstract notion by his own inquiry, that is not to say all is lost. We might claim, with Atkin and Karplus, that after the teacher has supplied the invention, the student can then investigate, *i.e.*, discover, some of its consequences. That is, fortified with the idea of "light ray" the student might be asked to find out how it could be used to explain reflection from mirrors. Perhaps so, but not, certainly, if the student is provided all of the apparatus right at the beginning, as is the usual case. To do so reduces the "experiment" to a mere puzzle, for it excludes the student from participation in the development of the experimental strategy to be employed in the investigation. For instance, just the fact that the student is provided only with a plane mirror limits severely the scope of the inquiry. Reflection takes place, after all, from spherical and parabolic surfaces, not to say irregular ones. One of the important techniques used in scientific inquiry is to seek out the simplest useable instance of a phenomenon for preliminary investigation. As the reflection experiment is commonly done students are bound to miss this point. A better strategy, better in the sense of having a more meaningful connection with the substantive content, would be to provide students an opportunity to observe reflection from an array of mirrors of different shapes, and then to require them to participate in working out some of the details of the experiment, including which kind of a mirror to use.

(3) The angles of incidence and reflection are defined for the student, and in a way that would not seem natural to him. The measurement of those angles with reference to the normal to the surface rather than to the surface itself is not self-evident. It is a matter of convention, the usefulness of which has to do primarily with Snell's law of refraction, and not with reflection from plane surfaces at all. The way this experiment is usually handled, however, deprives the student of an opportunity to learn that while definitions of physical quantities are arbitrary, consideration must be made of their likely usefulness in carrying out further investigations.

These few remarks concerning the laboratory investigation of the reflection of light are intended to indicate that even when one examines a relatively simple topic, it is not immediately and unequivocally clear just how it should be presented to the student so that it will contribute to the goal of teaching science as inquiry. Certainly this and other topics *can* so contribute, but not until each has been carefully analyzed from the standpoint of its relationship to the body of physical knowledge from which it is extracted. Only after such an analysis has been made can we possibly know which facts, definitions, presumptions, principles, and relationships are involved. At that point some investigation must be made as to which of these aspects of the topic particularly lend themselves to teaching by the method of inquiry. Thus there are two interrelated tasks to be accomplished. First, an analytical study needs to be made (from the standpoint of science as inquiry) of each of the usual topics encountered in introductory courses in the physical sciences. Second, some number of laboratory oriented experiences need to be devised which can contribute to the understanding of the nature of scientific inquiry *as it actually happens.*

Conclusion

In all of this discussion, whether dealing with the monumental concept of universal gravitation or the more modest one of light reflection, the emphasis has been on viewing scientific inquiry as part of the content of science itself. To separate conceptually scientific content from scientific inquiry is to make it highly probable that the student will properly understand neither. From this there follows an inescapable conclusion regarding the feasibility of teaching science as inquiry: science teachers must come to understand just how inquiry is in fact conducted in the sciences. Until science teachers have acquired a rather thorough grounding in the history and philosophy of the sciences they teach, this kind of understanding will elude them, in which event not much progress toward the teaching of science as inquiry can be expected.

References

1. Atkin, J. Myron, and Robert Karplus, "Discovery or Invention," *The Science Teacher*, **29**, 45–51 (1962).
2. Holton, Gerald, and Duane H. D. Roller, *Foundations of Modern Physical Science*, Addison-Wesley, Reading, Massachusetts, 1958.
3. Gagné, Robert M., "The Learning Requirements for Enquiry," *J. Res. Sci. Teaching*, **1**, 144–153 (1963).
4. Toulmin, Stephen, *The Philosophy of Science*, Hutchinson's University Library, London, 1953, pp. 17–85.

Critical Analysis: Opposing Viewpoints on Conceptual Schemes

Although many science educators and teachers are becoming convinced of the value of techniques placing primary emphasis on inquiry, investigation, and on the use of conceptual schemes in teaching, some thoughtful educators oppose their widespread introduction. Others disagree violently about what rigid conceptual schemes are worth and about the particular form that an "investigative" approach should take. In the following articles Russell, Glass, and Ausubel examine critically the merits of the conceptual schemes proposed by the National Science Teachers Association. I hope that you will not accept what the "authorities" represented in this book have proposed without personally subjecting their ideas to searching analysis and experimentation in your own classroom.

Theory Into Action[1]
as a Projection of
the Rational Tradition*

James E. Russell

Those of us who deal in educational policy must attempt con-
tinuously to evaluate the American system of education. Past evaluations
show us that the system has in general succeeded. More years of schooling produce better people by every standard we can measure, but all
that proves is that the planning we did in the past was at least partly
wise. It tells us little about the decisions that we ought to be making
now regarding the kind of school that we ought to have to enable our
children to adapt to a world in the future, of which we can say only
one thing—that we are quite sure it will not be like the world we grew
up in; it will be different.

Is there any way that we can look at the present and understand what
is happening? Is there some system by which we can put ourselves on
trend lines and see where these trends are taking us? Let me illustrate
the necessity for doing this.

You realize that a child aged six, now entering the first grade, is
entering a school system which is something in being. We are going
to go through a decade, and then we are going to go through another
decade. Say 20 years pass. That child will be 26 years old. For all you
know, that child may still be in school, or that child may be a young
parent at that time. If you extrapolate the age trends that we have now,
you have to assume that this child will at that time have 75 years of
useful life ahead of him.

What will we do now to bring about the sort of educational system
which will help that child to shape himself so that, starting 20 years
from now, he will be able to make the adaptations that the world will
call for in the succeeding 75 years?

[1]Publication No. 471–14282, available from NEA Publication Sales Division,
1201 16th St., N.W., Washington, D. C. 20036, $1.50 per copy.
*Reprinted from *The Science Teacher*, V. 32, No. 5, May, 1965, pp. 27–29.
©, by permission.

Scientists tell us that in the last decade they have learned half of all they know. They expect in the next decade again to double all they now know. We can anticipate that within 20 or 30 years the world will be very profoundly reshaped, and it will be reshaped not so much by its past as by what is yet in the future. The things that are becoming are far more important for what happens 30 years from now than the things that have happened.

What are these things that are becoming?

We recognize that our world is changing. We talk about change and we say things like this: The white middle classes are leaving the cities, and the lower and rural Negro and white groups are moving in. We say that we are facing a technological revolution and that we have revolutions in communication and in transportation, that we have the race for space and the harnessing of the atom and the rising expectations of the underdeveloped peoples. Each one of these things we see as some kind of a transformation of our lives, and we treat them as if they were profound changes, that is, as if these were the deep changes. Well, I don't think they are.

I think all these changes that I cited are surface reflections of just one change—just one—and that is the role of the mind. I can illustrate the point.

Take this matter of the white middle classes leaving the cities. Why are they going? They are going because of the infiltration of what we are calling "disadvantaged" persons who decay the cities.

Why, then, are the disadvantaged moving? If they cannot reconstitute their lives in the cities, why do they come there in the first place? They come because they have lost their role on the land; they have lost their role in the American economy. It used to be profitable to harvest the staple crops of the South by hand. It no longer is, because we have machines that do the job cheaper and better. Therefore, it pays the owner to enclose the land and push these people off. Consequently, they are in movement.

Why, after 25,000 years of technology, do we come only now to this kind of mechanisms? Obviously, this is because of recent advances in the basic sciences, upon which the technology depends—physics, chemistry, metallurgy, mathematics, and things like that.

Why, after all the centuries of growth in the sciences, why is it only now?

As you look back down this chain of events, what you come to when you get to the end is a system of thinking. You are looking at the flowering of the rational tradition of the West.

This is the thing that is changing our lives, and it is changing them at some sort of an exponential rate. It forces us to get our minds into dimensions where they don't easily go. We think we know what the word "rational" means. We understand that it operates in terms of certain common definitions, a consistency-contradiction relation. We understand that it has common values in the form of logic and understanding of logic. We understand that it calls upon us to test the results of reasoning by experience. We know that it operates in terms of familiar mental processes: recalling and imagining, evaluating and comparing, classifying and generalizing, analyzing and synthesizing, deducing and inferring. These things we see. But we do not know as a matter of common sense how to relate ourselves to it. I can illustrate the point.

If you want to relate, say, point F_1 to point F_2 and you have just two points, and if the relationship is going to be S and the distance between them is going to be X, and you put down on paper S equals X, you are talking about extension or what I call length. I know what that is because I can see this point and I can see that point and I can interrelate them.

You explain the same relationship in two dimensions and let one dimension be X_1 and the other dimension be X_2; now you have yourself in the Pythagorean and Euclidean world. You can express this relationship between F_1 and F_2 as a hypotenuse and you would say $S^2 = X_1^2 + X_2^2$, and I would still be with you. I would say: "I don't know why you are going to all this fancy language. But I learned the Pythagorean Theorem in the tenth grade, and I know that the square of the hypotenuse equals the sum of the squares of the other two sides."

Then you make one more step and you say: "Well, let's solve it for S. So we will take the square roots of both sides and say: $S = \sqrt{X_1^2 + X_2^2}$, and I am still with you. I think I understand extension in two dimensions. I understand area. I have bought and sold land. I know how to figure the size of a piece of paper.

You say: "All right. Now let's put it in three dimensions. We will have the same two we had, plus X_3, which will be the depth dimension. Our S is going to be the equivalent of a hypotenuse through a cube, and we will say:

$$S = \sqrt{X_1^2 + X_2^2 + X_3^2}.$$

Now we are in the world of Newton. This is the world of Newton's three absolute dimensions, of which this is the archetype proposition. I would say: "I don't know why you are doing all this, but I am still with you. I know what a cube is."

Those of you who teach physics will recognize that I am developing the Einsteinian spatial formulations. Frequently in the past when I talked about these things I used analogies for the Einstein formulations. These are not analogies. These are the exact formulations that Einstein used in the General Theory of Relativity, and they are exact in the sense that I am using the precise symbols that he used. He did not use $X = S$, but he did use the others and developed them, and he identified them as I have.

Now we go with Einstein and the man on whom he was relying, Minkowski. We go into non-Euclidean and Cartesian equations involving a fourth dimension, which is as follows:

$$S = \sqrt{X_1{}^2 + X_2{}^2 + X_3{}^2 + X_4{}^2}.$$

And I say: "Where do you get that X_4?" He says: "What do you mean 'where'? It isn't any where." I say: "Well, how do you draw it?" He says: "What do you mean 'draw it'? You don't draw it." "Well, how do you describe it?" "You don't describe it." "Well, I don't get it." He says: "You are talking about things you can touch and feel and hear and buy and sell. This isn't anything you can touch or see. It isn't accessible to the world of the senses. It is a rational construct. It is imaginary."

Well, then you might ask yourself a nice question. If it is imaginary, is it real?

Einstein said: "If you will use this four-dimension archetype as your basic spatial proposition, you will draw conclusions from it that accord more accurately with what can be observed than the propositions you draw from the Newtonian three-dimensional archetype." And on this basis he proceeded to develop the thesis of field effects on light, from which he hypothesized that if you could blot out the sun, as in a solar eclipse, you would find that the stars that appeared close to the sun would appear displaced because the sun's gravitational field would bend the light from those stars as it passed close to the sun.

In 1919 this led Eddington and other astronomers to the great expeditions to West Africa and Brazil, when there was a solar eclipse in those countries. They set up their telescopes; they looked for those displacements; and they found them.

This was more than just another useful discovery. This is not just an extension of those principles by which you build bridges and win wars. This was an event which said to mankind: Look people, if you want to look at the world and know what is really there, look with instrumentalities beyond your senses; look with the abstract power of your mind.

That imagined X_4 of Einstein is more real than those things which most of us nonscientists have taken to be the basis of reality all our lives. There is a story of Dr. Johnson and Bishop Berkeley having an argument over what is real. The Bishop said: "My good doctor, that stone there, how do you know it is real?" Johnson leaned back and kicked it and broke his toe in the process. He said: "That, sir, is how I know it." This is told by Boswell, because it shows what a great man Johnson was, and it is supposed to be evidence, on its face, that Dr. Johnson won the argument.

If there is one thing that the modern world is saying to us it is that Dr. Johnson had to be wrong. You could argue over whether Bishop

Berkeley was right, but you cannot argue Johnson's point. His concept was that he could tell something was real because he could feel it. Anyone who lives in an age of radiation and magnetism and the electron, and who thinks that you can measure reality by what you can see, has to be a fool.

Yet 1919 was just one year after educators of the United States embarked on a program of education which was focused on the concept of behavior. The great goals that were set for the schools were, in addition to intellectual goals, things like ethical behavior, good citizenship, worthy use of leisure time, homemaking, economic effectiveness —this means job effectiveness. They were goals set at this level. This is what I like to call the 20th century fallacy. This is the fallacy that the world for which we are educating the child is the world of his own experience; it is the world of his own behavior; it is the world in which he sees people and acts and interacts with human beings; yet, you can see from the nature of the argument I am developing that what is in front of us is the certainty that this is not the only world, that there are other worlds, and that these other worlds are becoming more important. The other worlds are worlds beyond sense, worlds, as Hayakawa said, of inferred structures and events.

Therefore, we come back to the trend line I am looking at. If you put yourself on the trend of our times, this trend tells you that the part of life which is dealt with in abstract rational terms, independent of sense experience, is becoming more important. This is the part of reality that is changing the world we see and live in. So all I have to do to put myself on this trend line is to say: "Well, what do I think it will be 20 years from now?" My answer is: I think this trend is going to continue, and we had better plan for it, too. In fact, we had better hope it continues. It means that my child 20 years from now is going to have to have developed abstract abilities, abilities to look at the world and deal with the world in terms other than mine; they cannot be drawn out of my experience. He will have to have access to the worlds of inferred structures and events.

For the child of the future I think that there are certain things that are not going to change. I think that the religious aspects of life, the emotional aspects, the esthetic aspects of life, the superstitial aspects will go on. We are going to continue to worship God, fall in love, admire beauty, and avoid black cats. But the power of thought is increasing.

When that child of the future faces up to some sort of a problem whose outlines I cannot perceive, what is he going to do? He is not going to be able to turn to our experience. There isn't any relevant experience. He is not going to be able to turn to the history or the whole accumulated experience of mankind. It is not going to do him any good to have a good character. He can take all the good ethical attitudes he wants and junk them; it will not solve the problem. Whether he understands its esthetic aspects also will not do any good. He will not be able to retreat from the problem or to ignore it. It will not even do him any good to pray. He will have to think.

It is therefore incumbent on those who are concerned with the re-shaping of American education that they deal with those parts of American life where the rational tradition may be exemplified, understood, and learned—where, in fine, one may gain access to the worlds of inferred structures and events.

It is against this background of considerations that I came to first see the volume called *Theory Into Action.* My first response to it was to be sensitive to some of its limitations. I think that it gives more stress to hard science than to soft, and to physical science than to life science. But as I held the little volume in my hand, I saw a vision of some of the structure of rationality and some of the things it has learned, and I said to myself: Here is an interdisciplinary approach saying to the world "these things we have learned." This document says something of what these inferred structures are and provides detail on the insights gained through rational approaches. There is a solid residue produced by the growth of knowledge. A child whose learning is aimed at these things will be participating in the growth of the rational tradition.

It is for this reason that I think there is implicit in this little document a very profound revolution, which, when its outlines are understood, will lead to a reshaping of American education—a profound and hopeful change for which those responsible deserve much praise.

Theory Into Action--A Critique*

Bentley Glass

I have been permitted by the officers of the National Science
Teachers Association to express my profound dissent from the choice
of seven "conceptual schemes" developed by an NSTA Conference of
Scientists in the hope that these concepts may be of great value in
planning science curricula. I have had to dissociate myself from the
conclusions of my colleagues not only because I disagree so fundamentally in principle, but also because I feel that any attempt to make
use of such a set of conceptual schemes in the development of science
curricula in the elementary and secondary schools of our nation would
do a great disservice to science as a whole, while proving disastrous
for the development of the biological sciences in particular. As Chair-
man of the Biological Sciences Curriculum Study for the past six years,
I could not compromise with what seems to me to be not merely an
inadequate, but indeed a prejudicial and injurious formulation of educational goals in science.

Such strong charges require explanation and defense. Let me say
first of all where the basic philosophical difference lies. The seven
conceptual schemes are stated entirely in terms of matter and energy,
the fundamental physical realities of the universe. That matter and
energy are the basis of all scientific phenomena and that all observations
relate to states of matter and changes induced by energy, who can
deny? The problem arises when we undertake to convert so basic an
axiom into a variety of conceptual schemes that will cover every science
adequately. Is it either true or practicable at the present stage of scientific development to regard all the laws, principles, and concepts of

*Reprinted from *The Science Teacher*, V. 32, No. 5, May, 1965, pp. 19–30,
82–83. ©, by permission.
†The conceptual schemes referred to by Glass are quoted on pp. 14–15 of this
book and also in a footnote to the article by D. P. Ausubel which immediately follows Glass' article.

biology, to take a prime example, as being adequately subsumed by stated physical principles? I hold that it is neither practicable nor true. The Conference has formulated seven statements, with none of which I would disagree. They may indeed supply an admirable basis for the organization of the study of physics, and possibly also of chemistry— although here I begin to have some doubt; but as a basis for organizing the study of the biological sciences they are not helpful—they are positively harmful.

Let us look at these seven conceptual schemes individually. Even in the light of their fuller exposition, as given in the report "Theory Into Action . . . in Science Curriculum Development," only three of them have much connection specifically with the phenomena of life. These are numbers II, III, and VII.

As for the four other concepts, while they underlie all living phenomena, they need not take much time in the biological curriculum if they are properly taught in the physical sciences. How true this is we may see from the admission, made in discussing Conceptual Scheme IV, that while all behavior of matter in the universe is "probably determined by electromagnetic, gravitational, and nuclear forces, the behavior of higher organizational units of living matter cannot be interpreted on this basis at this time." That is indeed so, whence it follows that for our present day we cannot usefully use this concept to assist in the organization of a biological curriculum, even though we admit its truth. The same may well be said for Concept V, the Second Law of Thermodynamics, which is highly important to the study of life, though one might scarcely think so from the brief sentence included in discussion of the concept. Many a physiologist and many an ecologist have stressed that the special and peculiar features of living systems relate to their seeming violation of the Second Law, to their astonishing ability to maintain their systems in relative constancy and even, for a time, in growth and reproduction, in spite of the constant flow of materials through them and the constant degradation of energy that occurs as they live through time. As for Concept VI, with its focus on heat, kinetic energy, and states of matter, the discussion again indicates how slight is its applicability to living systems, whereas had a choice been made of the capture of solar energy from light and its conversion into potential chemical energy, together with the transformations of potential chemical energy into kinetic energy of various kinds, the biologist might have taken heart.

Now let us look at the concepts that do deal more specifically with living organisms. Concept II is clearly of enormous biological significance. The flaw here is that its verbalization in terms of *matter* may mislead planners of curricula, if not into an outright omission of biological phenomena, at least into a failure of emphasis. The discussion, with its interesting description of sequence of organizational levels in the biological world, may help to avoid such an error. Nevertheless, what is overlooked, I believe, is a fundamental fact of nature, namely, that the lower levels of organization in the hierarchy are inherently simpler in the numbers and kinds of interacting units they contain, while the complexities grow inordinately greater at the higher levels. The hierarchy is no simple ladder. It is an inverted pyramid, resting on a tiny base, the internal structure of the atom in terms of fundamental particles. It is both theoretically and practically impossible to deal with successively more complicated levels of existence in the concise, *relatively simple* terms of nuclear physics. This is why biology is more complex, diversified, and admittedly less well formulated in terms of scientific law than are the physical sciences; and it is also why psychology and the social sciences are still more complex, diversified, and less well formulated in terms of scentific law. It may sound derogatory to the biological, and much more to the social, sciences to say that they are more descriptive. Yet it is true—in part because of the historical development of the sciences, which has seen the biological sciences pass from a descriptive to an experimental stage of methodology more recently than did the physical sciences. But it is true in a much deeper sense, true because of the very nature of the phenomena. The biological sciences deal with many levels of organization in the hierarchy: the molecular, the macromolecular, the cellular, the multicellular, the organism, the population, the community, and the biome. Physics, on the other hand, or chemistry, deals with but few. One simply cannot study all phenomena on many different levels at one time without becoming confused. In the planning of a science curriculum, we must take this diversification and increasing complexity at the upper levels of the inverted pyramid into account, as well as the less physical, increasingly descriptive state of scientific study at the uppermost levels of living organization.

In short, Concept II needs rephrasing in order to avoid misunderstanding and mistaken emphasis. One might suggest the following: "Matter exists in the form of units which can be classified into hierarchies of organizational level, from fundamental particles to galactic universe, from nonliving to living, from cell to individual, community, and biome. As one progresses up through the hierarchy, the organizational levels become more and more complex, more and more diversified, more and more difficult to describe in terms of general law."

Concept III comes closest to being a balanced statement of equal applicability to all of the natural sciences. Properly understood, its significance is to destroy the very validity of the sort of philosophical reduction of the biological sciences to the laws of physics which the rest of the total scheme so strongly implies. I have argued elsewhere and cannot repeat fully in the present instance why it seems clear that not all biological laws and principles are reducible to physical laws and principles, even though all phenomena are phenomena of matter and energy, space and time. One reason is that in the hierarchy of organizational levels new properties grow out of interactions and interrelations; and these new properties are, at least on the basis of our present scientific knowledge, unpredictable. The properties of the water molecule are not readily predictable from a full knowledge of the properties of the oxygen and hydrogen atoms. Even more, the properties of a living organism are not predictable simply on the basis of its chemical composition and its energetics. The specific organization of its parts is crucial. Still more obviously, the character of a living community cannot be specified simply on the basis of the numbers and kinds of its respective components. The environment, the distribution, and the interdependence of different kinds of organisms are the crux of the matter.

A second reason is that living cells, organisms, and communities are what they are because they have a history. The history may in some respects have followed predictable lines of natural selection within given types of environment, but very frequently two or more lines of evolution may have been equally possible, and chance may have determined which course was actually pursued. History is filled with *unique* events, just as each sexually reproducing population is composed of genotypically unique individuals. To the extent that uniqueness exists, evolution is not predictable, even though, looking back, we may explain the course it has taken on the basis of scientific analysis. Yet we cannot escape the fact that biological science, like much of geology, is a *historical* science that deals with an actual course of events, one which might at many turning points have gone differently. In this respect, the biological sciences are, and will forever remain, vastly different from the purely physical sciences.

But the most important reason of all why the laws of the biological sciences are not, all of them, reducible to the laws of physics is inherent in this same Concept III. At every level in the hierarchy of organization we meet with events that are stochastic, the outcome of random probabilities. The laws of Mendel depend upon the randomness of fertilization of eggs in given frequencies by sperms in given frequencies. The given frequencies of the genotypes of eggs or of sperms in a particular individual depend upon the random and independent assortment of the different pairs of chromosomes. The Hardy-Weinberg principle upon which all our modern calculations of evolutionary processes are based depends upon the randomness of mating of given genotypes in the gene pool of the population. These examples are taken exclusively from the field of genetics because that is the branch of biology commonly acknowledged to be most highly advanced, most mathematical in nature, most like the physical sciences in refinement and methodology. Yet it is perfectly clear that the basic laws of genetics cannot be reduced to laws of physics because they are in fact merely statements of the randomness of nature. If they reduce to anything, they reduce to the calculus of probability, not to physics, just as physicists are finding, since the development of Quantum Theory, that many of the basic laws of physics likewise reduce to a calculus of probability.

Concept VII is so vast in its biological implications that it in fact covers nearly everything within its enormous compass. One could very well treat the entirety of biology under the general concept of "Organisms through Time." It embraces the eons of organic evolution and the momentary changes of metabolic activity. It embraces the succession of living generations, and it concerns the growth and development of the individual. Of the eight major specifically biological themes stated by the Biological Sciences Curriculum Study to have guided its organization of subject matter and to permeate all of biological thought, there is not a single one, considered in its dynamic aspect, but is encompassed by this general statement. In fact, in the still more concise formulation: "All matter and all energy exist and interact in time and space," the universe itself is comprehended. Yet, for the very reason that it is all-inclusive, such a concept is of little or no practical value in the organization and planning of a science curriculum. For the latter, a more detailed categorization and application of principle to subject matter are required. One cannot propose to study at one and the same time the processes of evolution, the nature of genetic continuity, the growth and development of individual organisms, the dynamic relations of the components of a living community, the metabolic turnover, and the homeostatic regulations that enable a living system—cell, organism, or community—to maintain its essential being in the face of the inimical conditions of the outer world and the inescapable degradation of energy. The very essence of a curriculum study involves the determination of the relative emphasis, sequence, and the interrelations of concepts and content.

One is reminded that a great Greek philosopher, perhaps the most scientific among them, Heracleitus, held that change was the central idea that explained all existence. In unforgettable words, he said: "No man ever steps into the same river twice." This rhetoric can, of course, be interpreted in two ways. It is never the same river, for the water has flowed unceasingly in the meantime, and on the second occasion the man steps into new water. If the river is the water, as well as the course it takes, the river is indeed never twice the same. This, I feel sure, is the way the physical scientist interprets the dictum of Heracleitus. The biologist, on the contrary, looks at the meaning rather differently. It is never the same man who steps into the river twice. He has lived, he has aged, he has changed in the meantime. He may have memories of the former man he once was, but his substance has been steadily and unceasingly exchanged and renewed, until after seven years or so there is perhaps no atom within him that was there at the beginning.

Here again, and because of the very comprehensiveness of this concept, the biologist must fear the mistaken emphasis. The change in the river is no more important than the change in the man. In fact, since science is an inescapably *human* way of looking at the phenomena of nature, including man himself, one might defend the view that the study of science should begin with the nature of man and proceed outward toward the larger and more distant environment. I do not wish to defend that position here, but I do regard it as defensible, and if it be accepted, where is then the value of attempting to force all statements of major scientific conceptualization into a strictly physical mold? If you put all of biology under three of seven concepts, and the three are themselves stated in a strictly physical way, does this formulation in no way imply that the place of the biological sciences in the science curriculum should be considerably less than a half share? If not—if study of the life sciences be admittedly more equal in value to the study of the physical sciences—then one of two courses of action lies open. One can, on the one hand, organize the course of study of the biological sciences and the physical sciences in relative independence, with as much coordination between them as is reasonable in the present era, but without losing sight in performing each task of the primacy of the particular biological or physical view. Or, on the other hand, one can attempt to organize the program of study into units that represent areas or problems of human experience, each of which might well involve both physical and biological content and points of view. In the past, our high school, college, and university instruction have been developed on the basis of the first type of curriculum planning. The junior high school, for almost a half century, has pursued the second type by means of a "general science" program. The danger of the first type of curriculum study and planning is fragmentation and uncoordinated rivalry between special parts of science. Botany and zoology compete for shares of time and attention. Inorganic and organic chemistry split the pie, and biochemistry is left out in the cold. Nuclear physics vies with mechanics and with thermodynamics for a larger place in the sun. These rivalries of fragmented, incomplete portions of a larger science are highly unfortunate in their effects and have been combatted by such groups as the Biological Sciences Curriculum Study. It is indeed appalling that a future high school teacher, while in training in college, in many institutions cannot find a basic course in which microorganisms, plants, and animals are all considered, and in which the principles of genetics can be learned by useful cross comparisons between the results of animal and plant crosses, without senseless duplications of the same subject matter in "zoological" and "botanical" courses; and it is horrifying and anachronistic that a student can study "biology" without learning on the one hand of its macromolecular foundations or on the other without discerning the principles of population growth or community interdependence. The interrelationship of the living system and its environment requires study and understanding at every level of organization from the molecular to the biome. The existing curriculum studies have accomplished much to prevent this kind of unbalance in the future.

In contrast, the attempt made by the Committee in its report to unify the treatment of all the sciences by reducing curriculum planning to the strictly physical point of view embodied in the seven concepts seems not only to be philosophically unsound but also educationally unwise. It is generally admitted that at present considerable improvement has been made in the preparation of more modern science courses in the secondary schools of the United States. A beginning is now being made in the development of science units for the elementary school. Very little is currently being done, however, to improve the teaching of science in the junior high school, generally acknowledged to be the weakest link in the chain of science education. It seems to me that a considerable effort must be made by several, or many, groups to prepare well-coordinated science programs, truly worthy of the name of science, for the seventh, eighth, and ninth grades. It is not likely that any single group of planners and writers, no matter how competent and how dedicated they may be, can alone achieve an ideal program in science for these school years. Rather than a monolithic, authoritative plan, let us rather try to develop a number of possible sequences and programs for these grades and then test them thoroughly in the schools. In my own opinion, the greatest need in these years is for development of a good physical science program that will make it possible for students to enter tenth-grade biology—BSCS or other—with a knowledge of the fundamental constitution of matter, of transformations of energy, and of chemical change, I also believe, however, that a considerable portion of the junior high school years should be devoted to biological study, and not on account of its scientific value only. Many students leave school upon completing the junior high school, and they, as future parents and citizens, like the rest of us, need some practical introduction to biology upon the basis of which they can make many of the future decisions so important to themselves as individuals, to their families, their communities, and their nation. The future of democratic society in a scientific age rests upon the ability of its individual citizens to appreciate the natural forces and phenomena that are the setting and the essence of man's biological existence, and to value the scientific way of investigating them. The power of man's civilization rests upon science today, and not alone on the conquest of the atom or the control of physical and chemical energies in the external environment. It rests equally upon a knowledge of man's own nature and of his one-ness with his environment, upon his knowledge of nutrition, disease, heredity, and the community of organisms. Man's freedom from the chains of superstition and ignorance depends fully as much upon Darwin, Mendel, and Pasteur as upon Copernicus, Galileo, Newton, and Einstein. We must therefore see that the junior high school curriculum is well balanced and not top-heavy with physical science. The danger of the Committee's formulation is exactly the latter. By emphasis and implication as much as by specific formulation, the physical sciences are thereby enthroned as the truly significant aspects of science, and the methods of the physical sciences as sufficiently representative of all the sciences.

For my part, I shall not try to formulate any great concepts that embrace all of the sciences on an equal footing. Perhaps, some day, it may be possible to do so, as the monist philosophers of ancient Greece dreamed it might be, and as Einstein in his later years endeavored to do. For curriculum planning in the elementary and secondary schools here and now, I shall be satisfied as a biologist to add to the seven great truths formulated by the Committee the more modest "themes" of the Biological Sciences Curriculum Study. These themes, in point of fact, we found to be of very little use in detailed curriculum planning. What they turned out to be were concepts that coursed through and permeated every chapter and verse of whatever we did, no matter what points of view and patterns of organization we attempted to develop. Whatever the emphasis of a particular BSCS "version," we found the same themes to be of constant significance. That is why, in the end, we called them "themes." Very likely, the seven major conceptual ideas formulated by the Committee will turn out to possess a similar character. They will be of little value in actually planning courses and programs in science education. They are scientific ideas that must be held securely in the mind, and must never be forgotten or ignored while a program of study in the physical sciences is being developed. They are not the sole or even the most appropriate themes for educators to keep constantly in mind while developing programs in biology, or for students to keep constantly in mind while studying biology. Nor are they in any way likely to be of value in securing a good balance of the biological and physical points of view in the practical work of selecting content, choosing emphases, and coordinating physical and biological concepts and methods, all so necessary in preparing an effective new science course at any educational level.

An Evaluation of the Conceptual Schemes Approach to Science Curriculum Development*

David P. Ausubel

Although some psychological considerations are pertinent to the consideration of the validity of the "conceptual schemes"[1] approach to the development of a science curriculum, the evaluation of the validity of this approach really lies more within the competence of a philosopher of science. Since I am primarily an educational and developmental psychologist, I am, properly speaking, out of my depth in discussing this problem with you. The basic issues involved in this assessment of validity are indeed more philosophical than they are psychological. Nevertheless, as a social scientist, I have my own particular biases in the philosophy of

*Reprinted from the *Journal of Research in Science Teaching*, V. 3, pp. 255–264 (1965). ©, by permission.

[1]The seven conceptual schemes formulated by the NSTA Curriculum Committee as a basis for science curriculum development in "Theory into Action" are as follows:

1. All matter is composed of units called fundamental particles; under certain conditions these particles can be transformed into energy and vice versa.

2. Matter exists in the form of units which can be classified into hierarchies of organization levels.

3. The behavior of matter in the universe can be described on a statistical basis.

4. Units of matter interact. The bases of all ordinary interactions are electromagnetic, gravitational, and nuclear forces.

5. All interacting units of matter tend toward equilibrium states in which the energy content (enthalpy) is a minimum and the energy distribution (entropy) is most random. In the process of attaining equilibrium, energy transformations or matter transformations or matter–energy transformations occur. Nevertheless, the sum of energy and matter in the universe remains constant.

6. One of the forms of energy is the motion of units of matter. Such motion is responsible for heat and temperature and for the states of matter: solid, liquid, and gaseous.

7. All matter exists in time and space and, since interactions occur among its units, matter is subject in some degree to changes with time. Such changes may occur at various rates and in various patterns.

science, and these will emerge quite unambiguously along with my discussion of the relevant psychological principles, both in classroom learning theory and in intellectual development.

THE PHILOSOPHICAL POSITION

My philosophical position, briefly put, is simply this: Even though there is undoubtedly some interdisciplinary overlapping between sciences with respect to both content and methodology, each particular discipline tends idiosyncratically to develop its own unifying concepts and undergirding themes, as well as its own scientific method, depending on its own idiosyncratic history, content, problems, objectives, and methodology.[2] Hence, any general statement of conceptual schemes that purportedly underlies *all* science is likely to be characterized by one or both of the following two features:

1. It is stated at such a high level of generality that it pertains more to the philosophy of science than to the phenomenological and conceptual levels at which science is actually conducted and taught. To be sure, it is explicitly stipulated that the seven Conceptual Schemes are not thought of "as topics for individual units or courses;" but even if this is true, their curriculum derivatives, if they are to apply to *all* science, must be of such a general nature as to be philosophical rather than substantive in character. Principles at this level of generality, in my opinion, are too abstract to be meaningful to elementary and high school students. The philosophy of science should not be taught to scientifically unsophisticated individuals. Before one can understand or formulate a philosophy of science, considerable sophistication in a wide variety of sciences and in the history of science is required. The qualification also applies, of course, to the professional philosopher of science if we expect him to distinguish between what is known *now* in the various disciplines, from what is truly *knowable* in these same fields as a function of their *inherent* properties and limitations.

Epistemology, in other words, is not only a function of the nature of a given discipline. It is also a function of the cognitive properties of the knower. In part, this is immutable—a reflection of genetically limited capacities for conceptualization, information processing, and problem

2The Committee preparing the NSTA position paper explicitly concedes this point in its preliminary statement by saying, "The process of science has no discernible rules . . . which no two scientists perform in precisely the same way." But it then goes on to lay down seven conceptual and five process themes that undergird all science. Throughout the document (*e.g.*, pp. 4, 9, 11, and 33) reference is made to *the* process of science and *the* conceptual schemes of science, as if science were a unitary and monolithic rather than a multiform enterprise.

solving. In part also, it is a reflection of cognitive maturity. As Piaget insists, there is such a thing as "genetic epistemology." What can be known at any given age level, therefore, is partly a function of the general maturity of the knower's cognitive processes, as well as of his over-all sophistication in science and in any particular scientific discipline. The latter qualification, of course, also applies to adults. In short, these seven Conceptual Schemes are not consonant with principles of genetic epistemology, that is, their level of generality presupposes more cognitive maturity and/or subject matter sophistication than is possessed by elementary and high school students. I agree with Paul Hurd that "it is wasteful to teach facts divorced from a meaningful concept." However, the issue at stake here is the level of generality of a concept that is meaningful to a student at a given level of cognitive maturity and subject matter sophistication.

2. The second typical feature characterizing a set of conceptual schemes purportedly applying to *all* science is that it applies *only* to the *limited* group of sciences represented by the disciplinary affiliations of the authors of the conceptual schemes in question. Thus, this particular set of conceptual schemes applies well to the physical sciences, hardly at all to the biological sciences, and still less well to psychology and the social sciences. I know that scientists other than those in the physical sciences participated in the preparation of this position paper. Hence, I find it difficult to understand how they were able to go along with it. The only explanation I can offer is that the physicists and chemists on the Committee were unusually persuasive. In my opinion, it would do students a great dis-service to lead them to believe that these same conceptual schemes apply equally well to all sciences, particularly the biological and social. Imagine what the resulting disenchantment would be!

One aspect of this position paper, however, that I can endorse without any qualification whatsoever, is its insistence that "uncertainties in science should be presented clearly and frequently to students" and that neither scientific fact nor theory are immutable.

Let me be more specific now about the Conceptual Schemes themselves. In my opinion, Conceptual Schemes I and II have little applicability to biology, psychology, or the social sciences. At most, these principles apply, for example, to psychology in a substrate rather than in an explanatory sense. For instance, suppose we are interested in ascertaining the nature of thought. Thought, in turn, depends upon the percepts and concepts available in the conscious field. These phenomena, in turn depend upon neuroanatomical and neurophysiological processes in neural tissues. At the same time, neural tissue conforms to the energy phenomena and metabolic requirements of all living matter. Living cells, in turn, are composed of complex protein molecules which, in turn, are composed of more fundamental physical particles. What these Conceptual Schemes fail to make explicit is that the laws governing the properties of lower levels in this hierarchy of phenomenology apply to the higher levels in only a substrate but not in an explanatory sense.

Ultimately, of course, thought depends in a substrate sense on the special anatomy and physiology of the brain and on general cellular metabolism. Dead men do not think and brain damage may distort thought processes. It is quite conceivable, however, that the nature of thought as a psychological process is *not* dependent in any way—explanatory-wise or substrate-wise—upon a particular set of corresponding neurophysiological processes, but only on the availability of the concepts and percepts involved, which, from a phenomenological standpoint, are obviously immaterial in nature. In other words, the ultimate substrate dependence of thought on the nervous system may be only indirect, that is, reflective of the dependence of percepts and concepts on an intact cerebral cortex. But phenomenologically speaking, percepts and concepts are entirely immaterial in nature despite this dependence; and it is not beyond the realm of probability that the manipulation of these immaterial conceptual entities in various thought patterns may, in turn, involve purely immaterial processes that conform to purely psychological laws, and involve cerebral physiology only insofar as various associative pathways are structurally and functionally intact.

The third Conceptual Scheme, with respect to the statistical description of the behavior of matter, has a little more relevance for biology and psychology. But even here its relevance is vitiated by the choice of an unfortunate example, i.e., Mendelian laws of heredity. It is asserted that "on the basis of the Mendelian laws, it is possible to predict the distribution of characteristics among a significant population of offspring." Actually, Mendelian laws predict the distribution of only those traits that are uniformly or dichotomously distributed in a given species, that is, determined by single-gene effects. Most normal and pathological traits, on the other hand, are normally distributed and are determined by polygenic rather than by single-gene or Mendelian principles.

The fourth Conceptual Scheme regarding the interaction among units of matter has only farfetched applicability to the behavior of living organisms. Consider the statement that "the behavior of a worm or a human being can be predicted best in terms of exchanges of energy and information between the organism and the environment." Here exchanges of energy and information between organism and environment are blithely considered qualitatively comparable, whereas actually there is a world of difference between them, particularly at the human level where information is largely symbolic in nature.

The fifth Conceptual Scheme (regarding equilibrium states) also has only remote reference to behavior, especially at the mammalian level. The easiest way to maintain behavioral equilibrium is to remain cognitively inert. But curiosity, venturesomeness, groping for new knowledge, and the drives for competence and mastery represent deliberate efforts to destroy existing equilibrium states. The restoration of homeostatic equilibrium through such drives as hunger and thirst, on the other hand, is now regarded as a relatively unimportant source of activity among human beings and other primate species.

The application of kinetic and electric field theory to the selective diffusion of molecules across such semipermeable membranes as the placenta and the kidney tubules (as proposed in the sixth Conceptual Scheme) also has more substrate than explanatory value. In multicellular organisms the determinative variables regulating the differential diffusion of various electrolytes across semipermeable membranes are typically hormonal or enzymatic in nature.

Similarly, the application of the seventh Conceptual Scheme to biological, behavioral, and social processes constitutes little more than a platitudinous truism that has no explanatory value whatsoever for changes occurring over time. Lastly, the five "major items in the process of science" are stated at such a high level of generality as to constitute part of the philosophy of science. For any particular science they have little explanatory value either for the inquiry process itself or for the methodology of that science.

The Psychological Argument

A parallel psychological case revolving about the nature of problem solving and transfer can be made against the seven Conceptual Schemes. The position paper emphasizes that "because we are interested in *how* the pupil gains knowledge and understanding, the implication of cognitive processes for curriculum development must be considered." In this respect, the underlying basis of the Conceptual Schemes has obviously been influenced by Bruner's notion of the "heuristics of discovery." Once the heuristics of discovery have been mastered they constitute, according to Bruner, "a state of problem-solving or inquiry that serves for any kind of task one may encounter." Similarly, Suchman's Inquiry Training Program "is not proposed as a new way to teach science, but as a way of teaching basic cognitive skills . . . (that belong) in the science program and in every other curriculum area that requires . . . reasoning and the formulation and testing of hypotheses." [2]

The principal difficulty with this approach, as the faculty psychologists discovered, is that critical-thinking ability can be enhanced only within the context of a specific discipline. Grand strategies of discovery, like scientific method, do not seem to be transferable *across* disciplinary lines—either when acquired within a given discipline or when learned in a more general form apart from specific subject-matter content. This principle has been confirmed by countless studies, and is illustrated by the laughable errors of logic and judgment committed by distinguished scientists who wander outside their own disciplines. The only kinds of transfer that have been empirically demonstrated in problem-solving situations are the transfer of specific skills, the transfer of general principles, and the transfer of general approach or orientation to a specified class of problems. Hence, critical thinking cannot be taught as a generalized ability; in practice it can be enhanced only by adopting a precise, analytical, and critical approach to the teaching of a *particular* discipline, an approach that fosters appreciation of scientific method in *that* discipline. Also, from a purely theoretical standpoint alone, it hardly seems plausible that a strategy of inquiry or a set of conceptual schemes, which must necessarily be broad enough to be applicable to a wide range of disciplines and problems, can ever have, at the same time, sufficient particular relevance to be helpful in the understanding of a specific principle or the solution of the specific problem at hand. And from the standpoint of elementary and high school pupils, one wonders whether conceptual schemes or principles of inquiry pitched at this level of abstraction could *ever* be meaningful enough to be used successfully in problem solving and in acquiring understanding of scientific subject matter.

Much of this "heuristics of discovery" orientation to the teaching of science is implied by the view that the principal objectives of science instruction are the acquisition of general inquiry skills, appropriate attitudes about science, and training in the operations of discovery. Implicit OR explicit in this approach is the belief either that the particular choice of subject matter chosen to implement these goals is a matter of indifference (as long as it is suitable for the operations of inquiry), or that somehow, in the course of performing a series of unrelated experiments in depth, the learner acquires all of the really important subject matter he needs to know. Thus, Hibbs states:

> It does not matter whether the student learns any particular set of facts, but it does matter whether he learns how much fun it is to learn— to observe and experiment, to question and analyze the world without any ready-made set of answers and without any premium on the accuracy of his factual results, at least in the field of science. [3]

And Suchman contends that

> more basic than the attainment of concepts is the ability to inquire and discover them autonomously . . . The schools must have a new pedagogy

with a new set of goals which subordinates retention to thinking. Instead of devoting their efforts to storing information and recalling it on demand, they would be developing the cognitive functions needed to seek out and organize information in a way that would be most productive of new concepts. [2]

Finally, Paul Hurd in this position paper contends:

> To state the goals of science education is to describe the cognitive skills expected in the student rather than the knowledge assumed essential to attaining these skills.

All of this implies, of course, that the inquiry process *per se* in science education is more important than the acquisition of a particular body of knowledge.

In my opinion, any science curriculum worthy of the name must be concerned with the systematic presentation of an organized body of knowledge as an explicit end in itself. Even if it is relatively superficial and organized on an intuitive basis, as it must be in the elementary school, the science curriculum should make a start in this direction and give the student a feeling for science as a selectively and sequentially organized structure of knowledge. This is no less important than imparting the view that science is a method of inquiry.

It is also somewhat unrealistic to expect that subject-matter content can be acquired incidentally as a by-product of problem-solving or discovery experience, as in the typical activity program or project method. Such incidental teaching pays too little attention to graded and systematically organized content, to substantive and programatic aspects of presentation, and to practice and feedback variables.

The development of problem-solving ability is, of course, a legitimate and significant educational objective in its own right. Hence, it is highly defensible to utilize a certain proportion of classroom time in developing appreciation of and facility in the use of scientific methods of inquiry and of other empirical, inductive, and deductive problem-solving procedures. But this is a far cry from advocating that the enhancement of problem-solving ability is the major function of the school. The goals of the science student and the goals of the scientist are not identical. Hence, students cannot learn science effectively by enacting the role of junior scientist.

> The scientist is engaged in a full-time search for new general or applied principles in his field. The student, on the other hand, is primarily engaged in an effort to learn the same basic subject matter in this field which the scientist learned in his student days, and also to learn something of the method and spirit of scientific inquiry. Thus, while it makes perfectly good sense for the scientist to work full-time formulating and testing new hypotheses, it is quite indefensible . . . for the student to

. . . (do) the same thing . . . If he is ever to discover he must first learn; and he cannot learn adequately by pretending he is a junior scientist.

To acquire facility in problem-solving and scientific method it is also unnecessary for learners to rediscover every principle in the syllabus. Since problem-solving ability is itself transferable, at least within a given subject-matter field, facility gained in independently formulating and applying one generalization is transferable to other problems in the same discipline. Furthermore, overemphasis on developing problem-solving ability would ultimately defeat its own ends. (Because of its time-consuming aspects) it would leave students with insufficient time in which to learn the content of a discipline; and hence, despite their adeptness at problem-solving they would be unable to solve simple problems involving the application of such content.

Under these circumstances, students would fail to acquire the minimal degree of subject-matter sophistication in a given discipline that is necessary for abstract intellectual functioning in that discipline, much less make original research contributions to science.

DEVELOPMENTAL CONSIDERATIONS

One major concern of the NSTA Position Paper "is with identifying the broad principles that can apply to *any or all* curriculum development efforts in science. It calls attention to the aspects or issues of science teaching and the most promising approaches in each area, and encourages the development of a coordinated curriculum, based on them from kindergarten through grade 12 and beyond."

The implication here is that the same seven Conceptual Schemes are equally useful for curriculum programs at *all* age levels, except perhaps for differences in the level of abstraction at which materials are presented. How warranted is this assumption? I am not so sure that the same "big ideas" can be grasped in kindergarten as in grade 12. This assumption in the position paper again relies heavily on Bruner's conception that *any* subject can be taught meaningfully to students at *any* grade level, provided that one takes account of the child's developmental level of cognitive functioning.

By suitably adapting methods of teaching to the child's level of cognitive functioning, both Bruner and Inhelder believe that it is possible to teach preschool and primary school children any subject that can be taught to adolescent students. It is quite possible, of course, that prior intuitive understanding of certain concepts during childhood could facilitate their learning and stabilize their retention when they are taught at a more formal, abstract level during adolescence. In fact, this procedure may be the most effective means of discouraging rote memorization of verbally presented propositions in the secondary school.

However, it undoubtedly overstates the case to claim that *any* subject can be taught to children in the preoperational stage or in the stage of concrete operations provided that the material is presented in an informal, intuitive fashion with the aid of overt manipulation or concrete–empirical props. It is readily conceivable that some topics, such as "set-theory" in mathematics, can be successfully learned by fourth-grade pupils when recast in accordance with their characteristic ways of thinking and conceptualizing experience. This hardly rules out the possibility, however, that the comprehension of many other ideas presupposes a certain minimal level of life experience, cognitive maturity, and subject-matter sophistication, or that some ideas simply cannot be expressed without the use of certain higher-order abstractions. These latter kinds of concepts would be *intrinsically* too difficult for preschool and primary school children *irrespective* of the method of presentation. Moreover, even assuming that all abstract–verbal concepts could be restructured on an intuitive basis, it would still be unreasonable to expect that they could *all* be made comprehensible to children at any age level. Although the intuitive comprehensibility of any given restructured idea is best determined empirically, it would surely be plausible on a *priori* grounds to expect that a certain proportion of these ideas could *not* be rendered understandable to typical pupils in some of the preschool and elementary grades. [7]

The position paper also contends, on theoretical grounds, that "concepts are most easily acquired when familiar and concrete perceptual materials are used," but then goes on to endorse many practices that are obviously inconsistent with this precept at the elementary school level of instruction. The elementary-school child is completely dependent upon current or recently prior concrete–empirical experience for the meaningful understanding or manipulation of relational propositions. He tends to appreciate relationships between abstractions intuitively— as rather immediate logical extensions of his own personal experience, rather than in the truly abstract sense of relationships between general variables. [8] Hence, general laws and methodological canons of science, in their own right, have little meaning and intellectual appeal for him; they make sense only insofar as they are relatable to more tangible types of experience. "Utility" is a major example of this type of experience, but is certainly not the only possible example.

As far as elementary school children are concerned, therefore, one cannot hope to reduce science to "first principles" and basic abstract laws. [9] At the very best, one can strive for a semiabstract, intuitive grasp of these laws on a descriptive and manipulative level that is tied to particularized experience. On the methodological side, abstract principles of scientific inquiry and strategy also have much less meaning for children than a purely concrete–empirical explanation of how it is possible for mankind to know the facts and generalizations under discussion. [10]

Similarly, the suggestion that sciences be studied in the order of their phenomenological complexity, i.e., that one start with "the basic concepts of physics and chemistry before tackling the complex phenomena of biology and geology" [11] is logically sound but psychologically unfeasible. More important pedagogically than the logical structure of knowledge is the pupil's intellectual readiness to handle different kinds of subject matter; and from the standpoint of relevant experience and readiness, the phenomenologically "simple" laws of physics are far more abstract and difficult than the phenomenologically "complex" laws of biology and geology which are so much closer to every-day experience. This is not to deny the possibility that some aspects of physics might be profitably introduced in the elementary-school curriculum. However, before this could be done in the "rigorous fashion (physics) deserves," the teaching of elementary school mathematics would first have to be sufficiently improved to make possible a more functional intuitive understanding of the quantitative relationships that figure so prominently in the physical sciences. [11]

On the other hand, the position paper's endorsement of the concrete–perceptual approach to science teaching is entirely too generalized and unqualified. It fails to take account of important developmental changes that occur in cognitive functioning beginning with the adolescent period. At the high school level and beyond, *routine* reliance on current or recently prior concrete–empirical props is necessary neither for understanding abstract principles nor for solving abstract problems. Expository verbal teaching through definition and other forms of verbal exposition becomes much more feasible at this age. The dangers of "verbalization without understanding" are not nearly as great as Hurd seems to imply.

BREADTH VERSUS DEPTH

Many factors counsel a choice of breadth over depth in the content of elementary school science. First, from a logistical standpoint, the young child is not prepared for depth of subject matter coverage. His limited attention span and his dependence on concrete-empirical props slow down greatly his rate of learning new material, thereby making it difficult for him to assimilate a wide array of information about a given topic; and the paucity of higher-order abstractions in his cognitive structure and the particularized, semiabstract, and relatively imprecise nature of his concepts detract from his ability to organize and integrate this material in usable fashion. Second, because both his intellect and personality are still relatively uncrystallized and lacking in self-consistency, the elementary-school child is a "generalist." It is appropriate, therefore, to diversify the range of intellectual stimulation as widely as possible, because only in this way can all of the diverse potentialities both within a group of children and within a single child be brought to fruition. A broad curriculum, within the limits of pedagogic soundness, makes it possible for more pupils to experience success in the performance of school activities, and hence to develop the necessary self-confidence and motivation for continued academic striving and achievement.

Breadth, of course, inevitably implies a certain amount of superficiality. This superficiality, however, is not necessarily opprobrious. Whether it is desirable or undesirable cannot be judged in absolute terms, but only in relation to the student's intellectual readiness for depth. It should also be pointed out in this connection that superficiality itself is always a relative state of affairs; the graduate-school curriculum is just as superficial to the post-doctoral scholar as the elementary-school curriculum is to the college undergraduate. The spiral curriculum—the reintroduction of the same topics in progressively greater depth as intellectual readiness and maturity increase—is predicated on this assumption.

Superficiality is also not synonymous with triviality or with slipshod, unsystematic, or outdated teaching. Good teaching is as thorough as is possible at the appropriate level of breadth and depth: and even at the elementary-school level it allows for the occasional introduction of atypical depth, both substantively and methodologically, to give the student a taste of scholarship and of research inquiry. But, as will be pointed out later, the probing in depth of isolated areas, apart from the systematic presentation of subject matter—merely as a means of enhancing inquiry skills or methodological sophistication—is indefensible at any age level, and particularly in the elementary school. It is a type of activity suitable for the scholar and research scientist—*after* he has acquired substantive and methodological sophistication in his field. [12]

The Role of the Laboratory in Science Education

This brings us to the role of the laboratory in science education. I agree wholeheartedly with the authors of the position paper that

a heavy emphasis should be placed on the nature of science or the *process* by which new knowledge is obtained. Instruction should be planned to develop understanding of the basic ideas of science concomitant with the appreciation of the methods of science; these two aspects should not be treated independently.

The trouble with this statement, in my opinion, is that it is not sufficiently explicit. It emphasizes the role of the laboratory in teaching the process of science, and the importance of coordinating laboratory and expository instruction. They certainly should not be treated independently. But it is necessary, in my opinion, to be much more explicit about the respective roles of laboratory and expository teaching in transmitting knowledge of subject-matter content, on the one hand, and understanding of scientific methodology, on the other. *Primary* responsibility for transmitting the content of science should be delegated to teacher and textbook, whereas primary responsibility for transmitting appreciation of scientific method should be delegated to the laboratory. This does not imply, however, that laboratory and classroom should be uncoordinated or that related substantive and methodological principles should not be considered together whenever relevant.

Yet, science courses at all academic levels are traditionally organized so that students waste many valuable hours in the laboratory collecting and manipulating empirical data which, at the very best, help them rediscover or exemplify principles that the instructor could present verbally and demonstrate visually in a matter of minutes. Hence, although laboratory work can easily be justified on the grounds of giving students some appreciation of the spirit and methods of scientific inquiry, and of promoting problem-solving, analytic, and generalizing ability, it is a very time-consuming and inefficient practice for routine purposes of teaching subject-matter content or of illustrating principles, where didactic exposition or simple demonstration are perfectly adequate. Knowledge of the methods whereby data and principles in a particular discipline are acquired need not necessarily be gained in *all* instances through self-discovery in the laboratory. In many situations, this purpose can be accomplished much more efficiently through didactic exposition in conjunction with demonstrations and paper-and-pencil exercises.

Laboratory work in the present context refers to inductive discovery experience and should not be confused with demonstrations and simple exercises. Nevertheless, it involves a *contrived* type of discovery that is very different from the truly autonomous discovery activities of the research scholar and scientist. The immature or unsophisticated student is only confused by the natural complexities of raw, unselected, and unsystematized data. Before he can discover concepts and generalizations efficiently, the problem must be structured for him, and the available procedures and methods of handling data must be skillfully "arranged" by others, that is, simplified, selectively schematized, and sequentially organized in such a way as to make ultimate discovery almost inevitable. Occasional independent design of experiments may have a salutary effect in conveying the actual spirit of scientific inquiry, but should hardly be a routine procedure.

Thus, in dividing the labor of scientific instruction, the laboratory typically carries the burden of conveying the method and spirit of science, whereas the textbook and teacher assume the burden of transmitting subject-matter content. The laboratory, however, should be carefully integrated with the textbook; it should deal with methodology related to the subject-matter content of the course and not with experiments chosen solely because of their suitability for illustrating various strategies of discovery. It goes without saying of course, that laboratory methods should be used only when the underlying methodology and substantive principles are thoroughly understood, rather than followed mechanically in cook-book fashion. [12]

SUMMARY AND CONCLUSIONS

In my opinion, on philosophical grounds, no set of conceptual schemes or principles of scientific method are applicable to *all* science. Each science has its own idiosyncratic undergirding themes and methods of inquiry. An all-encompassing set of conceptual themes is likely to be characterized (*1*) by a level of generality that is reminiscent of the philosophy of science, and hence beyond the cognitive maturity and scientific sophistication of elementary and high school students; and (*2*) by only farfetched relevance and applicability to many scientific disciplines. The seven Conceptual Schemes prepared by the NSTA Curriculum Committee are characterized by both of these features. They are both stated at a level of generality that has little applicability to the phenomenological and conceptual levels at which science is actually conducted and taught, and are applicable at this philosophical level to the physical sciences but not to the biological, behavioral, and social sciences.

Psychologically, little transfer, either in the understanding of scientific propositions or in problem solving, is possible across interdisciplinary fields. Hence, a science curriculum at the elementary-school level that stresses the "heuristics of discovery," and ignores substantive content as an end in itself, is psychologically and pedagogically unsound.

From a developmental standpoint the seven Conceptual Schemes are not equally suitable for *all* age levels; some subject-matter principles cannot be transmitted to young children no matter how they are presented. Routine reliance on concrete–empirical experience is unnecessary both for problem-solving purposes and for transmitting scientific subject-matter content to adolescent pupils. At the elementary-school level, on the other hand, the child's dependence on concrete–empirical experience makes unfeasible such suggestions as teaching him "first principles," basic abstract laws, or methodological canons of science either at the level of generality contemplated in this position paper or divorced from his everyday experience. Similarly unfeasible psychologically is the proposal to teach sciences in the "order of their phenomenological complexity."

The principal function of the laboratory is not to transmit subject-

298

matter content or to demonstrate principles of science on an audio–visual basis, but to teach scientific method. Curriculums in science must also be concerned with transmitting organized bodies of knowledge rather than with the mere development of inquiry skills in which subject matter content is only of incidental concern in the development of such skills.

The solution to the problem of curriculum development in science lies not in abandoning the "conceptual schemes" approach. This would be throwing away the baby with the bath water. This approach is philosophically, psychologically, and pedagogically sound provided that it is *modified* so that a *separate* set of conceptual schemes is made available for each particular discipline. To seek one set of conceptual schemes that attempts to encompass all science is as illusory as seeking the fountain of youth or the philosopher's stone.

REFERENCES

1. Bruner, J. S., "The Act of Discovery," *Harvard Educ. Rev.*, **31**, 21–32 (1961).
2. Suchman, J. R., "Inquiry Training: Building Skills for Autonomous Discovery," *Merrill-Palmer Quart., Behav. Develpmt.*, **7**, 148–167 (1961).
3. Hibbs, A. R., "Science for Elementary Students," *Teachers College Record*, **63**, 136–142 (1961).
4. Ausubel, D. P., "Learning by Discovery: Rationale and Mystique," *Bull. Nat. Ass. Sec. Sch. Teachers*, **45**, 18–58 (1961).
5. Ausubel, D. P., "In Defense of Verbal Learning," *Educ. Theory*, **11**, 15–25 (1961).
6. Bruner, J. S., *The Process of Education*, Harvard University Press, Cambridge, Mass., 1960.
7. Ausubel, D. P., "Can Children Learn Anything that Adults Can—and More Efficiently?" *Elem. Sch. J.*, **62**, 270–272 (1962).
8. Inhelder, B., and J. Piaget, *The Growth of Logical Thinking from Childhood to Adolescence*, Basic Books, New York, 1958.
9. (a) Karplus, R., "Beginning a Study in Elementary School Science," *Amer. J. Phys.*, **30**, 1–9 (1962) and (b) M. H. Shamos ("Science for Citizens," *Sat. Rev.*, Sept. 16, 1961), as well as (c) the NSTA position paper (pp. 7, 18), deplore the emphasis in elementary-science education upon the practical utilitarian aspects of science and the attempt "to relate science primarily to everyday experience." They advocate, instead, stress upon the concepts and methods of science.
10. Atkin, J. M., and S. P. Wyatt (*Astronomy: Charting the Universe*, trial edition, University Illinois, Urbana, Illinois, 1961) emphasize the "how we know" aspects of astronomy, using didactic exposition and simple exercises and demonstrations.
11. Reference 9b.
12. Ausubel, D. P., "Some Psychological Considerations in the Objectives and Design of an Elementary School Science Program," *Sci. Educ.*, **47**, 278–284 (1963).

Science in the
Total Framework of Instruction

In the present days of emphasis on science it is well to examine the problem of how important scientific literacy is to people. If science is important, how can science teaching be more nearly directed into the mainstream of life, and how can science curricula be better integrated into the overall framework of public education? Should the humanities and arts continue to be neglected as has been increasingly true during the past few years? What are some basic values and goals toward which science educators should strive?

Science, Heuristics, and Humanism*

Donald W. Stotler

The newer post-Sputnik approaches in science education have served us well. They have met the immediate challenge while providing us with springboards to the future. We have devoted so much time to the installation of these springboards, however, that all too little time has been devoted to what lies beyond. What are we diving into? Let us consider what can be done now to prepare for changes which will take place during the next three decades, less than half the expected lifetime of today's citizen.

As we look ahead, it is not enough to teach the science processes typically used today. Leading scientists are pointing out modifications needed in the science enterprise, such as:

1. *Increased mental agility in moving from one's own science discipline or interacting system to others.* This should result in increasingly interrelated science disciplines.

2. *More vision in seeing one's own specialty as a part of the cosmological whole.* This should help illuminate values and purpose in life.

3. *Greater willingness to use science processes in the social arena and in one's own life.* This should aid in liberating mankind for the art of full living. Peter Odegard has pointed out that, "Rationally induced changes in human behavior are as reasonable, and as scientific, as rationally induced changes in the physical environment.[1]

*Reprinted from *The Science Teacher*, V. 32, No. 7, Oct., 1965, pp. 28–31. ©, by permission.

[1]Peter Odegard. Editorial, "The Social Sciences and Society." *Science*, 145:1127. September 11, 1964. Excerpted from *The Educational Record*, 45:190. 1964.

4. Increased recognition of the stimulus to learning and creativity which is provided by an esthetic environment. This should lead to science laboratories more enlivened by art, music, recreation, and the comforts of life.

Such modifications will tend to merge the two main goals of science education—namely (1) to teach the nature of the science enterprise to future scientists and (2) to produce science-literate citizens who can cope with modern problems. How can this important merger be hastened? It would seem that those of us in science education are obligated to direct science more nearly into the mainstream of life. Aren't the warm sentiments of science as important as its cold sediment of facts and concepts? Can't we do more to create and sustain values and purpose in the lives of people?

The place to begin is where we are. What is the nature of our raw material, the newborn child? How is he enabled to fit into his culture? The child emerges physically as a brain, sense organs, acting mechanisms, and viscera. At birth he is also provided an ill-fitting garment— the physical universe. Two general bequests, one individual and one cultural, help him grow into this ill-fitting garment: (1) The *individual bequest* is already programed into each child at birth as a result of evolutionary processes. It consists of a set of fundamental tools for learning—curiosity, initiative, and experimental-mindedness. This human birthright need never be formally taught if the individual is liberated to use his learning tools under mature guidance. To the extent the tools are blunted, the human race is, in a real sense, subverted. (2) The *cultural bequest* consists of human values and knowledge. Most often they are simply imposed at the expense of the individual's birthright. This makes him less creative and adaptable, and therefore mankind is less creative and adaptable.

It seems clear that an ideology is successful to the extent that it provides some means of creative self-renewal for one and all. Long-term success requires that revolutionary ideas be actively sought out, carefully tested, and then acted upon. This keeps the stream of events moving fast enough and broad enough to prevent log jams and sporadic, revolutionary breakup. The ideology which can produce the most new ideas in the least amount of time and put them to the most productive use will be most likely to prevail. Will this not be the ideology which can weave the birth bequest of curiosity, initiative, experimental-mindedness, and the cultural bequest of knowledge and values most harmoniously into the whole man?

Obviously new speculation about the role of science education is needed, even at the risk of oversimplification. Speculation concerning the influence of population mobility on education will serve as the underlying theme of this presentation. The problem of population mobility is at least as important as the population and knowledge explosions with which most of us are more familiar. Comparing people to molecules, our population will, in a few decades, change from its present semifluid state to a highly interactive gaseous state. This mobility will not be related mainly to employment. Most will result from the normal pursuit of cultural variety, which is becoming the hallmark of this century. The problem of students moving from school to school during the school year calls for careful thought lest mankind become the victim rather than the instrument of change.

CURRICULUM WITHOUT
A SET BEGINNING OR END

In order to meet the student mobility challenge, we must provide classrooms where the learning is organized to unfold without a set beginning, middle, or end. In such a classroom each learner would simply enter the room, begin where he is, and progress as far and as fast as he is able in terms of the circumstances. What can be done to enhance these circumstances? Based upon my own experience in the summer of 1964 at both Alaska Methodist University and Indiana University, I believe that the challenge can be met in the education of teachers by programing the classroom environment and then freeing the individual to learn on his own within the boundaries of certain ground rules. This allows learning to be more self-initiated, self-paced, and self-corrected. Presumably, it would work as well with youth.

In fact, so little is known about how individuals learn that it would probably be wiser for us to program the environment rather than the individual, even if the pressure of population mobility were not on the horizon. The following conditions are recommended for setting up specific experimental trials of this approach, whether for teacher education or regular classroom:

Environment. The room should be completely flexible and multipurpose, with adequate areas for storage, laboratory work, and library, and esthetically pleasing and comfortable. An esthetic learning environment seems to complement Jacob Bronowski's definition of science—"the attempt to find in the complexity of nature something which is simple and beautiful."

Objectives. Two general objectives, inclusive of the more typical ones, are made clear at the beginning: Each person is to improve in his ability (1) *to search* and (2) *to help others to search.*

Time. The group should meet long enough to let life move through the room more as it is naturally lived. Time blocks of no less than two hours and preferably three are needed to get equipment organized for research and to gain some learning continuity and momentum.

Freedoms. Since the responsibilities in this approach are formidable, it would be well first to clarify the freedoms—which are the essence of the freedoms enjoyed by research scientists. Each person is encouraged to:

1. Start with what he knows.
2. Select for study something within his environment about which he is curious.
3. Change his investigation at any time.
4. Select his own reading within preselected limits.
5. Group and ungroup in terms of his own initiative and the circumstances involved.
6. Have free access to audio-visual aids (including teaching machines), equipment, tools, and supplies as long as they are used in a safe, nondisruptive way.
7. Seek consultant help from others in the room and from outside experts.
8. Arrange excursions beyond the laboratory.
9. Serve as delegate if his group needs feedback from some outside activity in which he is interested.
10. Do the kind and amount of outside work necessary.

Responsibilities. Freedom within the science enterprise, like all freedom, is sustained through the responsible action of its practitioners. The following responsibilities should be made very clear to the group:

1. While it is not specified *what* materials and problems each learner investigates, it is specified that each use his environment persistently to gain the two main objectives—*how to search* and *how to help others search*. Like a scientist, each should be engaged in an experiment-centered search for predictability. Since all research is based upon sampling, the push is for a sampling adequate for predictability.

2. Each learner should keep a science-style daily log of his own design, and, like a scientist, write at least one scientific paper based upon the data recorded in the log. This is then presented in one of the science conclaves held by the group for this purpose.

3. While the research is going on, the group is responsible for organizing and maintaining its working environment.

4. Besides the responsibility of probing for insight into one or more of the environmental diversities, the learner also must share new insights with others.

Besides learning science and citizenship by "sciencing" in a more life-like setting, the group plays its ideas against the larger cosmological picture. A game is made of seeing whether any insight can be raised which cannot be related to the growing pool of other insights offered.

The push is toward an economy of explanation. These sessions tend to provide an intellectual flexibility which permits movement from one construct or system to another.

The learner furnishes the initiative in pursuing the elusive diversity and establishing patterns which can be applied to new situations and extended to larger patterns. The *learned* (the teacher), by his questions and consultative help, brings about the explanation of more phenomena with fewer generalizations. This recognizes that the logic of the learner and the learned may be quite different. No insistence is made that clear, precise, statements of concepts be verbalized at the inference sessions.

In this way, the learner's birthright of curiosity, initiative, and experimental-mindedness is less bruised and more used while his knowledge and value system are elevated toward the level of sophistication of the learned. This "unverbalized awareness" approach, according to studies such as the one by Hendrix,[2] leads to more power in later transfer of learning than either "tell-and-do" on the one hand or "conscious generalization" on the other.

Concepts. If the underlying goal for the group is the search for experiment-based predictability and ways to get others involved in the search, will concept development be neglected? In the first place, an overemphasis on a pre-arranged story or fixed sequence of concepts to be discovered may have its own dangers. Aldous Huxley pointed out the need "to look at the world directly and not through the half opaque medium of concepts, which distorts every given fact into the all too familiar likeness of some generic label or explanatory abstraction."

The problem is *not* whether there is a learning structure. Learning *is* the process of structuring. The problem is, who does the structuring? By studying relative disorder to achieve order and predictability, the learner builds his own sequence. This is not to say that the teacher is passive. As the group gets launched with its own dynamics, the teacher, after the manner of Louis Agassiz, places more and more of his intellectual resources at the learner's disposal at critical junctures without becoming directive.

It is suggested the teacher keep in mind the advice of Alfred North Whitehead who said, "Let the main ideas which are introduced into a child's education be few and important, and let them be thrown into every combination possible." The NSTA publication *Theory Into Action in Science Curriculum Development* can serve admirably as the teacher's main guide to these few and important ideas. In other words, the basic ideas presented in *Theory Into Action* can serve as the target in the teacher's mind toward which the group is shooting in its inference

[2]Gertrude Hendrix. "A New Clue to Transfer of Training." *Elementary School Journal*, 48:197–208. December 1947.

sessions as they generate more and more explanations with fewer and fewer generalizations.

Evaluation. Much of the dynamics in this approach is produced by making the means of evaluation explicit at the first session. Evaluation for elementary school teachers, for example, might be:

1. Teacher observation concerning the individual's use of his birthright of curiosity, initiative, and experimental-mindedness.

2. Teacher observation concerning the effectiveness with which the individual used his log as a basis for feedback and direction in his day-to-day learning.

3. The appropriateness of the paper drawn from his log.

4. Ability to use in a new context the interacting skills of observation, classification, interpretation, and experimentation. The enrollees may be told that four skills will be tested the last day by having objects at certain centers in the room—(1) to observe, (2) to classify, (3) to develop theories about, and (4) to make use of in experiments. For learners with more sophisticated backgrounds in science, the behaviors set forth for evaluation would be more sophisticated.

Is such an approach compatible with population mobility? At the two summer institutes referred to earlier it was evident that several similar institutes could have been conducted simultaneously in different rooms. As long as some system was developed to account for the whereabouts of the learners and to see that too many didn't show up at the same institute at once, they could just as well have been free to migrate. It might even have enhanced the learning, for one important skill in a highly mobile population will be the ability to move from one environment to another with a maximum of continuity and minimum of trauma.

EDUCATIONAL CONTINUITY AND THE COMPUTER

However, if we are to move into a year-round school program with students moving frequently from one school to another throughout the nation—and even internationally—there is a need for additional mechanisms. For one thing, how can overcrowding of certain schools be prevented? Here certain hotel chains might provide a clue. Some have an electronically interlaced computer service. The location and numbers of room vacancies in the system are immediately available.

In addition to knowing how many students are coming in a given day, there is a need for attendance and other students records to be available to the personnel of that school. This could be provided by a computer system. In fact, an appropriate name for this system might be TAG (Teachers Automated Guide). It would be the "tag" that permitted continuity as students moved from school to school. Available to teachers could be consoles, connected electronically with one or more central computers and consisting of (1) a TV screen, (2) a device to print anything which appears on the screen when desired, and (3) a message input mechanism for feedback to the computer. TAG might be programed to respond to the following questions:

THE INDIVIDUAL

1. What main science experience has Johnnie had?
2. What behavioral skill might Johnnie profitably learn next?
3. What subject matter in terms of interacting systems (man-discovered and man-created) is suitable for Johnnie to probe while acquiring a given behavioral skill?
4. How can I evaluate to see if Johnnie has learned a given behavioral skill—and can use it in a new context?

HIS GROUP

5. At about what behavioral level is the group as a whole?
6. In what subject area is the group as a whole most interested?
7. Given a content area and a behavioral level, what would be a good "guestimate" for a science bookshelf? Equipment and supplies? Audio-visual material? Field trips? Resource people?
8. What is available, for example, in astronomy at various levels?

TAG seemingly should be programed using the following criteria:

1. Alternatives, not directives (the teacher, not the device, should be the decision maker).
2. Learning sequences based upon increasingly sophisticated behavioral skills.
3. A wide variety of content areas to select as vehicles for learning a given behavioral skill.
4. Suggested doing activities rather than memorizing.
5. Progressively greater insight into a few important ideas (such as those listed in *Theory Into Action*).
6. Progressively greater insight into those processes which have led to these few important ideas (processes such as those listed in *Theory Into Action* by NSTA).
7. Suggested laboratory activities which draw upon both quantitative and qualitative relationships.
8. An integration of method and content through suggested laboratory activities.
9. Useful data concerning individual students.
10. A framework which would not need to be drastically reorganized if other disciplines were to be included.

TAG should provide an ideal access to Whitehead's recommendations that the main ideas taught should be few and important but *thrown into every possible combination.* The newer approaches in science, if divided into separate open-ended "scholarly bits," could be sorted by a computer into the needed "every possible combination."

HUMANISM VS TECHNOLOGICAL PRESSURES

In order to program TAG so it can yield scholarly bits concerning all of the observed universe and at different conceptual levels, the scholars from all disciplines will have to be brought together repeatedly to interact with educators. The tendency in this interplay will be the explanation of more phenomena and fewer generalizations.

TAG may also have significance for emerging nations. Could a computer feed modern curriculum to consoles in smaller rural schools without the necessity of the large, factory-like schools now used in the more technologically advanced nations? We won't know until such experiments are tried.

In one sense if TAG succeeded, chances would be good for generating the newest ideas in the least amount of time and putting them to the most productive use. The question then might be "Could the individual stand the pace and withstand the feeling of being a lost migrant in a knowledge and population explosion?"

The answer to this may be that if new ideas are really put to the most productive use, the individual will be provided humanistic retreats from overdoses of impersonal efficiency. Let us now consider a humanistic retreat within convenient walking distance of the home and consisting of a multipurpose combination of public park, library, community center, youth center, and TAG-equipped school.

At first it may be inconsistent to push full force for a mobile, impersonal, efficient, technologically centered world while also pushing full force for community retreats conveniently near both home and the temporary residences of those migrating. These more leisurely retreats would abound in natural beauty, creative arts, reflective thought, recreation, and sociability.

Perhaps our neuroses have been developing because we have sought progress by pushing for the impersonal world to the exclusion of the personal world. Would not even the world of technology gain if a state of homeostasis between personal and impersonal worlds could be established and maintained in which people were happier as well as wealthier?

In order to gain homeostasis, the multipurpose community center would apparently need to be convenient to homes and temporary residences and to be of manageable size. It might be limited to about

200 youths, ages five to fifteen, plus the people who live in the area from which these youth are drawn. The public school function of the center would consist of perhaps ten years of compulsory schooling. As recommended by Margaret Mead, these years would be termed primary education, and the other years would be termed secondary education.

The best way to continue one's secondary education would be to help with the primary education. Here, retired people could help the professional educators. The same would apply to employed people, for as the actual work week is further reduced it would seem advisable that employees continue to be paid on a 40-hour basis, but be expected to use extra time in serving the community center—as consultants, conductors of field trips, arrangers of exploratory on-the-job internships and keeping up to date themselves.

The center would have workshop areas; natural areas with water, trees, and other plants; places to raise smaller animals; and areas for recreational exercise. These facilities would be available to people at all times whether engaged in primary or secondary education. Those engaged in primary education would have frontier-like chores in maintaining the area. They would also be given opportunities to help care for the young of parents using the center. Since older people would be used in the center as consultants and aides, youth would have the privilege of gaining insight into people of all ages.

The environment of the center would be programed so the learner would simply intern in all the basic problems of the age and learn the techniques of constructive improvement. Reverence for all life would be the underlying theme. The creative arts and the sciences would serve a complementary function, for both the act of scientific creativity and the act of artistic creativity offer glimpses of order as stepping stones to new creative acts. Both are valid to the extent they can evoke a predictable feeling from all kinds of people in all ages.

It seems to be true that the fearful seek the predictable to avoid uncertainty, whereas the curious seek it as a springboard to new predictive constructs. Seeking the predictable is another way of seeking that in which one can place his faith. Perhaps the 20th Century will be most of all marked by the early loss of its faith in absolutes while finally gaining an equally satisfying and committed goal in life—the peaceful and unending search with no holds barred for predictability and faith. It is our responsibility as science educators, perhaps more than any other group, to see that the 20th Century does end on an optimistic note.

Is Science Getting
Out of Hand?*

Barry Commoner

We are living through a period of momentous change. The power of science is increasing with unprecedented speed, bringing with it great opportunities and critical problems. But the process has just begun, and before it sweeps us further into the new age, it is prudent to take stock, to consider where we are going and what may happen en route.

This question must trouble everyone who struggles to contain the ferment of modern science within the neat confines of the classroom. The amount of material that students need to learn is growing with alarming speed. With barely room enough in the curriculum for a little physics, chemistry, and biology, what can be done to accommodate the exciting new hyphenated sciences that speak of lasers and masers, DNA and RNA, radiation belts and space capsules? Or consider the plight of the chemistry teacher. After laboring to get across the basic idea that the bond between atoms is due to an unfilled electron shell, he is confronted with the announcement of a compound of a rare gas— xenon—the electron shells of which are lamentably filled with electrons. And then there is the problem of bringing modern science into the school laboratory. How shall we devise an experiment to demonstrate to the first grade the basic properties of the neutrino—using milk bottles, lolly-pop sticks, and the appropriate article from the *Scientific American?* What about the social and moral consequences of modern science? Will parents be upset if the fifth-grade students discuss not merely the production of test-tube babies, but the laboratory creation of life itself?

Yet, why complain? Aren't all these difficulties simply growing pains —the natural results of the recent recognition that science is important to education and to the nation? Should we not welcome the wave of

*Reprinted from *The Science Teacher*, V. 30, No. 6, Oct., 1963, pp. 11–16.
©, by permission.

excitement that now stirs the dry dust of the traditional science curriculum? Why dilute the gladness that Sputnik has brought in its bountiful wake: generous support of scientific research, grants for school laboratory equipment, summer fellowships and institutes, better salaries, a little of the long-missed appreciation of the meaning of science and of the value of those who teach it?

It is my purpose to suggest that we ought to pause, for a moment, in this headlong rush and give some thought to its effect on science, on science teaching and education, and on their service to the nation. So much has changed so fast in the brief time since the Russians launched both their own Sputnik and the rejuvenation of American science, that even a minor strain may be an important symptom of a basic fault in the scientific enterprise. Given the present rate of expansion and the enormous powers that lie at the hand of modern science, a small flaw —if unperceived—might soon produce a catastrophic failure. There is some merit in applying the traditional skepticism of science to the recent growth of science itself.

A few weeks ago there appeared in *Science* a remarkable paper "Are We Retrogressing in Science?" by a distinguished geologist, Dr. M. King Hubbert.[1] Dr. Hubbert makes several assertions regarding serious faults in the present state of science in this country. I should like to add to his observations some of my own, and prepare a brief catalog of a few of the major difficulties that now beset the development and use of science. This will show, I believe, that we are not merely suffering the natural pains of rapid growth but that certain weaknesses at the very heart of the scientific enterprise may threaten the future of science and its usefulness to the nation and to the world.

Here, briefly, are some of our more obvious troubles:

THE SCIENTIFIC INFORMATION CRISIS

Dr. Hubbert points to the phenomenal increase in the size and complexity of the scientific literature. There now appear to be some 100,000 scientific journals in the world, and the number is doubling about every 15 years.

Science is intended to discover and comprehend new information about nature. This means, of course, that in choosing a problem and in interpreting what he learns about it, the scientist must consider what is already known. The literature of science is the repository of this knowledge.

To function successfully, such a repository must be capable of storing

[1] *Science, 139:* pp. 884–890. March 8, 1963.

the new information and of delivering it to the inquiring scientist. The first of these functions is probably being met with moderate success. But the recovery of information from the literature is rapidly approaching a stage of crisis.

Twenty-five years ago the practicing scientist could keep up with the literature by spending part of every week in the library reading room glancing at a few dozen journals, noting the existence of perhaps twice that number of articles and reading a few thoroughly. By 15 years ago, the number of relevant articles had become so large that scientists began to rely increasingly on abstracts. And nowadays even the abstracts have become too numerous to read. One of the most revealing developments in the literature of science has been the publication of a new type of periodical which simply lists new articles appearing in several hundred scientific journals by title—about 2,000 of them weekly.

This enormous proliferation of scientific papers is usually accepted as a proper consequence of the growth of scientific research. The solution often proposed is that we attempt to tame the monster by creating a new one—computer-operated "information retrieval." This would, of course, accomplish the final ascendency of the title of the scientific paper over its content, for the only practical way to index papers in a computer memory is by the information contained in the title.

But a title, or even an abstract, cannot reveal the essential subtlety of a scientific observation: the limits imposed by techniques, the uncertainties and possible errors of interpretation, its relation to other facts and to ideas. Unless we can find a more fundamental solution to this problem, the basic precept that new scientific knowledge should incorporate and extend the old will collapse.

THE DECLINE OF THEORY

Here I should like to cite an example from a field with which I am particularly acquainted—biology. Perhaps the oldest—and most profound—theoretical problem in biology is what might be called the nature of the living state. By this I mean the effort to explain the curious paradox that a living organism, despite its unique capabilities for growth, self-duplication, and inheritance, is nevertheless a mixture of substances which are separately no more possessed of life than the more prosaic molecules that never occur in living cells. This question has been at the root of a long train of experiments, debates, and speculations that begins in classical times and continues unbroken through the development of modern biology and its attendant sciences.

The basic issues are simply stated. If the component parts of a cell are not alive, whence come the life-properties exhibited by the whole?

Apart from the untenable notion of a mystic nonmaterial "vital force," the debate has elicited two main positions: (a) There is, in fact, some special cellular component which possesses the fundamental attribute of *self*-duplication and which is, therefore, a "living molecule." (b) The properties of life are inherently connected with its complexity and arise from interactions among the constituents which are not exhibited unless the separate parts are brought together in the complex whole; thus, only the entire living cell is capable of *self*-duplication.

Both sides of the argument have had many notable proponents. In the nineteenth century, Verworn believed that the properties of life were embodied in a special type of molecule—as yet undiscovered, but nevertheless discoverable—the biogen; but Claude Bernard favored the emergence of life properties from the interactions of molecular components. More recently some of our most able physical scientists have argued both sides of the question. Schrodinger saw the properties of the cell contained in the aperiodic crystal structure of the chromosome. On the other hand, Niels Bohr has contended that the principle of complementarity—which in his view applies to all material systems—would deny even the *possibility* of discovering the attributes of life in any substance which can be studied only when it has been removed from a dismembered—and therefore dead—cell.

Now, the debate appears to be over. There is, we are told, a constituent which is indeed "a living molecule"—DNA—which has within itself the basic property of life, self-duplication, and which guides the behavior of all the other components of the cell.

Has this apparent victory actually resolved the old question; is it really the end of the great theoretical debate? I do not believe so. The apparent victory of DNA is not the result of a successful resolution of the long-debated alternatives. Instead the decision has been reached by a less arduous expedient—the basic theoretical question is largely ignored.

For example, if DNA is indeed a code which embodies all the features of the organism, then the adult must be fully specified by the DNA in the fertilized egg. But this idea conflicts profoundly with the evidence of embryology, which shows that development includes emergent phenomena, new features appearing from a previous, less specific stage. In the excitement over the "living molecule," this contradiction has hardly been mentioned. Nor has the basic theoretical question really been answered by the new biochemical experiments, which do not, in fact, support the idea that DNA is a self-duplicating molecule. Recent evidence on enzymatic synthesis of DNA shows that far from being self-duplicating in this system, part of the DNA specificity is derived from the necessary enzyme.

What is at issue here is not the validity of the magnificent experimental results which describe the structure and properties of DNA, but

313

the sweeping generalizations which they have engendered. These generalizations are unsound, I believe, not because they are founded on faulty data, but because they do not take into account *all* of the relevant data.

One of Dr. Hubbert's most serious criticisms of modern science is that it is afflicted with authoritarianism. Because of the fragmentation of knowledge and the absence of sound theory, he states, ". . . the only way of knowing anything outside of one's own specialty is to accept the word of an authority or specialist in the field." Dr. Hubbert supports this charge with examples from the physical sciences. I am afraid that authoritarianism may be equally evident in the biological sciences and in the DNA situation in particular.

Certainly there is good experimental evidence to support the notion that DNA does *influence* the hereditary characteristics of living cells in which it occurs. But the question which relates to the basic theoretical issue is whether DNA represents a self-contained code that by itself determines whether the organism is a turtle or a tiger.

Such a conclusion is not based on experimental fact, but on *dogma*. If you are shocked by my use of this word, let me hasten to add that it is not my own. The term "central dogma" is often used in current literature to describe the principles which are supposed to explain the governing role of DNA in inheritance. It was introduced into the scientific literature—probably for the first time since the Middle Ages—by *proponents* of the DNA code theory. You will find in the index to a report of a recent symposium[2] on molecular genetics the entry "Dogma, The" followed by 11 page references. On page 107 one of the participants makes the following remarkable statement: "The reason we call this 'dogma' is that it depends on personal bias, not logic." Shades of Galileo!

And consider the implications for education. Every freshman entering the main door of the biology building at Washington University is confronted by an exhibit case which contains, among an assortment of skeletons, a model of the famous DNA double helix, marvelously contrived of bits of colored paper. Every day as I pass this exhibit, I am struck by the same disquieting thought: Would any student detect a mistake among these exhibits? I have thus far restrained myself from conducting the required experiment, but I think that I can predict the result. If the skulls of the rabbit and the cat were interchanged, sooner or later some bright-eyed student would notice the discrepancy from what he had observed in the laboratory. But even if the DNA model were falsified sufficiently to convert the code into gibberish, it would go unnoticed. The *data* for the structure of DNA, unlike the *data* for the structure of the cat, are not experienced directly by a freshman. The paper model represents a *conclusion*, and even the best student in

[2]*Genetics—Transactions of the First Conference.* Macy Foundation, New York. 1960.

the class cannot criticize a conclusion if—due to the natural limits of his level of advancement in science—he can have no actual knowledge of the experiments on which it is based. The student need not accept the skeleton of the cat on anyone's authority but his own. But with respect to the DNA code, he must, at his stage of knowledge, accept the word of the "authorities." And what is true of the freshman may sometimes be true of his teacher!

I do not wish to press my own view that DNA is not "the secret of life." What troubles me here is the tendency to avoid a critical examination of the relation between experimental fact and the resultant generalizations and to evade a serious confrontation between the new chemical observations and the equally real complexity and subtlety of the living cell. I am troubled, too, by the tendency to favor simplicity over truth, to forego the intellectual rigors of the scientific process for illusory short cuts which our predecessors in science would have regarded with astonishment or amusement.

I agree with Dr. Hubbert who states, ". . . the acceptance of any conclusion, valid or otherwise, by an individual who is not familiar with the observational data on which it is based and the logic by which it is derived is a negation of science and a return to authoritarianism." And I must agree, if sadly, with his conclusion that "such a reversion, and the careless retreat from fundamentals that are its corollary, make up the pattern that one sees increasingly manifested today."

Failures in the Application of Science

The final test of scientific knowledge is its ability to predict the results of intervention by humans into natural processes. That modern science has suffered spectacular failures in predicting the outcome of new technological developments is only too apparent today. Fifteen or twenty years ago, when synthetic detergents were developed, no one seemed to be aware that inevitably—as is now happening—they would become the target of legislative prohibition. The new detergents were superior washing agents, easy on the skin, economical, and readily marketed—but they were not degraded in the sewage system. Thus, long after the detergents had become a common household item and had largely replaced soap, they were discovered to be an intolerable nuisance in the water supply. There is no way to gloss over this episode. It represents a failure on the part of modern chemical engineering— here and throughout the world—to predict successfully a vital consequence of a massive intervention into nature.

There are other examples. The really troublesome aspect of the insecticide problem is not the relative benefits and risks of massive dissemination of these new chemicals. More important is the fact—

which is not denied by even those who support present practices—
that many of the harmful ecological effects of these insecticides were
discovered only after they were already in use.

Or consider the effects of radioactive isotopes from the fallout dis-
seminated by nuclear explosions. None of the governments that have
been exploding these weapons can possibly claim to have been adequately informed about the biological consequences at the time when it
decided to proceed with this action. What may turn out to be the most
harmful result, the tendency of Sr^{90} to accumulate in the chromosomes
and thereby induce genetic defects, was reported for the first time in
January 1963.[3]

We are making massive use of powers which we do not fully understand. The reasons are varied and some of them relate to nonscientific
matters such as the pressure for economic or political advantage. Nevertheless, we cannot evade the fact that a primary purpose of science
—the guidance of man's interactions with the forces of nature—has, in
these grave instances, failed.

NONSCIENTIFIC DETERMINATION OF THE
COURSE OF SCIENTIFIC RESEARCH

The freedom to choose his own problem is often the scientist's
most precious possession. Of course, there is much good science that
derives from the solution of a given problem, and there are many
excellent investigators who advance science through such work. Nevertheless, the vitality of the total scientific enterprise is strongly dependent on the free inquiry into nature that we call basic science. At the
cutting edge of science, on the frontiers of knowledge, nature confronts
the scientist with a tangled obscurity, which only the most intense and
dedicated effort can hope, occasionally, to penetrate. This kind of effort
comes of devotion born of free choice. It can be guided only by science
itself, which in the clarity of its knowledge reveals as well the regions
of ignorance. There is, then, good reason to want, in basic science, a
pattern of development which comes from within and to resist the
determination of its course by external demands.

Until recently this principle has—with relatively minor exceptions—
been fully honored by the system of support of scientific research in
this country. Perhaps the oldest active government agency for the
support of science, the Office of Naval Research, has been notable for
its adherence to this principle. This principle is the basic guide to the
policies of the National Science Foundation, the National Institutes of

[3]Lüning et al. *Nature*, 197: 304. January 19, 1963.

Health, and others. Project-oriented research support has, until recently, been confined to specific areas and has not dominated the overall course of science.

However, this situation is being rapidly changed. In 1962 about one-third of the total federal obligation for basic research—and federal funds are now the major source of support for basic science—came from a single agency, the National Aeronautics and Space Administration. In a total federal budget of about $900 million for basic research, NASA was obligated to provide $350 million, while the National Science Foundation provided under $90 million. Unlike NSF, NASA is a mission-oriented agency, for the enabling legislation requires that it devote its full effort to the conquest of space. Moreover, for the next decade, the mission of NASA is even further narrowed, being centered on a single predominant project—Apollo—which is intended to take a man to the moon and back by 1970.

That this single mission is already determining the course of scientific investigation of space is quite evident from the extensive summary of space research recently published by the National Academy of Sciences.[4] The findings of this study state: "If the Apollo time schedule is to be met, data acquisition necessary to support engineering decisions for this mission must take precedence over the acquisition of other data of possibly greater basic scientific interest."

Unlike other mission-oriented agencies, NASA has needs which demand an appreciable fraction of our total scientific resources and which cut broadly across the entire range of scientific fields. To accomplish its mission, it must support investigations in all fields of science, including social problems regarding the impact of the space program on the nation. It has become the major source of graduate fellowships in science. Clearly, as it is presently projected, the NASA program will encompass a substantial portion of the nation's scientific effort. Since NASA-supported work is necessarily oriented toward the general area of space investigation and is for a decade dominated by a single mission, placing a man on the moon, the program is bound to have a considerable directive effect on the overall course of scientific investigation in the United States.

What is at issue here is that the space program, and, therefore, its determinative effects on the course of science, has not been created by the demands of *science*. Of course, investigations in space involve many exciting and important basic scientific questions. But this can be said of many other fields of science. The problem is to maintain a system of support which reflects the relative significance of each field within the total structure of science. The National Science Foundation was

[4]*A Review of Space Research*. National Academy of Sciences—National Research Council, Pub. No. 1079, Washington, D. C. 1962.

established for this purpose and in its organization is carefully designed to ensure a close coupling between the pattern of support and the structure of science itself. NASA has now developed a program of support in basic science which equals the NSF in size, but which no longer follows the principle, so laboriously established during the legislative debate on the National Science Foundation bill, that a national program of support for science should be science-oriented rather than mission-oriented. This major change in the nation's scientific enterprise has taken place, so far as I know, without any comprehensive discussion, within the scientific community or elsewhere, of its necessity or its consequences.

With respect to the single mission which now dominates the space program—Apollo—the origin of the decision is fairly clear. That the decision to land a man on the moon by 1970 was *not* dictated by scientific need is clearly stated in the review already mentioned. "The Apollo program was acknowledged as an integral part of the NASA effort, based on the President's decision that this undertaking be established as a national goal." The report also states, with respect to the Apollo project: "International competition and resulting political commitments have forced upon this complex mission a somewhat unrealistic timetable. Mission failure would cost lives, international prestige, and tremendous dollar investments."

These observations lead me to suggest that the space program as presently constituted will tend significantly to determine the course of basic research through considerations which originate outside the pursuit of science.

SOME REASONS FOR THE DIFFICULTIES

There is, then, some evidence to support the view that science may be getting out of hand: the crisis in scientific literature, serious failures in the proper application of science, a tendency toward authoritarianism and a neglect of theory, the direction of the course of science by restrictive external demands.

There are good reasons why these difficulties should be of direct concern not only to practicing scientists but to science teachers as well. One is that science teaching has a natural dependence on the fate of science itself. But, more than that, I should like to suggest that the understanding of these difficulties, and a search for effective solutions, must be based on principles which are common both to science and to education.

Some of the difficulties that I have mentioned result from the failure to understand that science is a *system* in which new observations and new ideas closely interact. Dr. Hubbert has, I believe, correctly diagnosed the reason for the information crisis. He points out that many modern scientists respond to the difficulty of keeping up with the vast literature relevant to any given science by restricting the scope of their interests. But having thus deliberately limited his field of competence, the scientist quite naturally tends to lose an interest and capability in relating his own segment of knowledge to its allied fields. And this is the real source of the trouble, for, as Dr. Hubbert points out, the progress of science comes from those overviews which sum up in a few relationships a whole realm of previously uncoordinated observations. It is such theory which reduces separate observations to orderly positions as special cases of general principles and frees science from the tyranny of numbers.

I do not believe that the present glut in the literature of science can be cured by mechanical or even electronic means. It is a failure of the entire *system* of science; it results from a tendency to ignore interrelationships, to evade the confrontation of one set of data with another.

Atrophy of the integrative process in science also leads to neglect of scientific theory. I believe that much of the present confusion about the significance of the new observations on molecular aspects of inheritance is due to excessive isolation of scientific fields and the resultant dependence on authority. If biologists are not prepared to review the actual data and logical foundations of the DNA code, they cannot properly relate this idea to the cell theory or to the principles of development. In the absence of such a confrontation, the biologist must either ignore the new work or accept its conclusions uncritically. In either case the conclusions derived from molecular observations remain immune to the corrective effects of biology, and their proper assimilation into the stream of science is delayed.

The same tendency toward fragmentation of knowledge is also the cause of failures in applied science. The biological defect in present detergents might have been foreseen if their development had involved not only chemists and engineers, but also biologists and biochemists. Present synthetic detergents resist bacterial attack in sewage disposal plants because the molecules are branched. And the general tendency of biological enzymes to halt at a molecular branch has been well known since the early biochemical work on starch degradation. This has been described in detail in textbooks for 30 years. Similarly, that Sr^{90} might become concentrated in the chromosome and so constitute a possible danger to genetic stability should have been evident to anyone familiar with cytological work on the role of calcium in the chromosome, which was first published 10 years ago.

Nature, unlike modern science, is not fragmented. A nuclear explosion is not only a matter of physics and engineering, but a gigantic experiment in ecology as well. If we permit our understanding of nature—

science—to split into isolated specialties, we risk the fate of the sorcerer's apprentice—who was so specialized that he knew only one of the two incantations necessary for a successful experiment with magic.

SCIENCE AND EDUCATION

We can hope to avoid these troubles only if we understand that science is a system in which new observations must reflect old ones, in which data must be built into theory, in which the narrow authority of the specialist must bow before the complexity of nature. And such an understanding can only be achieved through education—not only of students who are to become our practicing scientists, but also of the citizen, who, if he is to help guide its powerful uses, must understand the true nature of science.

Our apparent willingness to permit science to become dominated by external demands for particular results reflects another serious misapprehension about the nature of science and its relation to education. Both are, of course, important implements of social progress. But unlike a mechanical tool, which must itself resist change as it works, science and education are certain to be shaped by the uses to which they are put. If scientific work is ruled by a narrow purpose, the broad internal interactions which, as I have tried to show, are so essential to the growth of science, are bound to suffer.

Nor can we safely permit the whole of science to become isolated from the rest of learning, for there are important interactions between all fields of knowledge on which each of the separate disciplines depends for its own strength.

I believe that science and education are becoming constricted by certain present policies of support. Science is a subsidiary part of education, and one would suppose that any effort to strengthen science should be predicated on adequate support for the entire educational base. But we seem to have turned this relationship upside down. While exhibiting a considerable reluctance to provide the total support needed to sustain our schools and universities, the nation is eager to expand that part of the educational system which deals with science. Even federal support of education becomes acceptable if it is earmarked for science. Most of our universities have become so dependent on these outside funds that if such funds were withdrawn their total competence as educational institutions would sharply decline. I believe that we have balanced the fate of our system of higher education on too narrow a fulcrum—science.

The same sort of process appears to be going on *within* science. Space research is, after all, only a part of science. Yet, if present plans persist, we may soon be supporting a major part of basic research in the United States through activities undertaken in the name of space. If this happens, the broad structure of our scientific establishment will be sustained through a constricted purpose, investigation of space. Moreover, at least for the next decade, the space program itself seems to be balanced, and—in view of the palpable risk of failure—somewhat precariously, on a single project to land a man on the moon.

We are engaged in a spectacular balancing act: Education is supported by science, science by space, and space by the man on the moon.

Will it work? What is the harm, if Congress is willing, in supporting space research because of the political importance of getting onto the moon, of supporting science in the name of space, and of sustaining higher education through the expedient of grants for science?

One danger is obvious. If an appreciable part of the total structure of science is justified by the effort to invade the moon, the whole scientific enterprise may be seriously dislocated if this particular project should be abandoned. And since the adoption of the project was, after all, predicated on its apparent political significance, we cannot be certain that it will survive the natural fluctuations of the tides of politics.

But I have already indicated a more serious fault in this situation. If the free choice of problem which is so essential to the pursuit of basic science is curtailed by draining support and personnel into *any* narrow channel, the march of science will surely falter. And it is a truism that in the not-so-long run all the consequences of science, including its most practical fruits, depend on the healthy development of basic research.

Can society be properly served by a system of higher education which is increasingly sustained through the artificial expedient of support for science? I believe not. Education has an essential unity, and failure to support adequately the study of history and literature—which clarify society's goals and illuminate the human condition—thereby injures the whole.

Of course, the penalty will not be paid at once; research in the problems that happen to interest society at the moment *will* go forward for a time. But gradually the scientist's vision will narrow to the limits of his immediate problem; and when that vanishes (because it is solved), he will discover that seeing nothing, he is blind. Real scholarship is all of a piece. Physics will only flourish within the sound of poetry.

I believe that the policy of supporting education through science, and science through space, is dangerously unsound. We should recognize this policy for what it is—a short-sighted, pinch-penny effort to buy a few selected fruits of the tree of knowledge, without accepting the honest responsibility of nourishing the whole living, growing organism.

The nation is ready to pay for knowledge of science, engineering, and medicine, but it must recognize that this knowledge cannot be truly achieved in the absence of equally strong support for the humanities and the arts—for all the forms that truth can take.

I believe that every scientist, every scholar, and every teacher must proclaim and work for the unity of knowledge. This is our duty to the nation and to the welfare of man.

Individuality and Common Purpose: The Philosophy of Science*

Robert Sonné Cohen

Philosophy is a persistent attempt to grapple with foundations. When foundations are shaken, philosophy is practical and urgent. When the times are revolutionary, then the effects upon philosophy are revolutionary, too. And when the foundations of scientific knowledge undergo revolutionary transformations, then the philosophy of science receives extraordinary challenge. If the challenge is met rather than missed, the reciprocal effect upon scientific thought can be productive and liberating. The effect upon scientific education can be similar. But the way to liberation from old mental habits is through thickets of problems, tough and thorny.

Little need be said about the occurrence of these layers of revolutionary change. When seen against the world background of other and ancient societies, Western European civilization has never been stabilized; and seen against our own European and American history, twentieth century civilization has appeared to be rapidly and perilously changing. All is involved. Economic and social life have rapidly become so industrialized that only the most perceptive nineteenth century observers could recognize us. Political dominations and psychological manipulations have been accompanied by gross changes in religious life, in morality, and in all manner of the arts. And with an internal sweeping energy, the barely stabilized mechanism of the Galilean and Newtonian scientific outlook upon Nature has, almost within a generation, been replaced, absorbed, transformed. As a result, philosophy has become polarized into two modern traditions: first, devotion to contemporary science generated a desire for precision, analysis, and specialization within the profession of philosophy itself; and second, distaste for a technologically transmuted world brought a spectrum of counter-

*Reprinted from *The Science Teacher*, V. 31, No. 4, May, 1964, pp. 27–33. ©, by permission.

scientific attitudes. This modern anti-science has defeatist and escapist aspects, but, at the same time, it reestablishes a human concern, a viewpoint from which to observe what science has done as well as to observe what society has become. In their reestablishment of a classical task, the anti-scientific philosophers are our judges and critics. As we shall see, to say this is high praise. *For philosophy is criticism.*

PHILOSOPHICAL ANALYSIS

But why philosophy at all? Why not simply the self-critical procedures of science, the honored techniques of logical consistency, detailed elaboration, careful observation, and ingenious experimentation? Because philosophy, as the theory of foundations of science, can offer several benefits.

It is, first of all, analytic. It can make clear what we scientists know, how we know, to what extent we are certain and to what degree uncertain, and how far our own stipulations and definitions, our models and metaphors, have determined and distorted our view of reality. How are concepts related to the theories in which they are embedded? Even to working scientists and science teachers, a few questions will indicate some areas of achievements of recent philosophical analysis of the sciences.

1. What is an explanation? Are the laws of natural phenomena descriptions which correlate past and future observations, or perhaps conceptual umbrellas which cover observationally distinct types of phenomena? Are they causal?

2. Indeed, what is a causal explanation? Is cause a metaphor derived from the daily life of actions and effects? And if the causal metaphor is correct, where is the metaphorical active agent, and the causal connection? Where, in the difficult indeterminacy of microphysics as we know it—or, for that matter, where in the sophisticated realms of statistical and probabilistic analysis—do we locate causal understanding?

3. At least we might say that causes come first and effects second, and hence that the causal order of Nature is inseparably the order of time and sufficient to explain the nature of time. Or is it true that reversals of time may occur, as some scientists now believe, reversals for which the physical effects may occur at a moment prior to their sources? Then, in partial retreat, we may interpret the temporal order as itself a statistical effect, just as the law of entropy was interpreted in statistical mechanics. But how shall we understand our deeply intuitive feeling for the distinction between past and future?

4. To what extent do successful predictions validate a theory? And to what extent do negative outcomes falsify our theories? No question of the logic of science has received more attention, and no question is so open to scientists in every field and at every stage of their study. It serves, for many of us, as the disturbing introduction to the need for self-examination and for philosophical reflection, since with a few thoughtful examples before him, the elementary student can see how theories can be "stretched" to cover uncomfortable facts. And he can see the irresolvability of alternatives, the half-truth of true predictions based on partial perspectives, and then he will wonder just how to relate evidence with theory.

5. Consideration of evidence means, for most of us, understanding what is an experiment. The design of experiments is perhaps not a philosophical task but the demand for clarity provokes philosophical queries. Can we understand the twin characteristics of every experiment —accuracy and vagueness—and can we pinpoint simple phenomenal properties in the world which is so grossly complicated? From kindergarten to graduate research, we can be creatively disturbed by the need to have a precise comprehension of vagueness and a complex understanding of simplicity.

6. Whether in experiment or in theory, we work with ideally isolated factors and parts. We never seek the whole, except when mystically or metaphysically entranced with the whole of the world. We seek to understand a bit of a broader experience and a broader situation, and we assuredly know that we are doing it. Even the cosmologists, dealing with the entire universe, isolate their subject matter, since they consider only a few, allegedly basic, properties. They neglect, ignore, the remainder. And they should, for every science, thus far, has progressed by isolating. The simplest experiment, performed free of the wind, or at constant temperature, or repeated only at steady barometric pressure, is no different in this regard from the subtlest attempts in neurophysiology or in nuclear chemistry. So we must ask, is the universe the simple additive sum of the isolates? Is it to be understood as a superposition of externally described forces, and effects, and entities? Science has succeeded, so the answer is yes. And yet we know that isolation of an occurrence for experiment can at the same time destroy the larger object of study.

We isolate, narrow down, and hope that the context will not affect the outcome; and that the next generation will expand the isolate to include another cautiously apprehended part of its environment. Isolation is plausible enough but it is puzzling and a little distressing, for it prejudices the formation of concepts as much as it enables the conduct of experiments. How shall we best express the old truth of biology, that function depends on position within the whole, that the individuals in our world "do not blindly run, but run in accordance with the whole of which they form a part"? These are open questions, raised by philosophies of process and organism, by nonlinear speculations in physics and field speculations in social psychology by the polarities in the views of Whitehead and Teilhard and the ancient Nature-mystics and the modern dialectical philosophers, and they are implicit in the high school chemistry laboratory.

7. The experimenter long ago provoked another question. How has he distorted the object of his search? How has the measuring instrument disturbed the measured entity? Do we know only what we observe, and do we observe an object only in its relatedness to our observing selves? Is there no object other than the observer? Not only does this raise subjective idealist questions about the scientific world, but also the ancient sceptical and relativist assertions that man alone is the measure of all things, and a prejudiced measure at that. It has provoked the operationalist view of the meaning of words. And for some time we have wrestled with the significance of the fundamentals of physical knowledge, for at the ultramicroscopic level we find quantum physical equations whose interpretation demands the inclusion of the observing entity as well as of the phenomenon observed. The ancient philosophical riddle of man in Nature, of the relation of subject to object, has been reborn in the apparently impersonal relation of quanta and reality.

We see here a few open questions of contemporary philosophy of science. Each has its bearing upon scientific research, and also upon science teaching. And they could be supplemented by a dozen others. Is the world everywhere knowable in principle (though never completely in practice)? Are statistical explanations merely temporary? Are all entities ultimately explicable in terms of physics proper, and indeed what would this reductive explanation signify for the living and psychological and social properties of those physical entities which have them? Must our theories, taken as a general description of the world, be consistent?

SYNTHETIC CHARACTER

But enough has been said to sketch some puzzling aspects of the philosophical analysis of science. There is another story, for philosophy is not only analytic; it has a synthetic character as well. Despite our interdisciplinary border fields—biophysical chemistry, astrobotany, neuropsychiatry, historical sociology, chemical genetics—we are still divorced from one another in the sciences, ever greedily, or perhaps wistfully, looking at a summary review paper from a neighbor's field,

326

hoping to sniff his greener grass. But always these interdisciplinary fields produce the newest specialists, not the unifiers but the dividers. Only a philosophical temperament provides unity to the sciences, and then only by a way of thinking, not by aspiring to omniscience. This way of thinking asks, what is relevant? And how is relevance determined? What methods are common to all inquiry, asks the philosopher, but also he asks with equal care, which methods of thought and research are specific to each branch of science? The prime attention of scientific philosophers seems to be upon the unity of the sciences and their comparative methodology.

But synthesis also means linking science with *any* human concern. If philosophical analysis and unity of the sciences can provide deeper clarifications than individual scientists have of the *structural* nature of science, then philosophical synthesis will try to be deeper clarification of the *human* nature of science. To work at such a task is increasingly urgent. It is a response to a paralyzing fear of science as dehumanization and to a hesitant love of science for its imaginative powerful curiosity. To some, these are terribly simple fears, perhaps superstitious, perhaps exaggerated; to others they are sophisticated. The fears are all-too-simply listed: Scientists are magicians, with a fundamentally incomprehensible language, for the determining role of language upon cognition likewise determines the exclusion of outsiders. Scientists are manipulators of men as well as of viruses and molecules. The scientific curiosity has no inherent limitation, neither biased toward the good and the helpful nor gravitating toward evil and cruelty. But this curiosity is not merely ethically neutral, responding to some other human agent, like a weapon. Science is irresponsible, morally irresponsible, according to this view, like a child with a giant's muscles. It is that child-like curiosity, that lovely awe and wonder, the itch to know and to explore and to collect all manner of things, which suddenly may frighten a humane observer. How apt is Robert Boyle's phrasing—the experimenter must torture Nature. And how, the observer passionately wishes to know, how may he help this monstrous child to mature? If the metaphor were correct, perhaps he could teach the child, with love and with understanding, respect for the imaginative curiosity and the manipulative instinct. But who is such an observer? And who is such a teacher? At least in part, each humane man, in the twentieth century, has such fears, and by that he is instinctively philosophical.

The Human Situation

There are two distinct inquiries to be considered then, for the estimation of science today. Science itself, as pure and practical reasoning about the world we experience; and philosophy as critical reasoning about the human situation, of which science is a part. How simple it must have seemed to those hopeful rationalists in the Age of Reason, how certain that science *and its philosophy* were unqualifiedly part of the foundations of human enlightenment, the creators of human independence, and the forces which could eliminate practical miseries and spiritual illusions. In our time, we need philosophical clarity about science precisely because the civilizing role of science is in doubt. And before we can teach science properly, we had better try to establish the relation between science and humane goals once again. Let us state the critical challenge to science in such a way that it applies as well to pure science as to technology and industry.

AMBIGUITY

This civilization is both scientific and barbaric. How are these qualities linked? Things and people go faster, all of them might and some of them do last longer. Great chunks of Nature have been tamed. The possibilities seem endless, joyful, and wondrous, if only science can be linked with the fulfillment of life. The possibilities are brief, final, and degrading when science is joined with any denial of life. Which of the possibilities will be realized? In part, at least, this political question (with its psychological implications) can be illuminated by reflections on science. For the ambiguity and alternatives in the *use* of science have rough counterparts within science itself. Perhaps one side of the ambiguity, the success of science in its own terms, may offer hope that the method of observation and reason will also succeed in social life. Ultimately, that method evolved to a stage where we may say that the greatest invention was the method of inventing; the most profound discovery was the method of discovery.

Human goals are sometimes fantastic, sometimes impractical, sometimes plainly impossible; but we now have, in scientific reason, a way of finding out how to achieve our goals if they are achievable at all, and of diagnosing them when they are illusory. And by scientific education, we may teach ourselves how to reject the illusions and to work properly for our goals. But this task for education can permit deadening goals as well as enlivening ones, a bitter ambiguity of science and of science education.

Ambiguity is not itself an evaluative term, certainly not necessarily bad. But when the practical determinations are ethical, then theoretical ambiguity becomes less tolerable, and must be suspected. Where, then, are the ambiguities within science? A catalog of contrasts will show them. Science is cumulative, a progressively expanded and increasingly powerful development of human knowledge; and yet no scientific theory is immune to change and criticism, indeed, every theory seems doomed to be overthrown. In the world of science, the honest, devoted apprentice will honor his master and teacher by contradicting him. Newton today would be a follower of the physics of Einstein or Bohr, surely not a Newtonian. Science is a progressive accumulation and a series of overturned achievements.

Furthermore, even a single theory or simple explanation is open to doubt. We generalize from all-too-few observations of a restricted range of kinds of phenomena. We speak of general and universal laws of Nature, but our basis for confirmation of these laws is so far from universal that all of natural science rests upon an intelligent understanding of probabilities. And yet with this uncertain knowledge we have certain power.

Not only are we limited in the available evidence for a given theory, we are compelled to offer our theories as guesses, perhaps informed guesses, but more often wildly imaginative conjectures as to the nature of reality. In confronting any genuinely significant problem, we have insufficient facts, imprecise techniques, and incomplete contexts. We respond with uncomfortable simplifications, and even with implausible ideas. Then, when the facts have become a bit more sufficient and the techniques more precise, when the contexts are completed, and the simplifications modified, and one might even say, when the ideas have become plausible, then, psychologically as well as epistemologically, the problem has lost its scientific significance. It has been replaced by having been, in our cleverly fumbling way, solved.

What could be more human? Men—a man, a family, a nation—must act upon their life problems with whatever knowledge they can get within the short time they have, a split-second, or a lifetime. Part of wisdom is to avoid illusions. One such illusion is to be enmeshed in an interminable and hopeless search for certainty. The converse, and another part of wisdom, is to learn reasonably to estimate the most likely course of action by means of the most probable interpretation of an insufficient supply of facts. This uncommon reasonableness is the nerve of scientific thinking, and it should be taught as such.

Fact is objective, theory is probable. How deceptively simple this statement is, for we use theories in the establishment of the facts by making use of instruments whose design and interpretation depend upon theoretical science. Because of the accident of our body size, and the scope of our organs of perception, we may observe only bits of the enormous universe. We narrow our range of facts still further, by the plausible prejudices of our previously established theories. So the facts are theoretically and intrinsically incomplete, inescapably shaky. And shall we think less of our theories because they are merely probable? They are no less objective for that; the truths we learn are *both* relative *and* objective. They are relative, rather than absolute or certain; relative to our observational perspective, in the history of ideas and the history of instruments. They are objective, rather than private or willful; objective in reference, and in their inter-subjective relation to observers and to observations.

Disciplined imagination makes theories; delicate experimental skills support them or discredit them with observations; the logic of statistical inference shows the relation of theory to observation; and informed rational courage enables men to use these merely probable scientific theories in social and personal practice. Not an existentialist leap into utter darkness, science is a fragment of reasoning about the unknown.

ART AND SCIENCE

Just as science is certain and uncertain, so it is also passionate while dispassionate. Within the cool objectivity of scientific inquiry is also a human response to the esthetic of Nature. From the beginning, men have found beauty in Nature, and have used that response as a vital part of life. The sources of art are in the same spring as those of science. Sometimes, observing the objects of their environment, men imitated those objects. At other times, pure forms and abstract symbols predominated in human expression. Even the art of the Stone Age caves has already shown this. Indeed, the history of art is as complex as the history of science, and artists have travelled far from the paleolithic hunters who imitated and the neolithic potters who ornamented. Nevertheless, artists still share the diverse feelings for Nature which civilization produced. In this respect, in the emotional apprehension of Nature, art and science are intimate, for science, too, was but an expression of man's relations with the natural world. Have we lost this?

Indeed, scientists are like artists. They play with form. But for scientists, forms are abstracted in logical structures, in calculi and geometries, in the shapes of viruses or galaxies, in the free creations of electron orbits, or in other regularities of groups, pattern, sequences. The artist's imagination, whether imitative or abstract, is universal and concrete. Artists have responded to the man-sized world of experience, to its normalities and its distortions. Science opens new worlds of forms, and with them extends enormously the ranges of human response. We see Nature as a delicate agglomeration of changing forms, whose hidden realities were classically set forth in the simplicity of mathematical equations, the language of pure forms. But why should this abstract beauty of Nature, conceived by the imaginative method of scientific hypothesis, be any less legitimate than the concrete beauty of sunset, lightning, spider's web, or human body? It is the artist's response, set against his

330

human situation of cultural place as well as natural epoch, which is decisive for art. The fusion of science with art is as needed as the awareness of social reality through art. But science is not yet art. The scientist's hypothesis is itself independent of his sensory experiences; indeed the working scientist is as much creating as he is discovering and observing. Scientists experiment and imagine; they calculate and, again, imagine; and, hence, it is well to say that they are both sensuously involved with their world and rationally involved with forms and relations. It is close enough to the sensuousness and tough thought of the working artist.

And, hence, our implied contrast of logic and experience, reason and passion, appears. Nature conforms to both sensuality and the rationality. Fulfillment and loveliness appear, the beauty of Nature along with knowledge of Nature, the symmetry and elegance of formal structures, the visual, tangible delights of experimental clarities. There is, for the scientist, a certain pleasure to be found in the patterns of things, the ways they fit together. In the process of disinterested factual inquiry, he finds a deepened emotional life. Our students might, too. But for our larger public, it is not so clearly possible.

POLITICAL ETHICS

The political ethics of science demonstrates a further ambiguity. Science seems to be both democratic and authoritarian, and where democratic, both individual and private, but also cooperative and socialist. These alternatives need not be at war, however, for they are aspects of the double foundation of scientific methods. A primary foundation of science is the verifying and falsifying authority over our theories which is presented by the experience of Nature, by observation and experiment, and by continued practical application. Such practice is open to each investigator, but from earliest times it could be had only by the cooperation of many men, recording for other generations, learning from other specialists, joining together in constructive labor and critical thought, in teaching, studying, and in learning together.

Science *accumulates*, it grows. It contrasts sharply with other aspects of human culture. A sculpture by Michelangelo, created in the sixteenth century, is not inherently less beautiful than one by Henry Moore today. The pacifism of Isaiah is no less noble for being nearly twenty-five centuries earlier than that of Gandhi. But the scientific vision of Galileo and Newton is inherently less comprehensive, less knowledgeable, less successful, *less true*, than that of Einstein and Planck; and the wisdom of Pythagoras and Aristotle is, in its turn, likewise less true than that of Galileo. The history of science must be written as progressive, at least in its own terms. We scientists, as both Bernard of Chartres, in the twelfth century, and Isaac Newton, 500 years later, remarked, see so far because we are like dwarfs standing on the shoulders of giants. And the giants are no less indebted to the multitude of lesser workers: craftsmen, observers, experimenters, farmers, shepherds, and other common folk. The achievement of science is the patient work of the many investigators who are necessary to deal with the complex phenomena of the natural world. Of necessity, science is a cooperative activity. The social arrangements which seem so sophisticated in our industrial economy of today, in production and distribution, are really a commonplace in the ancient science of astronomy, which reaches back to the agricultural revolution of pre-history. The regularities in the motions of the heavenly objects *must* be observed and recorded through the generations, accurately, faithfully, with deeply felt moral understanding of the debt to previous observers and the obligation to subsequent ones. If they had not been, there would have been no astronomy. The success of science is a lesson in human cooperation, through the depth of time.

LOGICAL THOUGHT

The second foundation of science is the self-imposed rigor of logical thought, the private authority of proof and disproof. Since each competent investigator knows this inner discipline, he tends to acknowledge the skills and genius of others. There are no dictators, whether self-imposed or mass-accepted, in a realm of healthy science, but there are recognized experts. By detailed communication and repeated assessments, the ideas and proposals of lesser as well as eminent scientists are accepted or rejected by the scientific public. It has justly been said that the international community of scientists—when true to itself—forms a cooperative republic. The citizens of this Jeffersonian republic are the educated voters. There is no president, there should be no parties. In fact, there is no dogma, no inflexible guide, nor any infallible authority. We have experts, but we ourselves establish them, and go on to judge them, and, at the next election, to change them. We scientists may not quite "throw the rascals out" but our politics are recognizably a democratic ethic. Each teacher and student of science has this ethic of participation and belief open to him. This may sometimes be a chilling contrast of self-assured individualism against the weighty cooperative standards of our peers through the ages. But it is the way of any free scientific community, and ours is now a world community.

Such personal participation in the search for knowledge has another notable characteristic. Repeated testing of theories, repeated assessments of the limits of our instruments, repeated criticisms of new ideas and of old ones, of one's own notions as well as those of other thinkers—these

332

should be the continuous background of a scientific life. The excitement of invention and discovery is matched by the excitement of an inner critique. Science is a permanent school, a persistent learning and doubting. If science has a philosophic spirit it is the spirit of rational and empirical self-criticism. And its slogan must be: anti-dogma. Self-reliance, initiative, rational cooperation, imaginative realism—almost a classic model for human life. We must wonder what prevents this model from leading our civilization?

In Social Terms

A culture which is characterized mainly by textual scholasticism and dogmatic disputation, by undisputed authorities and self-justified thoughts, would be the negation of a scientific culture; and, I suppose, such cultures have also been the opposite of democratic. A potential linkage between science and free society might therefore be strong and pervasive. Why, nevertheless, is there an evident potential for the frustration of humane living inherent in the science of the twentieth century?

In social terms, the present tendencies toward inhumane conditions have come with modern science, the industrial revolution, and the emergence of very large populations, whether industrial or not. These tendencies are alike in their treatment of men as though they were things. Even more bitterly inhumane is a standardization of men, occasionally at a high level of cultural environment (as in the wide availability of fine reproductions of music, the fine arts, and literatures), but most often at a minimum level.

Mass society has reflected in its mass culture the efficient, controlled, and standardized procedure of its base in industrial production and mass distribution. As the research scientist controls his measuring instrument, and observes and manipulates natural phenomena, and as the engineer applies science to the economical attainment of material goals, so powerful men may measure and manipulate other men for the attainment of specific goals. Of course, these goals may be good or evil, or ethically neutral. Ethics is not a science. Hence, humanists may not agree upon moral standards, and it may be difficult to judge a specific moral situation. But any habits of thought, and criteria for action, which make possible a mechanization of human beings will justly frighten a sensitive man. If actual science in social reality does no more than evoke such disrespectful ignoring of the individual, if it has qualities which generally and genuinely tend to promote such an attitude, then science has become part of the de-humanizing process. Is it possible that science, whose positive, even ideal, human qualities have seemed so clear, might also have so negative a consequence?

Again we find ambiguity. Science has succeeded by means of isolating phenomena, taking causes and conditions to experimental extremes, purifying and analyzing, and by virtue of *generalizing,* by ignoring any uniqueness in the individual object of investigation. The method of analysis, whether experimental or theoretical, fragments reality. Can the same method restore the fragments to a complete whole?

Link to Industrial Society

There is a further difficulty. Scientific explorations carry a burden of assumptions which bind science tightly to industrial society. The methods of scientific thinking, and particularly the techniques of forming and manipulating concepts, are clearly consonant with the methods and techniques of a rationalized industrial economy. Science and industry share causal analysis of determinate and precise relations among the parts of a process. Science has a goal of complete, efficient, and simple knowledge; industry a goal of determinate control. Now these causal criteria of success are not hidden. Other characteristics, less clearly established, have been suggested by social psychologists and social philosophers, if not by philosophical physicists.

The classical view of Freud finds industrial society and its technological reasoning to be marked by inner demands for order, parsimony, and obstinacy. The interpertation of the philosopher Simmel points to the nature of money, and a moneyed society, as a historical origin for the core of scientific thinking. Since money seems to be abstract, impersonal, objective, quantitative—money is rational. And if these interpretations have some validity, then the ambiguous pattern is renewed because the irrational aspects of industrial society and its money economy also demand closest scrutiny. Apparently, there are psychological motives behind technological reasoning—irrational motives; and we cannot easily assert that they are justified or self-justifying. These motives may, in fact, be satisfied by manipulating the world of man and nature, not by respecting it or appreciating it or enjoying it in wonder or in play.

We have seen that the attitude of mind which makes possible that manipulative power does so by its successful investigation of the causal laws of men and nature. Most striking of the contrasts shown by science is the extraordinary fusion of regularity and plasticity in our world. It is determinate but it can be transformed and remade. For worse or for better, the world of man and nature can be manipulated. What kind of social institutions can absorb the scientific spirit of cooperative inquiry and love of Nature but yet reject the equally scientific spirit of callous manipulative mastery? What kind of science education, indeed of total education, can be suggested for such differentiation of response?

334

Still, may there not be other attitudes toward Nature, and may Nature not have other qualities than those we have emphasized since Galileo? If so, there may be other formulations of rational inquiry and reasonable behavior. If these alternatives are to be explored, then the ambiguities within science ought to be kept vigorous. They must not be submerged or absorbed. Have these ambiguities suggested contradictions and inconsistencies? Whitehead once said that a clash of doctrines is not a disaster —it is an opportunity. Indeed, a contradiction may be a sign of defeat in formal logic, but in science it marks a first step toward a victory. And so, also, if a philosophy of science is to be helpful, it should cherish the tensions within science and the scientific life. It must transcend the present arid and limiting aspects of that larger culture with which science has reciprocally flourished, but only by retaining the reasonable achievements of science itself.

This point seems essential. There is no way back to a prescientific style of life. Indeed a rejection of science now would mean beginning the struggle for technical mastery of nature once again. It is the humane, esthetic, and ethical aspects of science which can yet provide a ground for cultivating humanistic social behavior. In that case, courageous science teachers need not reinforce the sophisticated inhumanity of this century. And then science need not terrify.

I have painted a dark picture of science as an irresponsible social institution, resonating with, if not instigating, certain oppressive qualities of life. But we have also indicated a spirit within the classic scientific community which is the same as the spirit of free and responsible men in any society. At our best, scientists live by a philosophy of individuality and common purpose, treating each other with the utmost of rigorous demands and offering each other a habit of profound respect. If we will respond to the problems of poor and oppressed men with this same mixture of imaginative technique and mutual respect, we will civilize ourselves and our world. And if we scientists and science teachers do not strike radically at the close connection between the scientific and the barbaric, we must expect the verdict which has been demanded by our pessimistic philosophical judges. It requires more than a curricular addition of literature and the arts, more than a required course in ethics. Furthermore, it needs more than replacement of technical specialization by what my colleagues call general engineering and our Soviet colleagues call polytechnical education. It means a far deeper attempt at philosophical and historical understanding of science as a human enterprise by each teacher and scholar, an understanding which demands the logic and social relations of science, the linguistics and psychoanalysis of science, its economics and its politics, and finally, its characteristic but regretfully only potential symbiosis with art.

VALUES AND GOALS FOR SCIENCE TEACHING

What do these reflections on the ambiguous character of science imply for the school? Perhaps we can propose Some Values and Goals for Science Teaching:

1. To provide enough understanding to enable the educated citizens to collaborate intelligently with those who are actively engaged in scientific pursuits.

2. To enable the citizen both to criticize and to appreciate the effects of the sciences on his society; to understand its history and its present alternative prospects.

3. To give a practical grasp of scientific methods of grappling with problems, at least sufficient for problems which the student will face in his individual and social life.

4. To help the pupil and citizen to understand the whole world better factually, and especially the world as it affects him concretely. He should not be a spectator of the mysterious doings of scientists or of their products.

5. To kindle enthusiasm for the intrinsic delights of scientific knowledge, in part because it will make life more enjoyable, in part because society has an extreme need of good scientists in every field of human difficulty.

6. To understand the place of science among other intellectual and esthetic pursuits: briefly, to see the sciences as being themselves a humanistic enterprise, as much as literature, the arts, history and religion, connected closely with them even while differing from them.

7. To help the pupil who has already chosen to become a scientist, technician, or engineer to comprehend the humanistic basis and significance of his life-specialty; and to overcome the ever-present danger that we may, in our schools and colleges, produce a specialized and narrow-minded technician, whether in the research laboratory or in the machine shop or at the factory bench, and to teach him humility in his role as scientist, serving, not dominating, society.

8. To help the citizen investigate ways of increasing the range and depth of understanding natural processes and to relate this problem of encouraging and exploiting science to the many puzzling complexities of industrial society.

9. To provide our students with rich and various experiences of individual thinking and critical attitudes on the one hand, and of co-operative enterprise and mutual aid on the other.

336

10. To help the pupil to understand the position of his future job or activity in the productive web of society as a whole, technically and scientifically as well as socially, so as to establish his sane and healthy self-knowledge and so that he may act more intelligently with others whenever there are joint undertakings.

11. To educate our students so that they may distinguish ends from means, probabilities from certainties, evidence from propaganda, questions from pseudo-questions, rational belief from superstition, and science from quackery.

It is not too much to ask teachers to take time to reflect upon such goals as these. The development of the sciences has given us, in this century, the means to a secure life. There are no longer any material obstacles to an abundant life and yet the lives about us, in this country and throughout the world, are mainly stunted and unhappy. We should educate children to think about these urgent problems of social ethics and technical application, about the practical relation of science and values. We must do this with wisdom as well as with technical methods, for as Whitehead sadly noted: "Some of the major disasters of mankind have been produced by the narrowness of men with a good methodology. Ulysses had no use for Plato, and the bones of his companions are strewn on many a reef and many an isle."

Science is still ambiguous and her lot is not yet completely cast. Created by man—himself a part of Nature—science is as natural as her subject matter. And the transformation of Nature by man is therefore to be seen as Nature transforming, conquering, and disciplining herself. We can help from within the most delicate spot of all, from within the rational citadel of technological society, since we can help in the education of younger scientists, and in the scientific education of all young people.

It can still be maintained that the true science is consonant with older philosophical ideals. Plato thought it was possible to bring reason among the nations and among men. In our time, devotion to this possibility must be joined with a sober, and hence scientific, passion to know how ideals can be made real. We have made rational machines; perhaps we can make ourselves and our companions on earth rational, not least, I believe, by a humane teaching in every science classroom. Sometimes these hopeful sentiments seem to be empty jugs. But only more scientific thought can fill them. Our problems can be seen by anyone but it is not so commonly seen that they may be solved by further research. One of our wisest scientists spoke directly. Albert Szent-Gyorgyi was asked to explain research. He said that "research is to see what everybody has seen and to think what nobody has thought."

Men in society, with science acquiescent, have been cruelly false to their own potentialities; when men begin to remake the world, their desires and values will be part of Nature. Put in optimistic terms, "the historical achievement of science and technology has rendered possible the translation of values into technical tasks." We need philosophers and scientists and teachers who will undertake the re-definitions of values in technical terms. This would, in Herbert Marcuse's fine phrase, be a materialization of values. Then, with a humane science, the moral ideal will become a dimension of the natural.

ACTIVITY 17
Essay Topics and Problems on Part Two*

1. Compare and contrast some of the views of J. S. Bruner and of D. P. Ausubel on approaches to science teaching.

2. Choose an activity requiring student experimentation and write a dialogue showing how you as a teacher would handle a set of student questions and situations which might arise during the experiment.

3. What authors quoted or discussed in this book believe that discovery approaches and approaches based primarily on the learning of skills rather than subject matter are *not* satisfactory in teaching science? Summarize their case. Summarize also the case made *for* the use of discovery approaches and skill-developing curricula, and identify some of their main proponents.

4. Discuss the proposition: Students in secondary school science courses should be treated as junior scientists.

5. What, in your opinion, should be the relative roles of "content" and "method" in science courses?

6. Discuss Bruner's hypothesis that any subject can be taught meaningfully to students at any grade level. Choose an advanced science topic and outline how you might teach it in first, fourth, eighth, and twelfth grades.

7. Based on what you have read in this book and on your personal feelings, draw up a design of the most ideal classroom and class schedule situation you can think of (assuming that you have unlimited financial support available).

*For instructors who use this book as a text in methods courses it is recommended that students be required to write on several of the topics in this list. Teachers using this book as a reference will also find that the exercise of writing short essays on these topics will sharpen their insight into some of the recurrent themes that run through this book.

8. Discuss the proposition: Truly modern scientists are more *creators* of models than discoverers of natural laws. This being the case, the emphasis in science courses should be more on the formulation of constructs (and models) than on the "discovery" of relationships.

9. Discuss the view of M. King Hubbert (quoted in Commoner's article in this book) that "the acceptance of any conclusion ... by an individual who is not familiar with the observational data on which it is based and the logic by which it is derived is a negation of science and a return to authoritarianism." What are the implications of this statement for science teaching?

10. What *is* an experiment?

11. Discuss what the relationships should be ideally, in your opinion, between science teaching and other parts of a high-school student's education.

12. Discuss the following proposition: Most "facts" are dependent upon the observer. (See especially the articles by Cohen and by Farre.) What are the implications of this statement for science education?

13. Discuss the nature and implications of the "information explosion." (See especially Bruner, Commoner.)

14. Formulate a scheme for discovering the "frustration tolerance" of members of your class and using techniques to keep students frustrated to the point of being interested but not to the point of withdrawing.

15. Based on your readings and experiments, discuss ways in which you might help a group of students to distinguish between observations and inferences, facts and theories, inferences and deductions, and between laws and models. Give and discuss carefully several examples of each of these categories of scientific knowledge, information, or thought.

16. To what extent are science educators and scientists agreed that experiential, activity-centered approaches are the best ways of teaching science? To what extent do you think science courses should be experience-centered? Concept-centered? Information-centered?

17. Outline an activity or series of activities which you think will lead to the learning of a skill which can be transferred from one science discipline to another. Devise a way of testing to see whether or not your students have in fact been able to manage transfer.

18. Discuss the views of some of the authors represented in

Part II of this book on the objectives of science teaching and on the matter of behavioral objectives.

19. Outline a unit of study requiring the use of research papers in a high school science class. Prepare a bibliography to accompany your unit.

20. Choose one of the articles in Part Two with a bibliography, look up all of the references cited, and prepare a short abstract of each.

Objectives of this Book

Now that you have read this book and performed the activities prescribed you should be able to:

1. Formulate behavioral objectives for science lessons in accordance with the general principles described herein.
2. Analyze materials and determine which are stated in conceptual terms; formulate conceptual statements for lessons you teach to your own classes.
3. Organize course materials within a framework of conceptual schemes.
4. Devise and use several different techniques of establishing a need to know.
5. Prepare and conduct both structured and unstructured activities for science classes.
6. Design and conduct working field trips for biology or earth science classes.
7. Create invitations to inquiry and teach them to groups of students.
8. Analyze textbooks and determine quantitatively how effectively different texts can be when used in conjunction with a discovery-oriented science program.
9. Analyze audiovisual materials and use them in a way that helps you to reach previously stated behavioral objectives.
10. Analyze several textbooks or your own course notes and determine which technical terms are essential to reaching your behavioral objectives and which are superfluous.
11. Analyze and evaluate your questioning technique using the methods described within this book or other methods with similar goals.
12. Recognize carefully stated generalizations and lead students to careful formulation of generalizations.
13. Write examination questions which specifically test for previously stated behavioral objectives.
14. Prepare and use a contract or other independent-study unit for a portion of a science class.
15. Read critically, analyze, and discuss articles from the literature on science education.